A Charlton Standard

Canadian Colonial Tokens

SIXTH
EDITION

BY
W. K. CROSS

The Charlton Press

TORONTO, CANADA • PALM HARBOR, FLORIDA

Library and Archives Canada Cataloguing in Publication

Canadian colonial tokens : a Charlton standard catalogue

Biennial.
5th ed.-
Continues: Charlton standard catalogue of Canadian colonial tokens
ISSN 1706-7049
ISBN 978-0-88968-321-1 (6th edition)

1. Tokens--Canada-Catalogs
CJ4911.C42   737'.3'0971075   C2003-901659-5

**Printed in Canada
in the Province of Quebec**

The Charlton Press

**Editorial Office
Box 820, Postal Station Willowdale B
North York, Ontario, Canada. M2K 2R1
Telephone (416) 488-1418 Fax: (416) 488-4656
Telephone (800) 442-6042 Fax: (800) 442-1542**

EDITORIAL AND PRODUCTION

Editor	W. K. Cross
Editorial Assistant	Jean Dale
Graphic Technician	Davina Rowan
Cover image	Scott Cornwell

CONTRIBUTORS TO THE SIXTH EDITION

Pricing Panel

The Publisher would like to thank the following individuals for their assistance in making this edition possible. Without their help, the necessary improvements would not have been made.

Willard Burton, Ontario; Brian Cornwell, Ontario; Michael Findlay, Ontario; Andy Grecco, Ontario; Greg Ingram, Alberta; Andrew McKaig, Alberta; Charles Moore, California; Nathalie Roby, Quebec

Contributors

D. M. Casey, Nova Scotia; Douglas M. Carlson, Florida; Darrel Chaisson, Ontario; Jim Charlton, Ontario; Chris Faulkner, Ontario; Alain Gallo, Quebec; Ian Haire, Ontario; Tim Henderson, New Brunswick; Greg Ingram, Alberta; Mel Kyle, Ontario; Peter McDonald, Quebec

Organisations

We would like to thank the following organizations:

Bank of Canada National Currency Collection:
For the illustrations of the rare and unique tokens in their collections.
Also for the photographs of the Blacksmith Tokens of Canada.

American Numismatic Association
For the line drawings of the Bouquet Sous which were "reprinted through the courtesy of *"The Numismatist"*, the official publication of the American Numismatic Association, 818 North Cascade Avenue, Colorado Springs, Colorado 80903."

TABLE OF CONTENTS

NEWFOUNDLAND TOKENS

PRIVATE TOKENS

ANONYMOUS TOKENS

PRINCE EDWARD ISLAND TOKENS

SEMI-REGAL TOKENS

PRIVATE TOKENS

ANONYMOUS TOKENS

NOVA SCOTIA TOKENS

SEMI-REGAL TOKENS

PRIVATE TOKENS

ANONYMOUS TOKENS

NEW BRUNSWICK TOKENS

SEMI-REGAL TOKENS

PRIVATE TOKENS

ANONYMOUS TOKENS

LOWER CANADA TOKENS

SEMI-REGAL TOKENS

ANONYMOUS TOKENS OF LOWER CANADA

UPPER CANADA TOKENS

PRIVATE TOKENS

ANONYMOUS TOKENS

PROVINCE OF CANADA TOKENS

SEMI-REGAL TOKENS

ANONYMOUS AND MISCELLANEOUS TOKENS

VEXATOR CANADIENSIS TOKENS

BLACKSMITH TOKENS

BRIDGE TOKENS

FUR TRADE TOKENS

MERCHANT TOKENS

TRANSPORTATION TOKENS

NON-CANADIAN TOKENS

CROSS REFERENCING TABLES

INTRODUCTION

It is now fifteen years since the release of the first edition of Canadian Colonial Tokens. With four editions now behind us most of the rough spots have been removed, errors eliminated, and we now settle down to only the odd improvement being made in this and coming editions.

Any assistance from our readers in regard to new information, errors, omissions, or suggestions for improvement of the fifth edition would be greatly appreciated.

SCOPE OF THIS CATALOGUE

This book has been specifically designed to cover that period of Canadian numismatic history from 1794 to 1867. During this particular time the shortage of official coinage seemed more the rule of the day than an occasional exception.

Throughout this time the foreign policy of Great Britain was simply one of rigid control. Her attitude was that the colonies were to produce the raw materials needed by the homeland and during times of civil unrest at home to allow the entry of immigrants into the colonies.

The colonists were also expected to pay for any imported goods in what the mother country considered legal tender coins. This resulted in British North America, like all British colonies, being constantly short of change.

This need for circulating coinage became quite acute considering the growth in the local colonial economies. Consequently the colonists resorted to their own ingenuity and made use of whatever metal pieces they could find, all this in spite of Great Britain's policy. Needless to say there was a proliferation of these local tokens from many sources, including some counterfeits of the same. These tokens varied greatly in the quality of their workmanship and fullness in weight. They have been the subject of much numismatic study and research for over 100 years.

This issue of *Canadian Colonial Tokens*: a Charlton Standard Catalogue, lists those tokens that were used or issued expressly for the purpose of general circulation in order to alleviate the constant shortage of change that plagued British North America.

Also in the 6th edition we have listed Bridge Tokens, Fur Trade Tokens, Merchant Cards or Tokens, Transportation Tokens and Non-Canadian Tokens prior 1868, or considered token collectors as belonging to that era. These issues while not listed in our previous editions are considered part of Colonial Canada.

THE LISTING OF COLONIAL TOKENS

The Colonial Tokens of Canada are catalogued from East to West with the last two chapters dealing with listing the Blacksmith and Anonymous Tokens. For the beginner, one of the main stumbling blocks is token identification. Since a high percentage of tokens do not carry the colony, province or other identifying designs or legends an attribution scheme is required. Thus we have divided the tokens of the colonies into three major categories: Semi-Regal, Private and Anonymous.

SEMI-REGAL TOKENS: This category is devoted to tokens issued or authorized by a colonial government authority. An example is the Thistle token of Nova Scotia. We have also listed the Bank Tokens of Lower Canada in this category since they were issued with the authorization of the colonial government.

PRIVATE TOKENS: The private tokens of an individual or business are identified next. These tokens may or may not carry the name of the individual or business. If they do not then their attribution by other numismatic researchers has been established beyond doubt. They are now readily accepted as being from a known issuer.

ANONYMOUS TOKENS: The last category does not carry any issuer identification, nor has it been attributed to any known issuer. That is, no known record has yet been found to indicate who actually did import these tokens into that colony. A great number of these tokens have been found in Canadian hoards and therefore are considered important in the early commerce of what is now known as Canada.

In summary, all tokens are first classified by colonial government, East before West. Each of those general classifications is subdivided according to whether the issue was of a Semi-Regal, Private or Anonymous nature. Within each of these classifications a final, specific listing of tokens appears according to the catalogue numbering system which follows.

CATALOGUE NUMBERING SYSTEM

Tokens in the "Charlton Standard Catalogue of Canadian Colonial Tokens" have been numbered according to the following rules:

SEMI-REGAL TOKENS: Are listed by date and denomination order.
PRIVATE TOKENS: Are listed by Breton Number.
ANONYMOUS TOKENS: Are listed by Breton Number.

Listings by Breton numbers within each of the above three groups were not strictly followed if a type or family grouping of tokens was more consistent. The latter format was developed to allow the beginner a logical entry into the field of token numismatics.

All token catalogue numbers consist of up to four parts, each signifying a particular characteristic of that token. The general structure of the numbering scheme is as follows:

PROVINCE OR TYPE: Ten different two-letter classifications are possible. Seven of these are used to indicate where the token originated or circulated. The remaining three, WE (Wellington Tokens), BL (Blacksmith Tokens) and AM (Anonymous and Miscellaneous Tokens) indicate type.

TOKEN NUMBER: A one or two digit number follows the Province or Type classification and indicates the placement of the token within that group.

MAJOR VARIETY: The single letter following the Token Number classifies major varieties of that token. In all cases, a new die was used in the production of that token. The letters "I" and "O" were omitted from the alpha sequence.

MINOR VARIETY: The number following the Major Variety code signifies a minor variation within that variety. In most cases the die of the major variety had been reworked. However, exceptions in classifying the minor varieties and new dies are considered insignificant when the changes are difficult to distinguish. Examples are the portraits of George IV on the Nova Scotia Thistle Halfpenny and Penny tokens.

VARIATIONS: Recut, retouched and deteriorated dies are not assigned numbers. However, the more important minor varieties have been listed under the category of Variations. Allowances have been made for expansion of this category in future editions of this catalogue.

TOKEN CHARACTERISTICS SUMMARY

PROVINCE OR LETTER	TOKEN NUMBER	MAJOR VARIETY LETTER	MINOR VARIETY NUMBER
NF- Newfoundland	Issuer	Major design	Minor die
PE- Prince Edward	Series	alterations	alterations
Island	Denomination	Date change	to a major
NS- Nova Scotia		Legend change	variety such
NB- New Brunswick			as retouching,
LC- Lower Canada			polishing,
UC- Upper Canada			recutting,etc.
PC- Province of Canada			Composition,
WE- Wellington Tokens			weight,
BL- Blacksmith Tokens			die axis,
AM- Anonymous and			edge.
Miscellaneous Tokens			

An example of this catalogue numbering system is UC-9A3

UC signifies Upper Canada; **9** is the ninth token in the Upper Canada Series; **A** is the first major variety; **3** is the third minor variety.

CROSS REFERENCE NUMBERS

All tokens have been cross-referenced to other classification numbers as listed by Breton (Br), Courteau (Co), Wood (Wo), Willey (W), Lees (Lees) and McLachlan (Mc).

Courteau numbers are appended with a letter(s) component referring to his monographs as listed below:

B. The Canadian Bouquet-Sous, 1908
BH. The Canadian 1820 Bust and Harp Tokens, 1907
BM. The Copper Tokens of the Bank of Montreal, 1919
BT. A Blacksmith Token, 1908
H. The Habitant Tokens of Lower Canada
NB. Coins and Tokens of New Brunswick, 1923
NF. Coins and Tokens of Newfoundland, 1930
NL. Non-Local Tokens of Canada, 1924
NS. The Coins and Tokens of Nova Scotia, 1910
PEI. Coins and Tokens of Prince Edward Island, 1922
T. Canadian Bust and Commerce (Tiffin) Tokens, 1934
UC. The St. George Copper Tokens of the Bank of Upper Canada, 1934
W. The Wellington Tokens Relating to Canada, 1914

TOKEN GRADING

Token grading is unlike grading Canadian decimal coins in that a knowledge of the many token manufacturers is important to fairly assess an item's condition. Different manufacturers of the colonial period were known to produce widely different qualities of tokens. This depended on their:

(a) degree of technical expertise;
(b) access to capital and thus decent minting equipment; and
(c) actual desire to produce a quality product.

Two examples, while extreme, help to demonstrate the range of quality produced. On the one hand, the Royal Mint in London had the technical expertise, equipment and desire to turn out quality items. On the other hand the Blacksmith token mints lacked that desire for quality and this can be seen by the examples of their work available today. While these Blacksmith tokens are obviously inferior looking items relative to Royal Mint products their grade or condition is not judged solely by the presence or absence of detail now remaining. That missing detail may never have been there right from the very moment the token was first struck. This knowledge of a manufacturer's workmanship then adds a totally new dimension to grading beyond that experienced by coin graders. The implication then, when grading tokens, is that grades assigned are intended to mean "for issue." Thus a Royal Mint token and a Blacksmith which are both graded as Fine will undoubtedly display vastly different amounts of absolute design detail remaining to a casual observer. In fact both will have equal detail loss from that which was there at the time the token was originally struck.

The mints which follow are ordered in terms of the quality of product they were renowned for generating. The best quality of production is listed first with the worst last:

Royal Mint	Wright & Bale
Boulton & Watt	Belleville Mint
Ralph Heaton & Co.	Jean Marie Arnault
Thomas Halliday	Various Blacksmith Mints
William Mossop	

The Royal Mint, for example, produced the coinage of the Bank of Upper Canada in 1850. This was a high quality coinage which can be graded similarly to the decimal coins which appeared from 1858 on. On the other hand, the tokens of Jean Marie Arnault probably came from the presses with detail comparable to coins in Extremely Fine condition.

Another factor affecting token appearance was the inability of the native mints to properly store their dies. Improperly stored dies rusted, resulting in relief spots on the finished token. The pimple effect this created cannot be considered damage to a token and must be viewed as part of the "as struck condition."

The following list indicates which items were manufactured by which mints and therefore serves as a handy guide in terms of the general quality of workmanship to be expected when determining a suitable grade:

MINTS	COINAGE
The Royal Mint	Bank of Upper Canada Tokens of 1850 and part of 1852
Ralph Heaton & Co.	Bank of Upper Canada Tokens of 1852, 1854 and 1857
	Quebec Bank Tokens of 1852
	New Brunswick Coinage 1854
Boulton & Watt	Rutherford Tokens of 1846
	Habitant Tokens of 1837 Lower Canada
	Bank of Montreal 1842-1844
	New Brunswick Halfpennies and Pennies of 1843
Thomas Halliday	Genuine British Copper Tokens of Nova Scotia
	Ships Colonies & Commerce Tokens PEI
Wright & Bale	Ships Colonies & Commerce Tokens of Lower Canada
Belleville Mint	Bouquet Sous
Jean-Marie Arnault	Bouquet Sous

MINTS AND MANUFACTURERS

For the most part the Colonial coinages of Canada were struck by private mints. Only a very few tokens were struck at official mints.

FOREIGN MINTS AND MANUFACTURERS

The Royal Mint, London, England.
Boulton & Watt, Soho Mint, Birmingham, England.
Ralph Heaton & Co., Birmingham Mint, Birmingham, England.
Thomas Halliday, Birmingham, England.
Wright & Bale, New York, N.Y., U.S.A.
Belleville Mint, Belleville, N.J., U.S.A.
Daniel and Benjamin True, Troy, N.Y., U.S.A.
Sir Edward Thomason, Birmingham, England.
William Mossop, Dublin, Ireland.
William Stephen Mossop, Dublin, Ireland.
John Sheriff, Liverpool, England.

NATIVE MINTS AND MANUFACTURERS

Jean-Marie Arnault, Montreal.
Blacksmith Mints, Upper and Lower Canada

In 1848 the Soho mint of Boulton & Watt was sold by auction with the equipment going to Ralph Heaton & Co. and most of the dies to W.J. Taylor. Taylor's purchases included the dies of:

The New Brunswick Coinage of 1843.
The 1837 "Habitant" Coinage of Lower Canada.
The Bank of Montreal "Front View" Tokens.
The Copper Company of Upper Canada.

DESIGNERS AND ENGRAVERS

Not all engravers were employed at the mints. Engravers such as the Wyon family and Halliday had their own places of business. Issuers and mints often contracted them for token design and dies. The following is a practical listing of the designers and engravers with the tokens they designed.

FOREIGN DESIGNERS AND ENGRAVERS

THOMAS HALLIDAY
> Wellington Battle Halfpennies and Pennies
> Ships, Colonies and Commerce Tokens
> Trade and Navigation Tokens
> Wellington Tokens
> Waterloo Halfpenny Token
> Victoria Nobis Est Halfpenny Token
> Genuine British Copper Tokens
> John A. Barry Tokens
> Hosterman and Etter Tokens
> Anonymous Halfpennies and Pennies of 1812 and 1813
> (Imitations Imported by Joseph Tiffin)

NOEL-ALEXANDRE PONTHON (BOULTON & WATT)
> Copper Company of Upper Canada

JOHN SHERIFF
> Sloop Halfpennies of Upper Canada
> Starr and Shannon Tokens

THOMAS WELLS INGRAM (BOULTON & WATT)
> Lesslie Tokens

WILLIAM MOSSOP

WILLIAM STEPHEN MOSSOP
> Nova Scotia Halfpenny For the Convenience of Trade

ISAAC PARKES
> Marquis Wellington Tokens

PETER WYON

THOMAS WYON THE ELDER
> Carritt and Alport Halfpenny Tokens
> Anonymous Irish Penny of 1805

LEONARD CHARLES WYON
> New Brunswick Halfpenny and Penny Tokens of 1854
> Nova Scotia Mayflower Tokens of 1856

JOHN GIBBS (BELLEVILLE MINT)
> Bouquet Sous Tokens
> Banque du Peuple Sous Tokens

JOHN PINCHES
> Bank of Upper Canada Tokens

NATIVE DESIGNERS AND ENGRAVERS

JEAN-MARIE ARNAULT
> Molson Halfpenny Tokens
> Rebellion Sou Tokens
> Bouquet Sou Tokens

JOHN S. THOMPSON
Reverse design for the Mayflower Coinage of Nova Scotia
JACQUES VIGER
Reverse design for the Bank of Montreal Tokens
MICHAEL WALLACE
Reverse design for the Nova Scotia Thistle Tokens

AGENTS

The British Act of 1803 preventing the counterfeiting of foreign coins, and the legislation of 1812-1817 with the acts relating to coins, tokens etc., resulted in the Mints of England in some cases even refusing to offer an estimate on coinage without proper official authorization. M.R. Boulton of Boulton & Watt in a letter to Albert Furniss stated that "I have always considered it expedient to have the sanction of the Provincial Authorities, of the Government at home, for my security in undertaking such a coinage as the one you propose...."

This reluctance on the part of the minters left the door open to independent agents to negotiate directly with the mints on behalf of the Colonial Issuers for coinage.

FOREIGN AGENTS

Joshua Scholefield, Birmingham, Engand.
John Langdon, Bank of Liverpool, England.
Messrs. Tarratt and Co., England.
Thomas Jones Wilkinson, Birmingham, England.
Captain Dudne, England.
John Walker & Co., Birmingham, England.
Cotterill, Hill & Co., Walsall, England.
Rowe, Kentish & Co., London, England.

NATIVE AGENTS

Albert Furniss, Montreal, Lower Canada.

FRATERNAL AFFILIATION

For many years coin clubs have been formed across Canada with new clubs being organized all the time. Token collecting is attracting the interest of hundreds of collectors. Excitement in this aspect of numismatics has now reached unprecedented heights.

The educational value of collecting tokens is being stressed at both the local and national levels. Coin shows, special meetings, seminars, slide presentations, films and lending libraries help add to the recent enthusiasm in Canadian token collecting.

The following numismatic organizations are recommended to anyone interested in learning more about the history of tokens:

Canadian Numismatic Association
5694 Highway #7, Suite 432
Markham, Ontario
Canada L2P 1B4

American Numismatic Association
818 North Cascade Avenue
Colorado Springs, Colorado
U.S.A. 80903-3279

Canadian Association of Token Collectors
Gord Nichols, Secretary-Treasurer
Box 28039
600 Ontario Street
St. Catherines, Ontario
Canada, L2N 7P8
E-mail: nicholsg@cogeco.ca
Website: www.nunetcan.net/catc.htm

DATA OR SPECIFICATION TABLES FOR TOKENS

Each major variety of a specific token number has a specification listing to the right of the token illustration. This information includes:

COMPOSITION

The metallic composition of each token is listed as copper, brass, pewter, nickel, silver or gold. The exact chemical composition is considered of little value since the analysis of a single token offers no guarantee that the metallic composition of the next token of that same series would be identical. The copper alloy of each batch of tokens struck can vary. This is especially true for tokens of native manufacture where the colour of certain items moves from a normal copper colour to a brassy yellow. This clearly indicates that the alloy was not consistent throughout the production of the flans.

The identification of a token as being of copper, bronze or brass content can be difficult even for experienced collectors. One example is that of a copper token having been cleaned with modern cleaning compounds and taking on the yellow colour of brass.

Copper: Elemental copper. Pure, not an alloy. Red copper colour.
Bronze: An alloy of 95% copper, 4% tin, 1% zinc. Chocolate copper colour.
Brass: An alloy of 75% copper, 25% zinc. Yellow brass colour.
Ancient Bronze: An alloy of copper and tin. Yellow brass colour

Thus by varying the amounts of zinc or tin added to a copper base the colour of the finished token can be altered. The above data also illustrate the irrelevance of knowing the exact chemical composition. However, knowing the correct chemical composition could link Native or Foreign manufactured tokens to one minter.

It should be noted that silver and gold tokens were issued only for presentation purposes.

WEIGHT

The weight of each token is specified as a range and expressed in grams. Copper or bronze token production did not require the same close tolerance as that of silver or gold. As a result weights may vary between examples of the same type. Also, the greed of the minters and issuers tended toward the production of light weight tokens, this tendency being curbed at times by the lack of public acceptance. If the number of tokens per pound of copper or alloy increased so did the profit.

Early weights were expressed as the number of pieces per pound avoirdupois. The colonial issues of Canada were based on the English halfpenny and penny.

NUMBER OF PIECES PER POUND

Dates	English Halfpenny	Weight in Grains	English Penny	Weight in Grains
1717-1775	46	152.17	-	-
1797-1799	36	194.44	16	437.50
1806-1860	48	145.83	24	291.67
1860-1967	80	87.50	48	145.83

CONVERSION TABLE

1 Pound Avoirdupois = 16 ounces
1 Pound (av.) = 7000 grains
1 Pound (av.) = 454.6 grams
1 Grain = 0.0646 grams

Semi-Regal Colonial Bank Tokens were intended to be issued at five-sixths the weight of British copper, approximating the ratio of Halifax Currency to Sterling. However, most were issued at full weight.

DIAMETER

The diameter of each token is expressed in millimetres. Collected data indicate that token diameters must also be stated as ranges since there are variations in diameter between tokens of the same type.

DIE AXIS

The position of the reverse design in relation to the obverse design is indicated by using small arrows to show the direction the reverse design is pointing.

Medal or upright axis: ↑↑, (ie. obverse, reverse same direction)

Coinage or upset axis: ↑↓, (ie. obverse, reverse opposite direction)

90 degrees east axis: ↑←, (ie. obverse, reverse 90 degree rotation east)

90 degrees west axis: ↑→, (ie. obverse, reverse 90 degree rotation west)

The 90 degree rotation (east or west) variation in die axis is usually found only in tokens of native manufacture.

EDGE

Three separate edge designs have been employed on Canadian Colonial tokens.

Plain: Without design.

Reeded: Straight up and down edge grooves with either flat or V - shaped bottom. Diagonal edge grooves may also appear.

Engrailed: A chain or twisted rope design impressed into the edge of the coin during striking. This design will have variations depending on the direction of the design, southwest to northeast or northwest to southeast.

REFERENCE WORKS FOR CANADIAN COLONIAL TOKENS

The following list of reference works is suggested for further research and study by the collector.

Atkins, J.: The Coins and Tokens of the Possessions and Colonies of the British Empire, 1889.

Baker, Warren: Some Overstruck Specimens of Br. 1008 and Other Notes on the Blacksmith Series. CNJ Sept. 1985

Batty, T. D.: Descriptive Catalogue of the Copper Coinage of Great Britain, Ireland, British Isles, and Colonies, 1900. Four Volumes.

Bowman, Fred: The Bouquet Sou Tokens of Canada, Num. July-Nov. 1955, CNJ Jan.-Feb. 1960.
The "Bon Pour Deux Sous" Token of Canada, Num. Oct. 1948.
The Case of the Bouquet Sou Breton 712, CNJ Apr. 1957.
Cdn. Borderline Tokens, CNJ, Vol.11 No 9. Sept.1966

Breton, P. N.: Illustrated History of Coins and Tokens Relating to Canada, 1894.
Popular Illustrated Guide to Canadian Coins and Medals, 1912.

Buth, L.: A New Variety of Canadian "Ships Colonies amd Commerce" Token, Canadian Numismatics, 1999.

Carroll, Major S. S.: More Varieties of the Rutherford Tokens, CNJ July 1955.

Chalmers, R.: History of Currency in the British Colonies, 1893.

Christmas, Rev.H.: Copper Coinage of the British Colonies in America, Numismatic Society of London 1862.

Courteau, Dr. E. G.: A Blacksmith Token, May 1908
The Canadian Bouquet Sous, 1908. (1)
The Canadian 1820 Bust and Harp Tokens, Num. May-June 1907. (2)
The Canadian Bust and Commerce Tokens, Num. Feb. 1934. (2)
The Coins and Tokens of New Brunswick, Num. Aug. 1923. (2)
The Coins and Tokens of Newfoundland, Num. Feb. 1930. (2)
The Coins and Tokens of Nova Scotia, 1910. Addendum to the Coins and Tokens of Nova Scotia, Num. Feb. 1922. (1)
The Coins and Tokens of Prince Edward Island, Num. Nov. 1922. (2)
The Copper Tokens of the Bank of Montreal, 1919.
The Habitant Tokens of Lower Canada, 1927.
The Non-Local Tokens of Canada, Num. May 1924. (2)
The St. George Copper Tokens of the Bank of Upper Canada, 1934.
The Wellington Tokens Relating to Canada, 1914. (1)

Curry, Michael: The Anticosti Token Re-examined, CNJ Oct. 1972.

Davis, W. J.: The Nineteenth Century Token Coinage, 1904. Reprint 1969.

Faulkner, C.: Breton 999: A Numismatic Record, CNJ Sept. 1984.
"Out the Past - An History of Breton 999," from "Aspects of the Numismatics of North American," edited C. Gilboy, published by Regina Coin Club in 1985.

Ferguson, J. D.: Sun Tavern Blacksmith Token, CNJ Aug. 1966.
Variety of Sou, Courteau 15, Numismatist, Sept 1946

Fleming, H. A.: Halifax Currency in the Collections of the Nova Scotia Historical Society, 1921.

Ford, J. J. Jr.: The Copper Company of Upper Canada. The Coin Collector's Journal, May-June 1951.

Fougere, J. J.: Nova Scotia Thistle Tokens 1823-1824, CNJ June 1987.

Gibbs, Jeremiah: Sir Isaac Brock and the Brock Halfpennies, Num. Nov. 1902, CNJ Jan. 1965.

Ingram, G. S. and
Marelig, B.:   The Bust and Harp Tokens of Canada, First Edition, 2004

Ingram, G. S.:   The Tiffin Tokens of Canada, First Edition, 2004

Jacobs, Wayne: The 1850 George & Dragon, A Numismatic Mystery, Numismatica
     Canada, 2003.
     Background to the Banqu Dy Peuple, Br 715, Numismatica
     Canada, 2002.
     The Birmingham Bouquet Cous: A New Citizenship, CNN June 2000.
     Breton No. 670: The Belleville Clue is and American Citizen,
     Numismatica Canada 2003.
     The Br 681 Bouquet Sou: LeRoux was right, Numismatica Canada,
     Vo. 4, 2005.
     Changes and Problems with the Nova Scotia Coinage of 1856,
     Numismatica Canada, 2002.
     The Derivation of Designs on Early Canadian Copper Currency,
     Numismatica Canada, Vol. 5, 2006
     The Fake Nor'wester: An Update, Numismatica Canada, 2002.
     The Field Marhsall Wellington Halpenny, 1805, Br 976,
     Numismatica Canada, 2003.
     Gleanings of the Belleville Mint, Canadian Token Sept. 2000
     On the Trail of a Fake Nor'wester, CNR Summer 2001.
     The Phantom Token, CNJ July 1962.
     The Shadowy Issu of the Bellevillw Mint, CNJ Feb. 1996.

Kennedy, Earle K.:   The Prince Edward Island Holey Dollar, 1979.

Kyle, M. H.:   Bank of Upper Canada One Penny 1852, Wide 2 Varieties,
     Numismatica Canada, Vol 2, 2003.

Lees, W. A. D.:   The Ships, Colonies and Commerce Tokens, Num. Jan. 1917.
     Reprinted 1961. Addenda in Num. Dec. 1919 and May 1926.

Leighton, Eric: An Ante-dated Nova Scotia Token, Numismatica Canada, Vol 2, 2003.
     Arthur, Marquis of Wellington, Numismatica Canada, Vol. 3, 2004.
     More on the Ante-date Token of Nova Scotia, Numismatica Canada,
     Vol 3, 2004.
     Nova Scotia's 1856 Mintage Figures, Numismatica Canada,
     Vol. 1, 2002

Leroux, Dr. Jos.:   The Canadian Coin Cabinet, First Edition, 1888.
     The Canadian Coin Cabinet, Second Edition, 1892.
     Supplements to the Canadian Coin Cabinet, 1890 and 1897.

Linecar, H. W. A.:   A Catalogue of Canadian Coins and Tokens in the British
     Museum, CNJ Jan.-Feb. 1960.
     British Commonwealth Coins, 1959.

Lorrain, M.:   A Newly Found Variety of the 1832 Nova Scotia Halfpenny
     Token, CNJ Nov. 1968.

Low, Lyman H.:   Hard Times Tokens, 1900.

McCullough, A. B.:   Money and Exchange in Canada to 1900. Dundurn Press, 1984.

McLachlan, R. W.:   Address to the ANA Convention, Num. Sept. 1912.
     A Descriptive Catalogue of Coins, Tokens and Medals Issued in
     or Relating to the Dominion of Canada and Newfoundland, 1886.
     Reprint 1975.
     A Hoard of Canadian Coppers, CA 1890.
     Annals of the Nova Scotian Currency, 1892.
     The Canadian Wellington Tokens, Canadian Antiquarian & Numismatic
     Journal, Jan. 1902.
     Coins Struck in Canada Previous to 1840, 1892.
     The Copper Currency of the Canadian Banks, 1903.
     The Copper Tokens of Upper Canada ANS, 1916.
     Fabrications in Canadian Coins, CA 1893-1894.

Is the Mysterious Bust on Canadian Coins Really That of Wellington? Num. June 1916.
Jean-Marie Arnault, Num. Mar. 1914.
The Magdalen Islands Coinage, CA Apr. 1886.
The Money of Canada From An Historical Standpoint, 1915.
The Real Date of the Canadian 1820 Bust and Harp, ANJ 1907.
Some Recent Frauds in Canadian Coins, CA 1892.
The Wellington Tokens Relating to Canada: A Review, Num. Nov. 1915.
When Was the Vexator Canadinsis Issued? CA Apr. 1915.

Metcalf, J.:   Prince Edward Island Hard Times Currency, CA 1889-1890.

Naftel, F. J.:   The Copper Coins of the Bank of Montreal, Bank of Montreal Staff Magazine, October 1936.

Nichols, G.:   Wood 42, Not a Blacksmith Copper, Numismatica Canada, Vol 3, 2004.

**Nichols, G. and
Faulkner, C.:**   Ships, Colonies & Commerce, CNJ Jan/Feb 1998.

Prenoveau, J. J.:   Le Jeton de John Shaw, CNJ Dec. 1962.
                          Le Sou de J. Roy, CNJ Apr. 1963.

Pridmore, Fred: The Coins of the British Commonwealth of Nations, Part III, The West Indies, 1965.
                          The Holey Dollar and Plug of Prince Edward Island, NC Nov.-Dec. 1960.
                          Notes on Colonial Coins, NC Oct.-Nov. 1964.

Reid, R. L.:   The Holey Dollar of Prince Edward Island, Num. Feb. 1929.

Russell, Dr. P. A.:   Canadian Colonial Tokens Struck by Boulton & Watt 1838-1845, CNJ May 1982.

Sandham, A.:   Coins, Tokens and Medals of the Dominion of Canada, 1869, Reprint 1962.
                          Montreal Trade Tokens, 1872. Numismata Canadiana. CA 1880-1881.

Shortt, Adam: Documents Relating to Currency Exchange and Finance During the French Regime, 1925.

                          Documents Relating to Currency Exchange and Finance in Nova Scotia, 1933.
                          The History of Canadian Metallic Currency. Transactions of the Canadian Institute, 1912.

Thomson, Geo. H.:   Die Varieties of Breton 715, CNJ, May 1997.

Willey, R. C.:   The Boston Sou, CNJ Mar. 1974.
                          The Colonial Coinages of Canada, CNJ Jan. 1979 to July/Aug. 1983.
                          Ships Colonies and Commerce Halfpennies of Lower Canada, CNJ Dec. 1974.

Wood, Howland: The Canadian Blacksmith Coppers, Num. June 1910.

Abbreviations: ANS - The American Numismatic Society
                          CNJ - The Canadian Numismatic Journal
                          Num. - The Numismatist (ANA)
                          NC - Spink's Numismatic Circular
                          CA - The Canadian Antiquarian and Numismatic Journal
                          AJN - American Journal of Numismatics (American Numismatic Association)

Notes: **(1)** Reprinted in Dr. Joseph Leroux's "Canadian Coin Cabinet" - a 1964 reprint by Canadian Numismatic Publishing Institution.
                          (2) Reprinted in "Canadian Tokens and Medals," an anthology by A.D. Hock, Quarterman Publications, Inc.

LEGEND INDEX TO COLONIAL TOKENS

The legends on tokens are an important numismatic characteristic. They either domiciled the token to a particular colony or carried a message which had either monetary or political significance to the colony. Thus the beginner token collector can also use this index to locate a token by means of the legend it carries.

Legends may be incorporated into the design of a token in one of four different ways:

1. Tokens with both a reverse and obverse legend
2. Tokens with only a reverse legend
3. Tokens with only an obverse legend
4. Tokens with no legends

On Canadian tokens the reverse legend usually indicates the name of the issuer. It is for this reason that we chose to use the reverse legend first in our heading listing.

Each token heading in this catalogue carries a token number followed by the legend on the token as illustrated by one of the four examples shown below.

Chapter heads and sub-heads are shown in normal type while all token legends are italicized.

EXAMPLES

1. TOKENS WITH BOTH A REVERSE AND OBVERSE LEGEND

NS-14
PAYABLE BY JOHN ALEXR BARRY HALIFAX — 1815 HALFPENNY TOKEN

Reverse legend   Obverse legend

2. TOKENS WITH ONLY A REVERSE LEGEND

LC-46   *HALFPENNY TOKEN 1812 — (BUST DESIGN)*

Reverse legend   No obverse legend

3. TOKENS WITH ONLY AN OBVERSE LEGEND

BL-30   *(HARP DESIGN) — HALF PENNY TOKEN (BUST OF GEORGE III)*

No reverse legend   Obverse legend

4. TOKEN WITH NO LEGENDS

LC-55   *(SEATED JUSTICE DESIGN) — (SAILING SHIP DESIGN)*

No reverse legend   No obverse legend

COMPLETE LEGEND INDEX OF CANADIAN COLONIAL TOKENS

The following index represents a complete listing of all legends appearing on Canadian colonial tokens as catalogued in the Charlton Standard Catalogue of Canadian Colonial Tokens. This listing is grouped into three divisions as follows:

(a) tokens with a legend on both obverse and reverse;

(b) tokens with a legend on only one side; and

(c) tokens with no legends on either side.

Within each of these three groups, legends are ordered in alphabetic sequence to minimize legend search time. Once the desired legend is located, you will have instant access to three additional pieces of information. These include:

(a) page number reference for the token in the "Charlton Standard Catalogue of Canadian Colonial Tokens" - 6th Edition;

(b) the Charlton token reference number; and

(c) the Breton token reference number.

In some instances a particular legend may have multiple entries for page numbers and/or catalogue numbers. For an explanation you may have to consult all of the appropriate pages in this catalogue.

LEGEND INDEX - CANADIAN COLONIAL TOKENS

TOKENS WITH LEGENDS ON TWO SIDES

LEGENDS	Charlton Standard Page No.	Charlton Catalogue Number	Breton Number
1814 — Wellington Halfpenny Token	165	WE-8	979
1816 — Half Penny Token	73	NS-29	—
Bank of Montreal Token Un Sous — Trade & Agriculture Lower Canada	86, 87	LC-3	714
Bank Token Half Penny — 1838 Bank of Montreal	97	LC-10A	524
Bank Token Half Penny — 1839 Bank of Montreal	98	LC-10B	524
Bank Token Half Penny 1837 — Province Du Bas Canada Un Sou	91-93	LC-8A to D	522
Bank Token Half Penny 1842 — Province of Canada Bank of Montreal	187	PC-1A	527
Bank Token Half Penny 1844 — Province of Canada Bank of Montreal	188	PC-1B	527
Bank Token Half Penny 1845 — Province of Canada Bank of Montreal	189	PC-1C	527
Bank Token Montreal ½ Penny — Trade & Agriculture Lower Canada	90	LC-7	673
Bank Token Montreal Un Sous — Trade & Agriculture Lower Canada	84, 85	LC-2	713
Bank Token One Half-Penny — 1850 Bank of Upper Canada	192	PC-5A	720
Bank Token One Half-Penny — 1852 Bank of Upper Canada	193	PC-5B	720
Bank Token One Half-Penny — 1854 Bank of Upper Canada	193	PC-5C	720
Bank Token One Half-Penny — 1857 Bank of Upper Canada	194	PC-5D	720
Bank Token One Penny — 1838 Bank of Montreal	99	LC-11A	523
Bank Token One Penny — 1839 Bank of Montreal	99	LC-11B	523
Bank Token One Penny — 1839 Bank of Montreal	100	LC-11C	525
Bank Token One Penny 1837 — Province Du Bas Canada Deux Sous	94-96	LC-9A to D	521
Bank Token One Penny 1837 — Province of Canada Bank of Montreal	189	PC-2A	—
Bank Token One Penny 1842 — Province of Canada Bank of Montreal	190	PC-2B	526
Bank Token One Penny — 1850 Bank of Upper Canada	194	PC-6A	719
Bank Token One Penny — 1852 Bank of Upper Canada	195	PC-6B	719
Bank Token One Penny — 1854 Bank of Upper Canada	196	PC-6C	719
Bank Token One Penny — 1857 Bank of Upper Canada	196	PC-6D	719
Banque Du Peuple Montreal Un Sou — Agriculture & Commerce Bas-Canada	88	LC-4	716
Banque Du Peuple Montreal Un Sou — Agriculture & Commerce Bas Canada	89	LC-5	715
Britannia 1814 — Broke Halifax Nova Scotia	54, 55	NS-7A-B	879
Canada Half Penny Token — For Public Accommodation	102	LC-14	533
Cash Paid For All Sorts of Grain 1837 — THS & WM Molson Montreal Brewers Distillers &&& Un Sou	103	LC-16	562
Commerce — 1781 North American Token	199	AM-5	1013
Commerce — 1813 Marquis Wellington	164	WE-7	978
Commerce & Trade — 1840 Prince Edward's Island Halfpenny	10	PE-4	916
Commerce Rules The Main — 1812 Success to Trade	198	AM-3	983
Commercial Change 1815 — Halfpenny Token Upper Canada	180	UC-8	726
Commercial Change 1820 — Halfpenny Token Upper Canada	181	UC-9	727
Commercial Change 1821 Jamaica — Halfpenny Token Upper Canada	182	UC-11	729
Commercial Change 1821 Upper Canada — Halfpenny Token Upper Canada	182	UC-10	728
Commerical Change 1833 — Halfpenny Token Upper Canada	184	UC-13	731
Copper Company of Upper Canada One Half Penny — 1794	173	UC-1	721
Cossack Penny Token — Vimiera Talavera Busaco Badajoz Salamanca	170	WE-13	985
Fisheries and Agriculture — 1855 One Cent	12	PE-6	920
Fisheries and Agriculture — Halfpenny Token	16	PE-8	921
F. McDermott Importer of English, French & German Fancy Goods, King St. Saint John, N.B. — Depository of Arts	79	NB-3	914
For Public Accommodation One Penny — 1805 Hibernia	198	AM-2	975
For Publick Accommodation — 1815 Ships Colonies and Commerce	17	PE-9B	996
For the Convenience of Trade — 1814 Half Penny Token	56	NS-8	880
Francis Mullins & Son Montreal Importers of Ship Chandlery &c. — Commerce Token	104	LC-17	563
Genuine British Copper (Seated Britannia Design) — 1815 Half Penny Token	71	NS-25	886
H — 1816 Halfpenny Token	74	NS-30	—
Halfpenny — 1815 Genuine British Copper	72	NS-26	887
Half Penny — 1830 Canada	101	LC-13A	532

TOKENS WITH LEGENDS ON TWO SIDES

LEGENDS	Charlton Standard Page No.	Charlton Catalogue Number	Breton Number
Half Penny — 1841 Canada	101	LC-13B	532
Halfpenny Token — Field Marshal Wellington	160	WE-2A	971
Halfpenny Token — Field Marshal Wellington	161	WE-2B	972
Halfpenny Token — Nova Scotia and New Brunswick Success	73	NS-28	895
Halfpenny Token — Victoria Nobis Est	140	LC-49	982
Halfpenny Token 1813 — Field Marshal Wellington	160	WE-1	969
Halfpenny Token 1382 — Province of Nova Scotia	49	NS-3B	872
Halfpenny Token 1823 — Province of Nova-Scotia	38	NS-1A	867
Halfpenny Token 1823 — Province of Nova Scotia	39	NS-1B	867
Halfpenny Token 1824 — Province of Nova Scotia	40	NS-1C	869
Halfpenny Token 1832 — Province of Nova Scotia	41	NS-1D	871
Halfpenny Token 1832 — Province of Nova Scotia	48	NS-3A	871
Halfpenny Token 1832 — Province of Nova Scotia	49	NS-3C	871
Halfpenny Token 1832 — Province of Nova Scotia	50	NS-3D	871
Halfpenny Token 1840 — Province of Nova Scotia	42	NS-1E	874
Halfpenny Token 1843 — Province of Nova Scotia	43	NS-1F	874
Halfpenny Token 1832 — Province of Upper Canada	185	UC-14	732
Halfpenny Token Nova Scotia — 1815 Commercial Change	58	NS-12	885
Halfpenny Token Nova Scotia — 1815 Starr & Shannon Halifax	58	NS-11	884
Halifax — 1815 Halfpenny Token	72	NS-27	889
Halifax Nova Scotia — 1816 Wholesale & Retail Hardware Store	61	NS-15A	892
Hibernia 1805 — Field Marshal Wellington	163	WE-5	976
JB (Script Initials) — Halfpenny (Warehouse Design)	220	BL-31	—
J. Roy Montreal Un Sou — Commerce Bas-Canada	106	LC-20	671
Montreal — 1816 Half Penny Token	100	LC-12	531
New Brunswick Half Penny Currency — 1854 Victoria Dei Gratia Regina	77	NB-1B	912
New Brunswick Half Penny Token — 1843 Victoria Dei Gratia Regina	77	NB-1A	910
New Brunswick One Penny Currency — 1854 Victoria Dei Gratia Regina	78	NB-2B	911
New Brunswick One Penny Token — 1843 Victoria Dei Gratia Regina	78	NB-2A	909
One Half Penny Token — 1815 Ships Colonies and Commerce	17	PE-9A	995
One Halfpenny Token 1820 — Trade & Navigation	70	NS-24	894
One Penny Token — 1812	133	LC-47B	958
One Penny Token — 1812 Bon Pour Deux Sous	136	LC-47E	—
One Penny Token — 1813	134	LC-47C	958
One Penny Token — 1813 Field Marshal Wellington	162	WE-3	974
One Penny Token — Field Marshal Wellington	162	WE-4A	970
One Penny Token — Field Marshal Wellington	163	WE-4B	—
One Penny Token 1812 — 1812	132	LC-47A	957
One Penny Token 1813			
— Vimiera Talavera Badajoz Salamanca Vittoria	170	WE-12	984
One Penny Token 1824 — Province of Nova Scotia	44	NS-2A	868
One Penny Token 1832 — Province of Nova Scotia	45	NS-2B	870
	51	NS-4	870
One Penny Token 1840 — Province of Nova Scotia	46	NS-2C	873
One Penny Token 1843 — Province of Nova Scotia	47	NS-2D	873
Payable at the Store of J Brown — Nemo Me Impune Lacessit	62	NS-16	896
Payable at W.A. & S.Black's Halifax N.S.			
— 1816 Wholesale & Retail Hardware Store	61	NS-15B	893
Payable by Carritt & Alport Halifax — 1814 Half Penny Token	56	NS-9	881
Payable by Hosterman & Etter Halifax — 1814 Halfpenny Token	57	NS-10A	882
Payable by Hosterman & Etter Halifax — 1815 Halfpenny Token	57	NS-10B	883
Payable by John Alexr. Barry Halifax — 1815 Halfpenny Token	60	NS-14	891
Payable by Miles W. White Halifax NS — 1815 Halfpenny Token	59	NS-13	890
Peter McAuslane St. John's Newfoundland			
— Sells All Sorts of Shop & Store Goods	4	NF-2	956
Pro Bono Publico Montreal ½ Penny Token 1837			
— Trade & Agriculture Lower Canada	90	LC-6	672
Prosperity to Canada La Prudence et la Candeur Token Halfpenny			
— Lesslie & Sons York Kingston & Dundas	174	UC-2	718
Prosperity to Canada La Prudence et la Candeur Token 2d Currency			
— 1822 Lesslie & Sons Toronto & Dundass	175	UC-3	717

TOKENS WITH LEGENDS ON TWO SIDES

LEGENDS	Charlton Standard Page No.	Charlton Catalogue Number	Breton Number
Province of Nova Scotia Halfpenny Token			
— 1856 Victoria D:G:Britanniar:Reg:F:D:	52	NS-5	876
Province of Nova Scotia One Penny Token			
— 1856 Victoria D:G:Britanniar:Reg:F:D:	53	NS-6	875
Pure Copper Preferable to Paper Half Penny Token			
— 1812 Trade & Navigation	64	NS-19A	963
Pure Copper Preferable to Paper Half Penny Token			
— 1813 Trade & Navigation	64	NS-19B	963
Pure Copper Preferable to Paper Half Penny Token			
— 1813 Trade & Navigation (Ship Design)	67	NS-21	965
Pure Copper Preferable to Paper One Farthing			
— 1813 Trade & Navigation	63	NS-18	964
Pure Copper Preferable to Paper One Penny Token			
— 1813 Trade & Navigation	65	NS-20A	962
Pure Copper Preferable to Paper One Penny Token			
— 1814 Trade & Navigation	66	NS-20B	962
Pure Copper Preferable to Paper Half Penny Token			
— For General Accommodation	197	AM-1	966
Quebec Bank Token Half Penny 1852			
— Province Du Canada Un Sou	191	PC-3	529
Quebec Bank Token One Penny 1852			
— Province Du Canada Deux Sous	191	PC-4	528
Responsible Government and Free Trade			
— 1860 Fishery Rights for Newfoundland	5	NF-4	955
RH (Script Initials) — 1812 Farthing Token	141	LC-50	991
RH (Script Initials) — 1814 Half Penny Token	141	LC-51	990
RH (Script Initials) — 1814 One Penny Token	142	LC-52	989
R & I.S. Rutherford Newfoundland St. John's — 1841	2	NF-1B	952
Rutherford Bros. Newfoundland Harbour Grace — 1846	3	NF-1C	953
Self Government and Free Trade — 1855 Prince Edward Island	14	PE-7B	919
Self Government and Free Trade — 1855 Prince Edward's Island	13	PE-7A	918
Self Government and Free Trade — 1857 Prince Edward Island	15	PE-7C	919
Sir Isaac Brook Bart. The Hero of Upper Canada 1812			
— Success to the Commerce of Uppr & Lowr Canada	177	UC-5	723
Speed the Plough — Success to the Fisheries	11	PE-5A, B	917
Speed The Plough Halfpenny Token — No Labour No Bread	176	UC-4	1010
St. John New Brunswick Half Penny Token — For Public Accommodation	79	NB-4	913
Success to Commerce & Peace to the World 1816			
— Sr. Isaac Brock The Hero of Upr Canada Fell Oct 13 1812	178	UC-6	724
Success to Commerce and Peace to the World 1816			
— Success to the Commerce of Uppr & Lowr Canada	179	UC-7	725
Success to Navigation & Trade — 1815 Halfpenny Token	69	NS-23	888
Success to the Fishery One Penny — 1815 Magdalen Island Token	83	LC-1	520
T. Duseaman Butcher Belleville — Agriculture & Commerce Bas-Canada	130	LC-45	670
To Facilitate Trade 1823 — Halfpenny Token Upper Canada	183	UC-12A	730
To Facilitate Trade 1833 — Halfpenny Token Upper Canada	184	UC-12B	730
Token Montreal Un Sou — Agriculture & Commerce Bas-Canada	109-123,127-130 125, 126	LC-21 to LC-36 LC-38 to LC-39	674-708 710-712
Token Montreal Un Sou — Trade & Agriculture Lower Canada	124	LC-37	709
Trade & Navigation 1838 — Pure Copper Preferable to Paper	68	NS-22	967
Vexator Canadinsis 1811	201	VC-1	558
Vexator (or Venator) Canadiensis ML 1811	201	VC-3	559
Vexator (or Venator) Canadinsis 1811	201	VC-2	558
Vimiera Talavera Almeida — Hispaniam et Lvsitaniam Restitvit Wellington	167-169	WE-11A-D	986-988
W.L. Whites Halifax House Halifax Cheap Dry Goods Store			
— One Farthing Payable at White's Halifax House Halifax	62	NS-17	899
Waterloo Halfpenny 1816 — The Illustrious Wellington	166	WE-10	981

TOKENS WITH LEGENDS ON ONE SIDE ONLY

LEGENDS	Charlton Standard Page No.	Charlton Catalogue Number	Breton Number
1812 (Seated Justice Design) — (Bust Design)	140	LC-48C	961
1820 (Harp Design) — (Bust Design)	153-157	LC-60B to F	1012
1825 (Harp Design) — (Bust Design)	152	LC-60A	1012
1858 — (Sailing Ship Design)	4	NF-3	954
Commerce — (Bust Design)	137	LC-47G	—
Commerce 1814 — (Bust Design)	136	LC-47F	—
Commercial Change — (Bust Design)	151	LC-59A, B	1007
PMC P.E.I Uniface (McCarthy Penny Token)	9	PE-3	—
Field Marshal Wellington — (Seated Britannia Design)	161	WE-2C	973
Half Penny Token (Bust of George III)	219	BL-29	—
Halfpenny Token — (Sailing Ship Design)	147	LC-56C	1005
Halfpenny Token 1812 — (Bust Design)	131	LC-46	960
	138	LC48A	960
	139	LC-48B	960
Halfpenny Token 1812 — (Sailing Ship Design)	146	LC-56A	1004
Halfpenny Token 1813 — (Seated Britannia Design)	143, 144	LC-54A, B	994
Halfpenny Token 1814 — (Seated Britannia Design)	144	LC-54C	994
Halfpenny Token 1815 — (Sailing Ship Design)	147	LC-56B	1004
Halfpenny Token 1815 — (Seated Britannia Design)	145	LC-54D	994
Harp Design) — Halfpenny (Warehouse Design)	219	BL-30	—
J. Shaw & Co. Importers of Hardwares Upper Town Quebec —	105	LC-19	565
One Penny Token 1812 — (Bust Design)	135	LC-47D	959
P.E.I Uniface (McCausland Penny Token)	9	PE-2	—
Pure Copper Preferable to Paper — (Irishman Design)	199	AM-4	1009
R & I.S. Rutherford Newfoundland St. John's —	2	NF-1A	952
R.W. Owen Montreal Ropery — (Sailing Ship Design)	104	LC-18	564
(Seated Justice Design) — 1820 (Bust of George III)	148	LC-57	1011
Ships Colonies & Commerce — (Bust Design)	149, 150	LC-58A, B	1002
Ships Colonies & Commerce — (Harp Design)	218	BL-28	998
Ships Colonies & Commerce — (Sailing Ship Design)	217	BL-26	999
Ships Colonies & Commerce — (Sailing Ship Design)	21-36	PE-10-1 to 10-46	997, 999 1000
	215-216	BL-24 A-C	997, 999
St. John's N.B. Halfpenny Token —	80	NB-5	—
T.S. Brown & Co. Importers of Hardwares Montreal —	102	LC-15	561
To Facilitate Trade 1825 — (Civilian Bust Design)	143	LC-53B	—
To Facilitate Trade 1825 — (Military Bust Design)	142	LC-53A	992
Trade & Commerce 1811 — (Bust Design)	164	WE-6	977
Wellington Halfpenny Token — (Seated Britannia Design)	166	WE-9	980
Wellington Waterloo 1815 — (Large Bust Design)	171	WE-15	1006
Wellington Waterloo 1815 — (Sailing Ship Design)	171	WE-14	1003

TOKENS WITH NO LEGENDS

LEGENDS	Charlton Standard Page No.	Charlton Catalogue Number	Breton Number
Harp Design) — (Bust Design)	158	LC-61	—
Sailing Ship Design) — (Laureate Bust Design)	217	BL-25	—
Seated Justice Design) — (Sailing Ship Design)	146	LC-55	1001

The old Bank of Montreal building on the left (without the fencing and tree) and the new Bank of Montreal building on the right, which appears on the 100th anniversary medal of 1917.

TOKENS OF NEWFOUNDLAND

In 1838 the British government abandoned the idea of introducing Sterling into British North America.

Meanwhile, local halfpenny tokens began to appear to satisfy the need for currency. The first of these were the Rutherford halfpennies, in use from about 1840 to 1850. Because of the vast numbers of P.E.I. halfpennies being brought into St. John's, further importation was forbidden by the government in 1851. To further complicate the situation, French coppers were also circulating at this time.

A proposed issue of 500 Pounds in pennies and halfpennies of distinctive design failed and in 1860 the government again forbade the importation of all private tokens.

In 1863 the decimal system was adopted and old coppers of all kinds were recalled and redeemed at weight.

BRETON CROSS REFERENCE TABLE FOR NEWFOUNDLAND TOKENS

Breton Cat. No.	Charlton Cat. No.	Page No.		Breton Cat. No.	Charlton Cat. No.	Page No.
952	NF-1A, B	2		955	NF-4	5
953	NF-1C	3		956	NF-2	4
954	NF-3	4				

PRIVATE TOKENS

NF-1   *RUTHERFORD TOKENS*

In 1840 George, Andrew, Robert and I.S. Rutherford left England to set up as general merchants. Robert and I.S. Rutherford settled in St. John's, with George and Andrew settling in Harbour Grace. The first tokens were issued shortly thereafter from St. John's and were struck by Boulton & Watt.

NF-1A   *R & I.S. RUTHERFORD NEWFOUNDLAND ST. JOHN'S —*

Composition: Brass, copper
Weight: 8.7 to 10.6 g
Diameter: 28.7 to 28.9 mm
Die Axis: ↑↑, ↑↓
Edge: Plain
Ref.Nos.: Br 952 (R-1); Co 1NF;
           Lr 320 (R-4);
           McL 487; W 180

Varieties: Composition, Die axis
A1   Copper; Coinage
A2   Copper; Medal
A3   Brass; Medal
A4   Brass; Coinage

Variations: A variety exists where the apostrophe in St. John's touches the fleece of the right hind foot, W 181.

Cat.No.	Description	VG-8	F-12	VF-20	EF-40	AU-50	AU-55	MS-60
NF-1A1	Copper; ↑↓	10.	18.	65.	275.	500.	725.	900.
NF 1A2	Copper; ↑↑	10.	18.	65.	275.	500.	725.	900.
NF-1A3	Brass; ↑↑	12.	25.	80.	350.	600.	825.	1,000.
NF-1A4	Brass; ↑↓	12.	25.	80.	350.	600.	825.	1,000.

NF-1B   *R & I.S. RUTHERFORD NEWFOUNDLAND ST. JOHN'S — 1841*

Composition: Copper, brass
Weight: 9.0 to 10.4 g
Diameter: 28.8 to 29.5 mm
Die Axis: ↑↑, ↑↓
Edge: Plain
Ref.Nos.: Br 952 (R-1); Co 2NF;
           Lr 319 (R-4);
           McL 488; W 182

Varieties: Composition, Die axis
B1   Copper, Coinage
B2   Copper, Medal
B3   Brass, Medal

Cat.No.	Date	Description	VG-8	F-12	VF-20	EF-40	AU-50	AU-55	MS-60
NF-1B1	1841	Copper, ↑↓	8.	25.	75.	300.	600.	825.	1,000.
NF-1B2	1841	Copper, ↑↑	8.	25.	75.	300.	600.	825.	1,000.
NF-1B3	1841	Brass, ↑↑	10.	30.	95.	350.	675.	925.	1,100.

NF-1C *RUTHERFORD BROS. NEWFOUNDLAND HARBOUR GRACE — 1846*

In 1846 the Harbour Grace Store issued halfpenny tokens. While the initials R.H. appear below the arms on the reverse it is doubtful that these tokens were actually struck by Ralph Heaton and Company as previously believed, as they did not receive the coining equipment from Boulton and Watt until the late 1840s.

Composition: Copper
Weight: 7.5 to 8.8 g
Diameter: 29.4 mm
Die Axis: ↑↑, ↑↓
Edge: Plain
Ref.Nos.: Br 953 (R-1); See below

Fine Wool / Long hooves
/ Rosettes **(C1 and 2)**

Coarse Wool /Short hooves
/ Stars **(C3 and 4)**

Varieties: Reverse design, Die axis
    C1 Fine Wool, Long hooves, Rosettes, Medal; Co 3-6NF; Lr 321 (R-4); McL 490; W 183, 184
    C2 Coarse Wool, Short hooves, Rosettes, Medal; Co 7NF; Lr 321 (R-4); McL 490; W 185
    C3 Coarse Wool, Short hooves, Stars, Medal; Co 8NF; Lr 322 (R-4); McL 489; W 186
    C4 Coarse Wool, Short hooves, Stars, Coinage; Co 8NF; Lr 322 (R-4); McL 489; W 186

Variations: Minor varieties exist as a result of worn and retouched dies.

Cat.No.	Date	Description	VG-8	F-12	VF-20	EF-40	AU-50	AU-55	MS-60
NF-1C1	1846	Fine, Rosettes, ↑↑	8.	12.	25.	110.	275.	425.	500.
NF 1C2	1846	Coarse, Rosettes, ↑↑	8.	12.	30.	110.	275.	425.	500.
NF-1C3	1846	Coarse, Stars, ↑↑	12.	25.	50.	135.	350.	500.	625.
NF-1C4	1846	Coarse, Stars, ↑↓	12.	25.	50.	135.	350.	500.	625.

NF-2   **PETER McAUSLANE ST. JOHN'S NEWFOUNDLAND**
            — SELLS ALL SORTS OF SHOP & STORE GOODS

Peter McAuslane, a blacksmith by trade, opened a dry goods store on Water Street in St. John's about 1844. It is believed that McAuslane struck one hundred of these pieces which once were thought to be intended as farthings due to their size. Most were probably lost in the fire of 1846 that destroyed his establishment.

Composition: Brass
Weight: N/A
Diameter: 20.0 to 20.6 mm
Die Axis: ↑↑
Edge: Plain
Ref.Nos.: Br 956 (R-5); Co 11NF; Lr 318 (R-8); McL 486

Cat.No.	Description	AG	G-4	VG-8	F-12	VF-20
NF-2	Peter McAuslane	1,500.	3,000.	4,500.	6,500.	9,000.

ANONYMOUS TOKENS

NF-3   **1858 — (SAILING SHIP DESIGN)**

A rare halfpenny was issued anonymously at St. John's in 1858. It was struck by Ralph Heaton and Company using Halliday's Ships Colonies and Commerce obverse design.

Composition: Copper
Weight: 5.0 to 6.1 g
Diameter: 25.4 to 25.6 mm
Die Axis: ↑↑
Edge: Plain
Ref.Nos.: Br 954 (R-4); Co 9NF; Lr 316 (R-5); McL 491; See below

Open "5" (A1)   Closed "5" (A2)

Varieties: Reverse
A1 Open "5"; W 188
A2 Closed "5"; W 187

Cat.No.	Date	Description	VG-8	F-12	VF-20	EF-40	AU-50	AU-55	MS-60
NF-3A1	1858	Open "5"	600.	800.	1,500.	2,000.	2,750.	—	—
NF-3A2	1858	Closed "5"	600.	800.	1,500.	2,000.	2,750.	—	—

NF-4   *RESPONSIBLE GOVERNMENT AND FREE TRADE*
              — 1860 FISHERY RIGHTS FOR NEWFOUNDLAND

     This token was issued in 1860 to commemorate the signing of a treaty by the major fishing nations to regulate the fisheries and establish fishing limits. The treaty also took steps to control the actions of foreign fishermen while on Newfoundland waters and in Newfoundland ports. The tokens were struck by Ralph Heaton and Company.

Composition: Copper
Weight: 4.8 to 5.8 g
Diameter: 26.0 to 26.2 mm
Die Axis: ↑↑
Edge: Plain
Ref.Nos.: Br 955 (R-2½);
            Co 10NF; Lr 317 (R-5);
            McL 493; W 189

Cat.No.	Date	Description	VG-8	F-12	VF-20	EF-40	AU-50	AU-55	MS-60
NF-4	1860	Fishery Rights	75	150.	200.	450.	750.	—	—

TOKENS OF PRINCE EDWARD ISLAND

Prince Edward Island formed part of the French colony of Acadia but was not ceded to Great Britain when mainland Acadia was lost by France in 1713. The Island was acquired by Britain by the Treaty of Paris and received its present name in 1798 in honour of Queen Victoria's father. Prince Edward Island was governed from Nova Scotia until 1769 when it was made a separate colony. The first act to regulate its currency was passed in 1785 when the Spanish dollar was rated at five shillings (5/-), the same as in Nova Scotia. Currency depreciation began when the first of the irredeemable treasury notes was issued. By 1827 the Spanish dollar was circulating at five shillings and six pence (5/6). In 1829 an act was passed by the legislative assembly but it was later rejected, probably due to its odd valuation of gold coins. By 1833 the dollar was circulating at six shillings (6/-), a premium of 20% over its intrinsic value because of the inflationary effect of the increasing volume of treasury notes. This was done in order to keep the coins circulating in Prince Edward Island and not being exported.

According to Pridmore, the late British colonial token authority, the treasury ordered the countermarking of coins with the letters "P.E.I.," also to keep them in local circulation. Today these coins are extremely rare.

By 1847, when an inquiry into local currency was ordered, the situation was still very unsettled as most government departments were valuing the dollar at six shillings (6/-), while the Customs department valued it at six shillings and three pence (6/3).

In 1849 the recommendations of the Committee of Inquiry were accepted and an act was passed regulating the currency and fixing the Spanish-American dollar at six shillings and threepence (6/3). This rating prevailed until the adoption of the decimal system in 1871.

BRETON CROSS REFERENCE TABLE FOR PRINCE EDWARD ISLAND TOKENS

Breton Cat. No.	Charlton Cat. No.	Page No.	Breton Cat. No.	Charlton Cat. No.	Page No.
916	PE-4	10	997	PE-10-10 to 13	24
917	PE-5A, B	11	997	PE-10-14 to 17	26
918	PE-7A	13	997	PE-10-18 to 22	27
919	PE-7B, C	14, 15	997	PE-10-23, 24, 26	29
920	PE-6	12	997	PE-10-25	30
921	PE-8	16	997	PE-10-27, 33	30
995	PE-9A	17	997	PE-10-28 to 32	31
996	PE-9B	17	997	PE-10-34, 35, 40	33
997	PE-10-1	21	997	PE-10-36, 37, 42, 45, 46	34
997	PE-10-2	21	997	PE-10-38, 39	35
997	PE-10-3	22, 215	997	PE-10-41, 43, 44	36
997	PE-10-4	22, 216	999	PE-10-5 to 5A	22, 217
997	PE-10-6 to 9	23	1000	PE-10-5B	22

SEMI-REGAL TOKENS

PE-1   *"HOLEY" DOLLAR AND PLUG OF 1813*

PE1A   *TREASURY ISSUE*

The principal coin used on Prince Edward Island in the early 19th century was the Spanish-American dollar. When a new governor arrived there in 1813 to take up his post however, he found that all coins were very scarce creating something of a commercial crisis. The scarcity resulted from the tendency of local businessmen to hoard coins to be sent abroad to pay for goods imported.

The governor decided that a remedy to the problem was the creation of a local coinage from mutilated Spanish-American coins, similar to that taking place in the West Indies and Australia. He ordered that a quantity of Spanish-American dollars be perforated to form two kinds of coins. The piece punched out of the centre (the plug) was to be a shilling and the large ring that remained ("holey" dollar) was to be a five shilling piece.

Each plug and holey dollar was given an official counterstamp. The nature of this counterstamp seems not to have been specified. Circumstantial evidence suggests it consisted of ten triangles arranged in a circle, like a symbol for the sun. On the holey dollar the triangles are well separated from each other and the symbol touches the king's forehead. However, on the plug the triangles are larger and run together at the corners.

The reasoning behind the creation of the plug and holey dollar coinage was that the coins would remain on the island, being overvalued (as they were by some 20 percent) compared to the unmutilated coins. Anyone using the mutilated coins for payments abroad would thus sustain a loss of 20 percent because the coins would only be accepted at the inflated rate on the island. This proved to be correct. The merchants saw a chance to make a quick profit by creating their own holey dollars. This forced the government to withdraw the official issue in 1814, leaving the merchants' forgeries behind. The merchants' pieces are thought to have continued in circulation for about another ten years.

Authenticating a holey dollar or plug is not an easy matter. Provenance, the appearance and placement of the counterstamp and the appearance of the hole in the centre of the dollar are all important. Differentiating the original issue from the merchants' imitations is made doubly difficult by the fact that from about 1890 onward forgeries have been made to sell to collectors. Most are made from genuine Spanish-American dollars. The forgeries made for collectors are, of course, worth much less than an original or merchants' imitation. Recently, lightweight counterfeits of the holey dollar and plug have also begun to appear. At the present time it is not possible to positively differentiate the originals from the contemporary merchants' imitations. It is assumed that certain of the holey dollars with counterstamps consisting of small squares or radiating lines instead of triangles are merchants' imitations, but it is also possible that the counterstamp on the merchants' imitations were always more like the originals and that all pieces with squares, lines, etc. are later forgeries for collectors. For this reason, we have listed the merchants' forgeries along with the originals. Pieces of particularly good appearance and with a good pedigree are worth a premium over the prices given below.

PE-1B   *MERCHANTS' ISSUE*

A thousand pieces proved insufficient in light of subsequent forgeries and on May 7, 1814, the government warned against such forgeries and announced that only the original treasury issue would be honoured by the treasury. On June 14, 1814, the government announced that these holey dollars and plugs were to be withdrawn and redeemed at the value at which they were issued. In August of 1814 it was announced that the exchange of official dollars and plugs would cease on September 28 of that year.

On withdrawal of the official issue, the local merchants, accustomed to an adequate supply of silver, agreed among themselves to accept forgeries for trade at the official value of 5/- for the ring and 1/- for the plug. As a result, forgeries were raised to the status of private tokens. They were used for the next ten years.

PE-1   *"HOLEY" DOLLAR AND PLUG OF 1813*

Composition: Silver
Weight: Ring: 21.8 g; Plug: N/A
Diameter: Ring: 39.2 mm; Plug: 16.0 mm

Die Axis: ↑↑
Edge: Lettered
Ref.Nos.: W 201, 202

Note: There is currently no way of authenticating the counterstamp used for the treasury issues. Thus, the merchant and treasury issues, while listed separately, are priced the same.

Cat.No.	Description	AG	G-4	VG-8	F-12	VF-20
PE-1A1	Treasury Ring	1,500.	2,000.	2,500.	3,000.	4,000.
PE-1A2	Merchant Ring	1,500.	2,000.	2,500.	3,000.	4,000.
PE-1B1	Treasury Plug			Extremely Rare		
PE-1B2	Merchant Plug			Extremely Rare		

Modern Copies

A crude eleven-point radiate counterstamp was applied to white metal cast copies of rings and plugs of Spanish-American Dollars made in the early 1960s by Regency Coin and Stamp Co. of Winnipeg. There was no intent to deceive collectors. These copies are easily recognized by the fact all rings are dated 1793, by the distinctiveness of the counterstamp, and by the fact that it is applied to the field in front of the king's nose on the ring and away from the throat on the plug.

PRIVATE TOKENS

PE-2   *P.E.I UNIFACE (McCAUSLAND PENNY TOKEN)*

This piece was issued as a penny token by Peter McCausland, a prosperous farmer and fisherman who owned the island of Rustico. The pennies were crude with extreme variation in weight. The specimen illustrated weighs only 125 grains, so light that it is difficult to believe that it would have been accepted as a penny even with the depreciated standard of the local currency.

Composition: Copper
Weight: 8.1 to 9.3 g
Diameter: 33.8 mm
Die Axis: Uniface
Edge: Plain
Ref.Nos.: W 236

Cat.No.	Description	AG	G-4	VG-8	F-12	VF-20
PE-2	Copper	750.	1,000.	1,500.	2,500.	3,500.

PE-3   *DMC P.E.I UNIFACE (McCARTHY PENNY TOKEN)*

This token is said to have been issued by Dennis McCarthy, a tinsmith from Charlottetown. It first came to notice over fifty years ago when a specimen was listed in the Wilson sale. A specimen was also offered in 1976 in the McKay-Clements sale.

Composition: Copper
Weight: N/A
Diameter: 34.4 mm
Die Axis: Uniface
Edge: Plain
Ref.Nos.: See below

Varieties: Uniface
   3A   DMC; W 237
   3B   DMC P.E.I; W 237a

Note: PE-2 and PE-3 are linked to the same maker by the punches used to form P.E.I.

Cat.No.	Description	AG	G-4	VG-8	F-12	VF-20
PE-3A	DMC			Extremely Rare		
PE-3B	DMC P.E.I			Extremely Rare		

PE-4

COMMERCE & TRADE —
1840 PRINCE EDWARD'S ISLAND HALFPENNY

The James Milner Sheaf of Wheat token was the first halfpenny struck and issued in Prince Edward Island. In 1840, Milner, with permission from the Colonial government, imported dies and presses from the United States.

Most specimens known are crudely struck on inferior planchets. This token was issued in poor condition which explains why so few were issued and why his production equipment was eventually sold for scrap.

Composition: Copper
Weight: 5.5 to 7.0 g
Diameter: 27.0 to 28.4 mm
Die Axis: ↑↓
Edge: Plain
Ref.Nos.: Br 916 (R-4); Co 3PEI;
Lr 352 (R-7);
McL 417; W 238

Cat.No.	Date	Description	AG	G-4	VG-8	F-12	VF-20
PE-4	1840	Copper	500.	1,000.	1,500.	2,000	3,000.

PE-5   *SPEED THE PLOUGH - SUCCESS TO THE FISHERIES*

Clift, Wood & Co. of Charlottetown are credited with first importing this token into Prince Edward Island. The hook variety was struck by Ralph Heaton & Sons around 1860 and large quantities were subsequently exported to Newfoundland.

The two major varieties, the clevis and the hook, were issued around 1859 and 1860 respectively.

PE-5A   *CLEVIS REVERSE Ca. 1859*

Composition: Copper
Weight: 5.2 to 6.0 g
Diameter: 25.9 to 26.1 mm
Die Axis: ↑↑
Edge: Plain
Ref.Nos.: Br 917 (R-1);
           Co 4-8PEI; Lr 357 (R-3);
           W 239-243

Clevis

Variations: Minor obverse variations exist in the fillet, the size and shaping of the tail and the lower fin. Reverse variations exist in the placement of the crossbar on the clevis.

Cat.No.	Date	Description	VG-8	F-12	VF-20	EF-40	AU-50	AU-55	MS-60
PE-5A	(1859)	Clevis reverse, ↑↑	10.	15.	40.	100.	300.	475.	600.

PE-5B   *HOOK REVERSE Ca. 1860*

Composition: Copper
Weight: 5.5 to 6.0 g
Diameter: 25.9 to 26.1 mm
Die Axis: ↑↑, ↑↓
Edge: Plain
Ref.Nos.: Br 917 (R-1);
           Co 9-12PEI;
           Lr 357 (R-3):
           W 244-246

Hook ━━━

Varieties: Die axis
     B1   Medal
     B2   Coinage

Variations: The same obverse variations exist as for PE-5A.

Cat.No.	Date	Description	VG-8	F-12	VF-20	EF-40	AU-50	AU-55	MS-60
PE-5B1	(1860)	Hook reverse, ↑↑	7.	10.	22.	75.	175.	325.	450.
PE-5B2	(1860)	Hook reverse, ↑↓	8.	12.	27.	90.	225.	375.	475.

PE-6   *FISHERIES AND AGRICULTURE — 1855 ONE CENT*

James Duncan, a hardware merchant in Charlottetown, issued the first Canadian decimal piece, the "cent" of 1855. Competing with other halfpenny tokens which went at 150 to the Spanish dollar (Duncan's piece went at 100 to the dollar) it is doubtful whether they were accepted. Later issues on thick flans were probably an attempt to gain acceptance at the higher value.

Composition: Copper
Weight: 5.0 to 6.2 g
Diameter: 26.0 mm
Die Axis: ↑↑, ↑↓
Edge: Plain
Ref.Nos.: Br 920 (R-1);
　　　　　　Lr 355 (R-3);
　　　　　　McL 420; See below

Plain fives **(A1)**

Recut fives **(A2 and 3)**

Varieties: Obverse, Die axis
A1 Plain fives, Medal; Co 41, 42PEI; W 247, 248
A2 Recut fives, Medal; Co 43PEI; W 249
A3 Recut fives, Coinage, Thick flan; Co 44PEI, W 250

Cat.No.	Date	Description	VG-8	F-12	VF-20	EF-40	AU-50	AU-55	MS-60
PE-6A1	1855	Plain fives, ↑↑	5.	10.	20.	90.	225.	350.	450.
PE-6A2	1855	Recut fives, ↑↑	8.	12.	30.	110.	300.	400.	475.
PE-6A3	1855	Recut fives, ↑↓	7.	11.	25.	90.	225.	350.	450.

PE-7   *SELF GOVERNMENT AND FREE TRADE —*

The Self Government and Free Trade tokens of 1855 and 1857 were issued by George and Simeon Davies and Henry Haszard. Besides having two distinct issue dates, the most noticeable difference between varieties is in the obverse legends which display the island name spelt two different ways.

PE-7A   *— 1855 PRINCE EDWARD'S ISLAND*

Composition: Copper
Weight: 4.8 to 5.3 g
Diameter: 26.0 to 26.1 mm
Die Axis: ↑↓
Edge: Plain
Ref.Nos.: Br 918 (R-1);
Lr 353 (R-4);
McL 420; See below

Thick top fives (**A1**)   Thin top fives (**A2**)

Varieties: Obverse
A1   Thick top fives; Co 13, 14PEI; W 251, 252
A2   Thin top fives; Co 15PEI; W 253

Cat.No.	Date	Description	VG-8	F-12	VF-20	EF-40	AU-50	AU-55	MS-60
PE-7A1	1855	Thick top fives	7.	10.	22.	70.	225.	350.	450.
PE-7A2	1855	Thin top fives	8.	12.	25.	75.	275.	400.	475.

PE-7B   *— 1855 PRINCE EDWARD ISLAND*

Composition: Copper
Weight: 4.7 to 5.1 g
Diameter: 26.0 to 26.3 mm
Die Axis: ↑↓, ↑↑
Edge: Plain
Ref.Nos.: Br 919 (R-1);
           Lr 354 (R-3);
           McL 424-426;
           See below

Five points
to "S"
(B1)

Five points
bewteen 'I' and "S"
(B2)

Varieties: Obverse
     B1 Top of "5" pointing to "S" of ISLAND; Co 16, 17PEI; W 254, 255
     B2 Top of "5" pointing between "I" and "S" of ISLAND; Co 18PEI; W 256

Variations: Courteau variations exist with date numbers slightly closer together.

Cat.No.	Date	Description	VG-8	F-12	VF-20	EF-40	AU-50	AU-55	MS-60
PE-7B1	1855	Pointing to "S"	6.	10.	22.	60.	175.	325.	450.
PE-7B2	1855	Pointing between "I" and "S"	6.	10.	22.	60.	175.	325.	450.

PE-7C   *— 1857 PRINCE EDWARD ISLAND*

Composition: Copper
Weight: 4.9 to 5.3 g
Diameter: 26.0 to 26.3 mm
Die Axis: ↑↑, ↑↓
Edge: Plain
Ref.Nos.: Br 919 (R-1);
Lr 354 (R-3);
McL 424-426;
See below

Large "AND"	Small "AND"	Large Quatrefoil	Small Quatrefoil
(C1 and 2)	**(C3 and 4)**	**(C1, 2 and 3)**	**(C4)**

Varieties: Obverse, Reverse, Die axis
C1 Large Quatrefoil, large "AND", Medal; Co 19-23, 33PEI; W 257-263
C2 Large Quatrefoil, large "AND", Coinage; Co 27, 28; W 257, 262
C3 Large Quatrefoil, small "AND", Medal; Co 25, 26, 34PEI; W 264-266
C4 Small Quatrefoil, small "AND", Medal; Co 35-40PEI; W 267-269

Variations: Varieties exist where the date points to different letters in the legend as in PE-7B. Variations also exist in die alignment, plain or hooked "E" and dot between 8 and 5 of the date (Co 24. 29-34).

Cat.No.	Date	Description	VG-8	F-12	VF-20	EF-40	AU-50	AU-55	MS-60
PE-7C1	1857	L Quatrefoil, L "AND", ↑↑	6.	10.	25.	90.	225.	350.	450.
PE-7C2	1857	L Quatrefoil, L "AND", ↑↓	6.	10.	25.	90.	225.	350.	450.
PE-7C3	1857	L Quatrefoil, S "AND", ↑↑	7.	12.	30.	115.	275.	425.	525.
PE-7C4	1857	S Quatrefoil, S "AND", ↑↑	7.	12.	30.	115.	275.	425.	525.

PE-8   *FISHERIES AND AGRICULTURE — HALFPENNY TOKEN*

The last token of Prince Edward Island was issued about 1858. It is the heaviest of the local tokens which suggests that it represented another attempt by a merchant to circulate cents. It was probably issued by James Duncan as the obverse is similar to that of Duncan's tokens of 1855. It seems that after 1858 Prince Edward Island was amply supplied with copper for there were no further halfpenny issues. The official adoption of the decimal system in 1871 rendered the tokens obsolete and they were replaced by the cents of 1871.

Composition: Copper
Weight: 5.5 to 6.5 g
Diameter: 26.4 to 26.6 mm
Die Axis: ↑↑
Edge: Plain
Ref.Nos.: Br 921 (R-1); Co 45PEI;
            Lr 356 (R-4);
            McL 492; W 272

Variations: Struck on thick or thin flans. Thin flans are the scarcer.

Cat.No.	Date	Description	VG-8	F-12	VF-20	EF-40	AU-50	AU-55	MS-60
PE-8	(1858)	Copper	10.	18.	35.	95.	275.	425.	525.

ANONYMOUS TOKENS

SHIPS COLONIES AND COMMERCE TOKENS

This is an extensive series of halfpenny tokens that circulated chiefly in Prince Edward Island between 1830 and the early 1860s. However, some of the varieties are known to have circulated in Lower Canada and Newfoundland. They are all listed under Prince Edward Island for ease of identification and pricing.

PE-9   *— 1815 SHIPS COLONIES AND COMMERCE*

The two tokens dated 1815 were struck after 1830 and antedated to evade the laws prohibiting anonymous tokens. PE-9B has the reverse of a private token issued in the Isle of Man after 1830.

PE-9A   *ONE HALF PENNY TOKEN —*

Composition: Brass
Weight: 4.5 to 4.8 g
Diameter: 27.9 to 28.1 mm
Die Axis: ↑↑
Edge: Plain
Ref.Nos.: Br 995 (R-1½);
Co 1PEI; Lr 783 (R-4);
McL 573; W 206

Cat.No.	Date	Description	VG-8	F-12	VF-20	EF-40	AU-50	AU-55	MS-60
PE-9A	1815	Brass	25.	55.	115.	300.	525.	—	—

Note: These dies were poorly prepared resulting in lack of detail. Look for surface wear to help in grading.

PE-9B   *FOR PUBLICK ACCOMMODATION —*

Composition: Brass, copper
Weight: 4.5 to 4.7 g
Diameter: 28.0 to 28.1 mm
Die Axis: ↑↑
Edge: Plain
Ref.Nos.: Br 996 (R-1½);
Co 2PEI; Lr 783a (R-4);
McL 574; W 207

Cat.No.	Date	Description	VG-8	F-12	VF-20	EF-40	AU-50	AU-55	MS-60
PE-9B	1815	Brass	30.	60.	175.	350.	600.	—	—
PE-9B	1815	Copper	50.	100.	250.	750.	900.	—	—

PE-10 *SHIPS COLONIES & COMMERCE — (SAILING SHIP DESIGN)*

The following tokens were designed by Thomas Halliday whose initial "H" appears on most of them. W.A.D. Lees in his list published in "The Numismatist" of January 1917, recorded fifty-four varieties of this token dividing the series into three groups: No "H," Single "H" and Double "H." R.C. Willey in his "The Colonial Coinage of Canada" (CNA Journal 1979-1983) followed suit with the exception of an unsigned group, and the Wright & Bale issues which were assigned to Lower Canada. We have grouped the complete series into one and listed all varieties under Prince Edward Island knowing that some of the tokens also circulated in Lower Canada and Newfoundland as well as Prince Edward Island.

IDENTIFICATION OF SHIPS COLONIES & COMMERCE TOKENS

The ships colonies and commerce tokens are divided into four major categories and within these are arranged in order by the numbering sequence used by Lee. These tokens are among the most difficult to identify. The flow charts on pages 20, 25, 28 and 32, plus the illustrations should help in the process of identification.

A: No mint mark — No guys; see flowchart 1 on page 20
B: No mint mark — Guys; see flowchart 2 on page 25
C: Single H mint mark; see flowchart 3 on page 28
D: Double H mint mark; see flowchart 4 on page 32

REVERSE

The ampersand on the token reverse is the major identifying feature. The next is the size and location of the reverse legend.

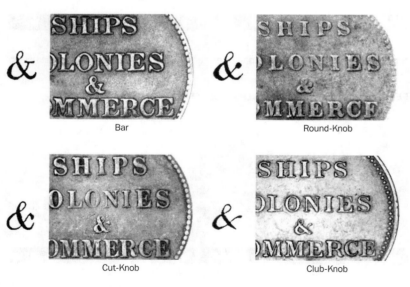

Bar   Round-Knob

Cut-Knob   Club-Knob

OBVERSE

The obverse characteristics of this token are used to help identify the major and minor varieties. The main characteristics are:

1. No mint mark
2. Single "H" mint mark
3. Double "H" mint mark
4. Wright & Bale mint mark

5. British flag, straight or curved
6. U.S. flag
7. No guys to the spritsail
8. Guys to the spritsail

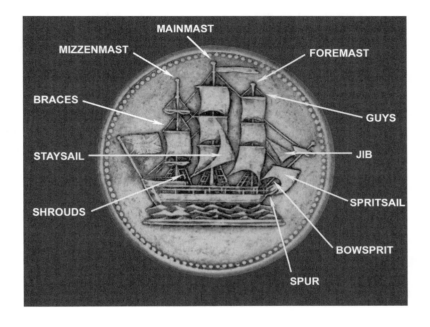

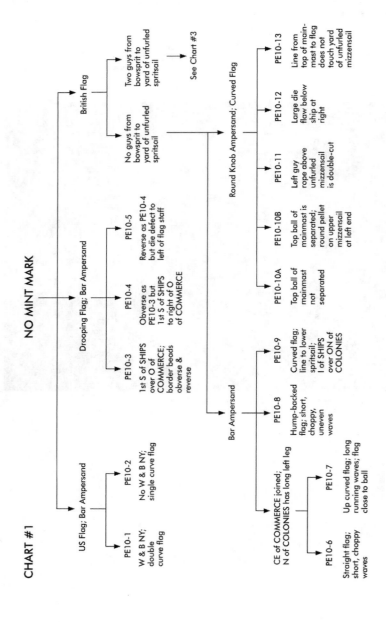

CHART #1

NO MINT MARK

US Flag; Bar Ampersand

PE10-1
W & B NY; double curve flag

PE10-2
No W & B NY; single curve flag

Drooping Flag; Bar Ampersand

PE10-3
1st S of SHIPS over O of COMMERCE; border beads obverse & reverse

PE10-4
Obverse as PE10-3 but 1st S of SHIPS to right of O of COMMERCE

PE10-5
Reverse as PE10-4 but die defect to left of flag staff

British Flag

No guys from bowsprit to yard of unfurled spritsail

Two guys from bowsprit to yard of unfurled spritsail

See Chart #3

Bar Ampersand

CE of COMMERCE joined; N of COLONIES has long left leg

PE10-6
Straight flag; short, choppy waves

PE10-7
Up curved flag; long running waves; flag close to ball

PE10-8
Hump-backed flag; short, choppy, uneven waves

PE10-9
Curved flag; line to lower spritsail; l of SHIPS over ON of COLONIES

Round Knob Ampersand; Curved Flag

PE10-10A
Top ball of mainmast not separated

PE10-10B
Top ball of mainmast is separated; round pellet on upper mizzensail at left end

PE10-11
Left guy rope above unfurled mizzensail is double-cut

PE10-12
Large die flaw below ship at right

PE10-13
Line from top of main- mast to flag does not touch yard of unfurled mizzensail

PE10-1 and 2   *NO MINTMARK; UNITED STATES FLAG*
BAR AMPERSAND

The New York firm of Wright & Bale cut the dies and struck the following tokens which circulated in Lower Canada. The ship is flying a striped flag resembling the flag of the United States. While it was first thought that these tokens were issued in 1829, their light weight could have made acceptance doubtful. Six years later they more likely would have been accepted. These tokens circulated in Lower Canada.

Composition: Copper
Weight: See below
Diameter: 25.6 mm
Die Axis: ↑↓
Edge: Plain
Ref.Nos.: Br 997 (R-0);
Lr 793 (R-2); See below

With
"W & B N.Y."
(10-1)

Without
"W & B N.Y."
(10-2)

Varieties: Obverse, Weight
10-1   With "W & B N.Y.," 3.1-4.1 g; Lees 1; W 557
10-2   Without "W & B N.Y.," 3.1-4.2 g; Lees 2; W 556

Cat.No.	Date	Description	VG-8	F-12	VF-20	EF-40	AU-50	AU-55	MS-60
PE10-1	(1829)	With "W & B N.Y.," ↑↓	22.	45.	150.	325.	600.	—	—
PE10-2	(1829)	Without "W & B N.Y.," ↑↓	12.	22.	75.	175.	350.	—	—

CCT-0002
CCT-0001

PE10-3 to 5A   NO MINTMARK; BRITISH FLAG DROOPING
BAR AMPERSAND

The tokens, PE10-3 to 5A, are listed here in order to complete the PEI section. These tokens are also listed in the Blacksmith section as they are also considered part of that series. For illustrations and technical data in greater detail see BL-24 and 26, pages 215 and 217.

Varieties: Obverse, Reverse

CCT-0003 3 Obv. and rev. border beads; First "S" of SHIPS over "O" of COMMERCE; Br 997 (R-0); Lees 3; Lr 793 (R-2); W 655

0004 4 Obv. border beads, First "S" of SHIPS to right of "O" of COMMERCE; Br 997 (R-0); Lees 4; Lr 793 (R-2); W 654

0005 5 Rectangular pennant with no balls where the guys join the main mast; Br 999 (R-4); Lees 5; Lr 793 (R-2); W 653

5A No obv. or rev. border beads; Br 999 (R-4); Lees 5A; Lr 793 (R-2)

Cat.No.	Description	AG	G-4	VG-8	F-12	VF-20
PE10-3	Obv. and rev, border beads	25.	50.	100.	225.	500.
PE10-4	Obv. border beads	1,000.	1,350.	1,800.	3,000.	4,000.
PE10-5	Rectangular pennant	1,250.	1,750.	2,500.	3,500.	4,500.
PE10-5A	No obv. or rev. border beads	—	—	—	—	6,000.

PE10-5B   LONG SHIP, UNION JACK FLAG

Composition: Copper
Weight: 5.9 g
Diameter: 25.9 mm
Thickness: 1.4 mm
Die Axis: ↑↑
Edge: Plain
Ref.Nos.: Br 1000 (R-4½);
                    Lees 5B; Lr 793 (R-2);
                    W 558

Cat.No.	Description	AG	G-4	VG-8	F-12	VF-20
PE10-5B	Long Ship		Only two known, Extremely Rare			

PE10-6 to 9   *NO MINTMARK; BRITISH FLAG*
NO GUYS
BAR AMPERSAND

The first series of the Ships Colonies and Commerce tokens (undated) cannot be attributed to a single minter. The first three tokens circulated in Lower Canada and the others in Prince Edward Island. There is no designer's initial or minter's mark on this series.

Composition: Copper
Weight: 5.0 to 6.2 g
Diameter: 25.9 to 26.2 mm
Die Axis: ↑↑, ↑↓
Edge: Plain
Ref.Nos.: Br 997 (R-0);
Lr 793 (R-2); See below

10-6 Choppy even waves

10-7 Long running even waves   **10-8** Short choppy uneven waves

                                                     Bar ampersand

10-9 Long running uneven waves

Varieties: Obverse, Reverse, Dies axis
   10-6   Choppy even waves, Straight flag, "CE" of COMMERCE joined, "N" of COLONIES has long left leg; Lees 6; W 559
   10-7   Long running even waves, Up curved flag close to ball, "CE" of COMMERCE joined; Lees 7; W 560
   10-8   Short choppy uneven waves, Hump-backed flag, Coinage; Lees 8; W 555
   10-9   Long running uneven waves, Curved flag; Lees 9; W 208

Cat.No.	Description	VG-8	F-12	VF-20	EF-40	AU-50	AU-55	MS-60
PE10-6	Choppy even waves	18.	40.	115.	150.	300.	425.	525.
PE10-7	Long running even waves	10.	20.	45.	100.	250.	375.	450.
PE10-8	Uneven waves, Coinage	8.	15.	25.	75.	325.	475.	600.
PE10-9	Long uneven waves	10.	20.	45.	95.	325.	475.	600.

PE10-10A to 13   NO MINTMARK; BRITISH FLAG (CURVED)
NO GUYS
ROUND KNOB AMPERSAND

Composition: Copper
Weight: 5.0 to 6.2 g
Diameter: 25.9 to 26.2 mm
Die Axis: ↑↑, ↑↓
Edge: Plain
Ref.Nos.: Br 997 (R-0);
 Lr 793 (R-2);
 W 209 to 211;
 See below

Round-knob
ampersand

Varieties: Obverse, Reverse, Die axis

10-10A Top ball of main-mast not separated; Lees 10
10-10B Top ball of main-mast is separated, Round pellet on upper mizzen-sail at left end; Lees 10A
10-11 Left guy rope above unfurled mizzen-sail is doublecut; Lees 11
10-12 Large die flaw below ship at right; Lees 12
10-13 Line from top of main-mast to flag does not touch yard of unfurled mizzen-sail; Lees 13

Cat.No.	Description	VG-8	F-12	VF-20	EF-40	AU-50	AU-55	MS-60
PE10-10A	Top ball not separated	8.	18.	45.	110.	275.	—	—
PE10-10B	Top ball is separated	125.	225.	375.	—	—	—	—
PE10-11	Double cut guy rope	125.	300.	600.	—	—	—	—
PE10-12	Flaw below ship	12.	25.	65.	150.	450.	525.	600.
PE10-13	Line does not touch	950.	1,650.	—	—	—	—	—

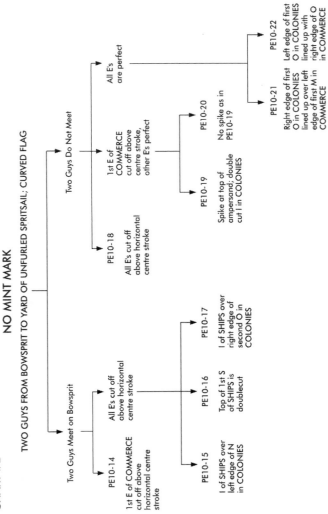

CHART #2

NO MINT MARK

TWO GUYS FROM BOWSPRIT TO YARD OF UNFURLED SPRITSAIL; CURVED FLAG

Two Guys Meet on Bowsprit

PE10-14 — 1st E of COMMERCE cut off above horizontal centre stroke

All E's cut off above horizontal centre stroke

PE10-15 — I of SHIPS over left edge of N in COLONIES

PE10-16 — Top of 1st S of SHIPS is doublecut

PE10-17 — I of SHIPS over right edge of second O in COLONIES

Two Guys Do Not Meet

PE10-18 — All E's cut off above horizontal centre stroke

1st E of COMMERCE cut off above centre stroke, other E's perfect

PE10-19 — Spike at top of ampersand; double cut I in COLONIES

PE10-20 — No spike as in PE10-19

All E's are perfect

PE10-21 — Right edge of first O in COLONIES lined up over left edge of first M in COMMERCE

PE10-22 — Left edge of first O in COLONIES lined up with right edge of O in COMMERCE

PE10-14 to 17   NO MINTMARK; BRITISH FLAG (CURVED)
TWO GUYS MEET
BAR AMPERSAND

Composition: Copper
Weight: 4.7 to 5.2 g
Diameter: 25.9 to 26.2 mm
Die Axis: ↑↑
Edge: Plain
Ref.Nos.: Br 997 (R-0);
Lr 793 (R-2);
W 212; See Below

Two guys meet

Two guys meet

Bar ampersand

Varieties: Obverse
10-14 First "E" in COMMERCE cut off above horizontal centre stroke; Lees 14
10-15 All "E's" cut off; Lees 15
10-16 Top of first "S" of SHIPS is doublecut; Lees 16
10-17 All "E's" cut off; Lees 17

Cat.No.	Description	VG-8	F-12	VF-20	EF-40	AU-50	AU-55	MS-60
PE10-14	First "E" cut off	35.	70.	125.	375.	550.	—	—
PE10-15	All "E's" cut off (see Chart 2)	60.	100.	200.	450.	675.	—	—
PE10-16	All "E's" cut off, first "S" doublecut	450	600.	750.	—	—	—	—
PE10-17	All "E's" cut off (see Chart 2)	50.	85.	175.	400.	600.	—	—

PE10-18 to 22   *NO MINTMARK; BRITISH FLAG (CURVED)*
TWO GUYS DO NOT MEET
BAR AMPERSAND

Composition: Copper
Weight: 4.7 to 5.2 g
Diameter: 25.9 to 26.2 mm
Die Axis: ↑↑
Edge: Plain
Ref.Nos.: Br 997 (R-0);
Lr 793 (R-2);
W 213; See Below

Two guys do
not meet

Bar ampersand

Two guys do not meet

Varieties: Obverse
  10-18   All "E's" cut off above horizontal centre stroke; Lees 18
  10-19   First "E" of COMMERCE cut off above centre stroke; Spike at top of ampersand; Lees 19
  10-20   First "E" cut off above centre stroke; Lees 20
  10-21   All "E's" are perfect; Lees 21
  10-22   All "E's" perfect; Lees 22

Notes: **1.** PE10-18, Lees 18: The only known copy is in the Bank of Canada Money Museum, Ottawa.
     2. This group, PE10-19-22, is extremely rare in high grade.

Cat.No.	Description	VG-8	F-12	VF-20	EF-40	AU-50	AU-55	MS-60
PE10-18	All "E's" cut	Only One Known						
PE10-19	1st "E" cut off, spike on &	35.	70.	125.	250.	—	—	—
PE10-20	1st "E" cut off, no spike	375.	600.	1,000.	—	—	—	—
PE10-21	All "E's" perfect	300.	450.	750.	—	—	—	—
PE10-22	All "E's" perfect (see Chart 2)	2,500.	4,000.	—	—	—	—	—

CHART #3

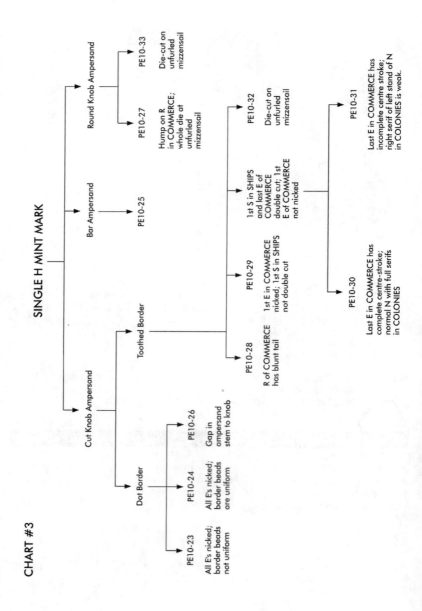

SINGLE H MINT MARK

Cut Knob Ampersand

Bar Ampersand

Round Knob Ampersand

Dot Border

Toothed Border

PE10-23
All E's nicked; border beads not uniform

PE10-24
All E's nicked; border beads are uniform

PE10-26
Gap in ampersand stem to knob

PE10-28
R of COMMERCE has blunt tail

PE10-29
1st E in COMMERCE nicked; 1st S in SHIPS not double cut

PE10-32
1st S in SHIPS and last E of COMMERCE double cut; 1st E of COMMERCE not nicked

Die-cut on unfurled mizzensail

PE10-30
Last E in COMMERCE has complete centre-stroke; normal N with full serifs in COLONIES

PE10-31
Last E in COMMERCE has incomplete centre stroke; right serif of left stand of N in COLONIES is weak.

PE10-25

PE10-27
Hump on R in COMMERCE; whole die at unfurled mizzensail

PE10-33
Die-cut on unfurled mizzensail

PE10-23, 24   *SINGLE H MINTMARK; BRITISH FLAG (STRAIGHT)*
   and 26   *CUT KNOB AMPERSAND*
                        DOT BORDER REVERSE

Composition: Copper
Weight: 5.0 to 5.1 g
Diameter: 25.9 to 26.2 mm
Die Axis: ↑↑
Edge: Plain
Ref.Nos.: Br 997 (R-0);
          Lr 793 (R-2); See below

      &   Cut knob
        ampersand

Single mint mark "H"

Varieties: Reverse
   10-23   All "E's" nicked, Border beads not uniform; Lees 23; W 214
   10-24   All "E's" nicked, Border beads are uniform; Lees 24; W 216
   10-26   Gap in ampersand stem to knob; Lees 26: W 218

Cat.No.	Date	Description	VG-8	F-12	VF-20	EF-40	AU-50	AU-55	MS-60
PE10-23	(1835)	Border beads not uniform	12.	25.	50.	150.	350.	—	—
PE10-24	(1835)	Border beads are uniform	25.	50.	125.	200.	300.	—	—
PE10-26	(1835)	Gap in ampersand	9.	15.	30.	100.	200.	—	—

PE10-25   *SINGLE H MINTMARK; BRITISH FLAG (STRAIGHT)*
BAR AMPERSAND

Composition: Copper
Weight: 5.0 to 5.1 g
Diameter: 25.9 to 26.2 mm
Die Axis: ↑↑
Edge: Plain
Ref.Nos.: Br 997 (R-0); Lees 25;
Lr 793 (R-2); W 215

 Bar ampersand

Cat.No.	Date	Description	VG-8	F-12	VF-20	EF-40	AU-50	AU-55	MS-60
PE10-25	(1835)	Bar ampersand	1,500.	2,750.	3,500.	5,000.	—	—	—

PE10-27 and 33   *SINGLE H MINTMARK: BRITISH FLAG (STRAIGHT)*
ROUND KNOB AMPERSAND

Composition: Copper
Weight: 5.0 to 5.1 g
Diameter: 25.9 to 26.2 mm
Die Axis: ↑↑
Edge: Plain
Ref.Nos.: Br 997 (R-0);
Lr 793 (R-2); See below

 Round knob
ampersand

Varieties: Obverse, Reverse
10-27 Reverse: Tail of "R" in COMMERCE has a small hump; Lees 27; W 217
10-33 Obverse: Die-cut on unfurled mizzen-sail;
Reverse: Tail of "R" in COMMERCE has a small hump; Lees 33; W 222

Cat.No.	Date	Description	VG-8	F-12	VF-20	EF-40	AU-50	AU-55	MS-60
PE10-27	(1835)	Hump on "R"	12.	25.	50.	135.	350.	—	—
PE10-33	(1835)	Die-cut on unfurled mizzen-sail	650.	1,250.	2,500.	3,750.	—	—	—

PE10-28
to 32

SINGLE H MINTMARK; BRITISH FLAG (STRAIGHT)
CUT KNOB AMPERSAND
TOOTHED BORDER REVERSE

Composition: Copper
Weight: 5.0 to 5.2 g
Diameter: 25.9 to 26.2 mm
Die Axis: ↑↑
Edge: Plain
Ref.Nos.: Br 997 (R-O);
Lr 793 (R-2); See below

 Cut knob
ampersand

Varieties: Obverse, Reverse
10-28 Blunt tail to "R" of COMMERCE; Lees 28; W 218
10-29 First "E" in COMMERCE nicked; First "S" in SHIPS not
double-cut; Lees 29; W 219
10-30 First "S" of SHIPS and last "E" of COMMERCE double-cut;
Last "E" in COMMERCE has complete centre-stroke; Lees 30; W 220
10-31 First "S" of SHIPS and last "E" of COMMERCE double-cut;
Last "E" in COMMERCE incomplete centre-stroke; Lees 31; W 221
10-32 Die-cut on unfurled mizzen-sail; Lees 32

Cat.No.	Date	Description	VG-8	F-12	VF-20	EF-40	AU-50	AU-55	MS-60
PE10-28	(1835)	Blunt tail to "R"	7.	12.	20.	60.	150.	225.	275.
PE10-29	(1835)	First "E" in COMMERCE nicked	7.	12.	20.	60.	150.	225.	275.
PE10-30	(1835)	Complete centrestroke "E"	6.	10.	15.	40.	100.	150.	175.
PE10-31	(1835)	Incomplete centrestroke "E"	6.	10.	15.	40.	100.	150.	175.
PE10-32	(1835)	Die-cut on mizzen-sail	7.	12.	20.	45.	100.	150.	175.

CHART #4

DOUBLE H MINT MARK

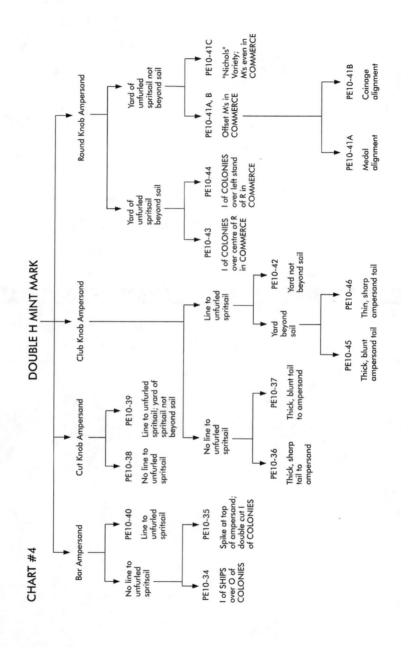

PE10-34, 35 *DOUBLE H MINTMARK; BAR AMPERSAND*
and 40

The Double "H" mint mark on this series of tokens is known to have been struck by Ralph Heaton & Sons of Birmingham. The dies with the "H" on the exergue line may have been acquired by the Heaton Mint from the successor of Thomas Halliday. Heaton, in order to distinguish his own strikings from the previous minters, may have punched the additional "H." This group is noted for the different varieties of the ampersand used on the reverse die.

Composition: Copper
Weight: 4.7 to 5.2 g
Diameter: 25.9 to 26.2 mm
Die Axis: ↑↑, ↑↓
Edge: Plain
Ref.Nos.: Br 997 (R-0);
Lr 793 (R-2); See below

 Bar ampersand

Double mint mark "H"

Varieties: Obverse, Reverse, Die axis
10-34 No line to unfurled spritsail; "I" of SHIPS over "O" of COLONIES; Lees 34; W 223
10-35 No line to unfurled spritsail; Spike at top of ampersand; Double cut "I" of COLONIES; Lees 35; W 224
10-40 Line to unfurled sprit-sail; Lees 40; W 229

Cat.No.	Description	VG-8	F-12	VF-20	EF-40	AU-50	AU-55	MS-60
PE10-34	No line to sail, "I" over "O"	15.	30.	50.	145.	300.	—	—
PE10-35	No line to sail, double cut "I"	15.	30.	50.	145.	300.	—	—
PE10-40	Line to unfurled spritsail	15.	30.	50.	145.	300.	—	—

PE10-36, 37
42, 45
and 46   *DOUBLE H MINTMARK; CLUB KNOB AMPERSAND*

Composition: Copper
Weight: 4.7 to 5.2 g
Diameter: 25.9 to 26.2 mm
Die Axis: ↑↑, ↑↓
Edge: Plain
Ref.Nos.: Br 997 (R-0);
            Lr 793 (R-2); See below

&   Club knob
       ampersand

Varieties: Obverse, Reverse, Die axis

10-36 No line to unfurled sprit-sail; Thick, sharp tail on ampersand; "C" of COLONIES over "C" of COMMERCE; Lees 36; W 225

10-37 No line to unfurled sprit-sail; Thick, blunt tail on ampersand; "C" of COLONIES slightly to the right of "C" of COMMERCE; Lees 37; W 226

10-42 Line to unfurled sprit-sail; Yard not beyond sail; Lees 42; W 231

10-45 Line to unfurled sprit-sail; Yard beyond sail; Thick, blunt ampersand tail; Lees 45; W 234

10-46 Line to unfurled sprit-sail; Yard beyond sail; Thin, sharp ampersand tail; Lees 46

Cat.No.	Description	VG-8	F-12	VF-20	EF-40	AU-50	AU-55	MS-60
PE10-36	Thick, sharp tail, "C" over "C"	10.	18.	50.	125.	200.	—	—
PE10-37	Thick, blunt tail, "C" to right "C"	11.	20.	50.	135.	225.	—	—
PE10-42	Yard not beyond sail	55.	125.	250.	400.	550.	—	—
PE10-45	Thick, blunt tail, Yard beyond	15.	30.	50.	135.	225.	—	—
PE10-46	Thin, sharp tail, Yard beyond	15.	30.	50.	135.	225.	—	—

PE10-38   *DOUBLE H MINTMARK; CUT KNOB AMPERSAND*
and 39

Composition: Copper
Weight: 4.7 to 5.2 g
Diameter: 25.9 to 26.2 mm
Die Axis: ↑↑, ↑↓
Edge: Plain
Ref.Nos.: Br 997 (R-0);
Lr 793 (R-2); See below

  Cut-knob
              ampersand

Varieties: Obverse, Reverse, Die axis
10-38   No line to unfurled sprit-sail; Lees 38; W 227
10-39   Line to unfurled sprit-sail; Yard of sprit-sail not beyond; Lees 39; W 228

Cat.No.	Description	VG-8	F-12	VF-20	EF-40	AU-50	AU-55	MS-60
PE10-38	No line to sprit-sail	9.	18.	45.	100.	225.	—	—
PE10-39	Line to sprit-sail	18.	40.	90.	175.	350.	—	—

PE10-41, 43 and 44   DOUBLE H MINTMARK; ROUND KNOB AMPERSAND

Composition: Copper
Weight: 4.7 to 5.2 g
Diameter: 25.9 to 26.2 mm
Die Axis: ↑↑, ↑↓
Edge: Plain
Ref.Nos.: Br 997 (R-0);
Lr 793 (R-2); See below

 Round-knob ampersand

Varieties: Obverse, Reverse, Die axis

10-41A Yard of unfurled sprit-sail not beyond sail; Offset "M's" in COMMERCE; Medal; Lees 41

10-41B Yard of unfurled sprit-sail not beyond sail; Offset "M's" in COMMERCE; Coinage; Lees 41

10-41C Yard of unfurled sprit-sail not beyond sail; Even "M's" in COMMERCE; Medal; Lees 41a

10-43 Yard of unfurled sprit-sail beyond sail; Weakly struck "I" in SHIPS and "L" in COLONIES; Lees 43

10-44 Yard of unfurled sprit-sail beyond sail; Well struck "I" and "L"; Lees 44

Cat.No.	Description	VG-8	F-12	VF-20	EF-40	AU-50	AU-55	MS-60
PE10-41A	Not beyond sail, ↑↑	18.	40.	95.	225.	500.	—	—
PE10-41B	Not beyond sail, ↑↓	9.	15.	45.	60.	200.	—	—
PE10-41C	Not beyond sail, even "M's"	22.	45.	125.	275.	—	—	—
PE10-43	Beyond sail, "I" over centre of "R"	22.	45.	125.	275.	—	—	—
PE10-44	Beyond sail, "I" over left stand of "R"	15.	30.	60.	150.	300.	—	—

TOKENS OF NOVA SCOTIA

When Halifax was founded in 1749, the governor was instructed to enforce the use of sterling. This proved to be a difficult task for a number of reasons. The Spanish dollar, then rated at 4/4 sterling, was virtually unobtainable unless 5/- was offered. In consequence, the local government paid 5/- for dollars. This rate eventually became the standard for Nova Scotia but in 1753 an attempt to establish this standard by law was disallowed by the British government. Nevertheless, this value of Halifax currency remained in effect.

In 1787 a currency act was passed that rated the British crown at 5/6, the shilling at 1/3 and the sixpence at 6 1/2d, with the Spanish dollar at 5/-. As British silver was overrated, copper began to disappear from circulation.

Many years earlier there had been several shipments of British halfpennies and farthings but legislation of 1787 drove them out of use. Local businessmen took matters into their own hands about 1812 and miscellaneous English pieces often struck over the Bristol Guppy tokens made their way into circulation. Later, issues from 1814 to 1816, of distinctive local design, most being struck in England, began to appear. Due to their variation in weight, size, design and purity of copper, the government ordered their removal in 1817.

No new pieces were issued to replace them until in 1820 a halfpenny appeared. The government issued halfpennies in 1823 and halfpennies and pennies in 1824, 1840, 1843 and 1856.

Plans to issue silver 15d tokens were abandoned in 1823 when it was learned that such a move would constitute a breach of royal prerogative. Had such pieces been coined, local currency could have been depreciated by as much as 25 per cent.

BRETON CROSS REFERENCE TABLE FOR NOVA SCOTIA TOKENS

Breton Cat. No.	Charlton Cat. No.	Page No.	Breton Cat. No.	Charlton Cat. No.	Page No.
867	NS-1A, B	38, 39	885	NS-12	58
868	NS-2A	44	886	NS-25	71
869	NS-1C	40	887	NS-26	72
870	NS-2B	45	888	NS-23	69
870	NS-4	51	889	NS-27	72
871	NS-1D	41	890	NS-13	59
871	NS-3A, C, D	48, 49, 50	891	NS-14	60
872	NS-3B	49	892	NS-15A	61
873	NS-2C, D	46, 47	893	NS-15B	61
874	NS-1E, F	42, 43	894	NS-24	70
875	NS-6	53	895	NS-28	73
876	NS-5	52	896	NS-16	62
879	NS-7A, B	54, 55	899	NS-17	62
880	NS-8	56	962	NS-20A, B	65, 66
881	NS-9	56	963	NS-19A, B	64
882	NS-10A	57	964	NS-18	63
883	NS-10B	57	965	NS-21	67
884	NS-11	58	967	NS-22	68

SEMI-REGAL TOKENS

THE THISTLE TOKENS OF 1823-1843

These tokens were issued under the terms of an act of the legislative assembly passed in 1817. The withdrawal of the private issues naturally resulted in a shortage of coppers by the early 1820s. When British coppers could not be obtained the provincial government ordered their own issues through the colony's agent Smith, Forsyth & Co. of Liverpool without the authority of the British Government.

The Act provided that the tokens should bear the British coat of arms on the obverse and the badge of Nova Scotia on the reverse. Michael Wallace, the colonial treasurer, instead ordered a coinage depicting a bust of George IV on the obverse and what was described in his words as "A handsome thistle" on the reverse.

NS-1   *HALFPENNY TOKEN 1823-1843*
                            — PROVINCE OF NOVA SCOTIA

NS-1A   *GEORGE IV HALFPENNY TOKEN 1823*
                            WITH HYPHEN IN NOVA SCOTIA

The halfpenny token of 1823 exhibits considerable variation in workmanship, indicating the dies were cut by more than one engraver. The weight was similar to that of the contemporary British halfpenny.

Composition: Copper
Weight: 9.3 to 9.6 g
Diameter: 28.3 to 28.8 mm
Die Axis: ↑↓
Edge: Engrailed, plain
Ref.Nos.: Br 867 (R-1);
Lr 410 (R-3);
McL 330-331;
See below

Varieties: Obverse, Edge
    A1 Laurel crown with fifteen leaves; Engrailed edge; Co 251, 252aNS; W 351, 352
    A2 Laurel crown with fifteen leaves, Plain edge
    A3 Laurel crown with fourteen leaves; Engrailed edge; Co 252NS; W 353
    A4 Laurel crown with thirteen leaves; Engrailed edge; Co 253NS; W 354
    A5 Laurel crown with twelve leaves, two small and three large locks; Engrailed edge; Co 256NS; W 357
    A6 Laurel crown with twelve leaves, five locks of equal size; Engrailed edge; Co 257NS; W 358

Cat.No.	Date	Description	VG-8	F-12	VF-20	EF-40	AU-50	AU-55	MS-60
NS-1A1	1823	Fifteen leaves	7.	15.	40.	115.	300.	—	—
NS-1A2	1823	Fifteen leaves, Plain			Very Rare				
NS-1A3	1823	Fourteen leaves	7.	15.	40.	115	300.	—	—
NS-1A4	1823	Thirteen leaves	12.	30.	75.	160	375.	—	—
NS-1A5	1823	Twelve leaves, unequal locks	35.	55.	125.	250.	450.	—	—
NS-1A6	1823	Twelve leaves, equal locks	70.	150.	250.	375.	750.	—	—

NS-1B   *GEORGE IV HALFPENNY TOKEN 1823*
                   NO HYPHEN IN NOVA SCOTIA

Composition: Copper
Weight: 9.5 g
Diameter: 28.3 to 28.8 mm
Die Axis: ↑↓
Edge: Engrailed
Ref.Nos.: Br 867 (R-1); See below

Stem does not
touch top of 8 **(B1)**

Stem touches
top of 8 **(B2)**

Varieties: Reverse
  B1 Stem does not touch top of 8; Co 254NS; Lr 411 (R-4); McL 333;
          W 355
  B2 Stem touches top of 8; Co 255NS; Lr 412 (R-4); McL 329; W 356

Cat.No.	Date	Description	VG-8	F-12	VF-20	EF-40	AU-50	AU-55	MS-60
NS-1B1	1823	Does not touch top of 8	12.	22.	75.	225.	450.	—	—
NS-1B2	1823	Touches top of 8	30.	55.	125.	300.	600.	—	—

NS-1C   *GEORGE IV HALF PENNY TOKEN 1824*

In 1824 an issue of 118,636 halfpennies was struck at the request of the colonial government, with John Walker acting as agent.

Composition: Copper
Weight: 8.6 to 8.7 g
Diameter: 28.4 to 28.9 mm
Die Axis: ↑↓
Edge: Engrailed
Ref.Nos.: Br 869 (R-1½);
    See below

Far "P" **(C1)**   Near "P" **(C2)**

Varieties: Obverse
  C1 "P" in PROVINCE far from bust; Co 258NS; Lr 416 (R-4); McL 337; W 359
  C2 "P" in PROVINCE near to bust; Co 259NS; Lr 417 (R-4); McL 338; W 360

Cat.No.	Date	Description	VG-8	F-12	VF-20	EF-40	AU-50	AU-55	MS-60
NS-1C1	1824	Far "P"	10.	20.	50.	125.	375.	575.	750.
NS-1C2	1824	Near "P"	10.	20.	50.	125.	375.	575.	750.

NS-1D   *GEORGE IV HALFPENNY TOKEN 1832*

The colonial government, through their agent John Bainbridge of London, placed an order for 800,000 halfpennies in 1832. The order requested tokens of similar design to those previously sent with a new date added. The manufacturer, following instructions, struck the tokens with an obverse bust of George IV and reverse dated 1832, even though William IV became king two years earlier.

Composition: Copper
Weight: 8.0 to 8.6 g
Diameter: 28.0 to 28.3 mm
Die Axis: ↑↓
Edge: Engrailed
Ref.Nos.: Br 871 (R-0);
See below

Long left ribbon **(D1)**   Long right ribbon **(D2)**   Ribbons of equal length **(D3)**

Varieties: Obverse
D1 Long left laurel ribbon; Co 265, 265aNS; Lr 422 (R-3); McL 340; W 366, 367
D2 Long right laurel ribbon; Co 266-271NS; Lr 423 (R-4); McL 344; W 368-373
D3 Laurel ribbons of equal length; Co 272-276NS; Lr 424 (R-3); W 374-380

Variations: Eight other variations exist with only very minor obverse and reverse differences.

Cat.No.	Date	Description	VG-8	F-12	VF-20	EF-40	AU-50	AU-55	MS-60
NS-1D1	1832	Long left ribbon	7.	12.	25.	75.	225.	350.	450.
NS-1D2	1832	Long right ribbon	6.	10.	25.	65.	225.	350.	450.
NS-1D3	1832	Equal ribbons	6.	9.	18.	60.	200.	300.	375.

NS-1E   *VICTORIA HALFPENNY TOKEN 1840*

An issue of some 300,000 halfpennies was released in 1840 and another issue of the same amount followed in 1843. As with earlier issues, these coins were circulated without Imperial authority. Some of the 1840 halfpennies are on slightly broader and thinner flans and are struck in a style suggesting that more than one engraver produced the dies. Crude cast forgeries exist.

Composition: Copper
Weight: 8.6 to 8.8 g
Diameter: 28.0 to 28.8 mm
Die Axis: ↑↓
Edge: Engrailed, plain
Ref.Nos.: Br 874 (R-0);
Lr 428 (R-3);
McL 351-357;
See below

| 1840 Large "0" (**E1**) | 1840 Medium "0" (**E2**) | 1840 Small "0" (**E3 and 4**) |

Varieties: Reverse, Edge
E1 Large "0" in date; Co 290, 291NS; W 394, 395
E2 Medium "0" in date; Co 292-294NS; W 396-398
E3 Small "0" in date, Plain; Co 296NS; W 400
E4 Small "0" in date, Engrailed; Co 295, 297, 298NS; W 399-402

Variations: Minor variations exist for these four tokens. These have resulted from touching up the dies. Obverse differences occur in the form and shape of the mouth and nose, where the coil is attached to the chignon, and with the size of the thistle on the reverse, and defective legend.

Cat.No.	Date	Description	VG-8	F-12	VF-20	EF-40	AU-50	AU-55	MS-60
NS-1E1	1840	Large "0"	9.	20.	70.	225.	375.	—	—
NS-1E2	1840	Medium "0"	7.	15.	45.	95.	300.	—	—
NS-1E3	1840	Small "0", Plain				Very Rare			
NS-1E4	1840	Small "0", Engrailed	8.	18.	55.	125.	350.	—	—

NS-1F   *VICTORIA HALFPENNY TOKEN 1843*

Composition: Copper
Weight: 8.6 g
Diameter: 28.0 to 28.8 mm
Die Axis: ↑↓
Edge: Engrailed
Ref.Nos.: Br 874 (R-0);
Lr 428 (R-3);
McL 351-357;
See below

BRACT   THORN

Thirteen Bracts, Eight Thorns

Varieties: Reverse
F1 Fifteen bracts, Ten thorns; Co 302, 303NS; W 406, 407
F2 Fourteen bracts, Fourteen thorns; Co 299; W 403, 405
F3 Thirteen bracts, Fourteen thorns; Co 300, 301NS; W 404
F4 Thirteen bracts, Nine thorns; Co 304, 304a, 305NS; W 408-410
F5 Thirteen bracts, Eight thorns; Co 306-308 NS; W 411-413

Variations: The variations listed on page 42 also apply to NS-1F1 to NS-1F5 varieties.

Cat.No.	Date	Description	VG-8	F-12	VF-20	EF-40	AU-50	AU-55	MS-60
NS-1F1	1843	Fifteen / Ten	7.	15.	40.	115.	300.	400.	450.
NS-1F2	1843	Fourteen / Fourteen	7.	15.	40.	115.	300.	400.	450.
NS-1F3	1843	Thirteen / Fourteen	12.	22.	60.	160.	375.	525.	600.
NS-1F4	1843	Thirteen / Nine	18.	35.	75.	190.	400.	525.	600.
NS-1F5	1843	Thirteen / Eight	7.	15.	40.	115.	300.	400.	450.

NS-2   ONE PENNY TOKEN 1824-1843 — PROVINCE OF NOVA SCOTIA

NS-2A   GEORGE IV PENNY TOKEN 1824

John Walker & Co. of Birmingham acting as agent for the colonial government procured the striking of the 1824 penny. The mintage of this issue was 217,776.

Composition: Copper
Weight: 17.0 to 17.4 g
Diameter: 34.1 to 34.3 mm

Die Axis: ↑↓
Edge: Engrailed
Ref.Nos.: Br 868 (R-1½);
Lr 413 (R-3), Lr 414 (R-4);
McL 336; See below

Three thin upper leaves (**A2**)   Three thick upper leaves (**A3**)

Varieties: Obverse
A1 Laurel crown with four upper leaves; Co 260NS; W 361
A2 Laurel crown with three thin upper leaves;
Reverse has double cut "K" in TOKEN; Co 261NS; W 362
A3 Laurel crown with three thick upper leaves;
"E" in PROVINCE is defective; Co 262NS; W 363
A4 Laurel crown with upper leaf touching "F" in OF; Co 263NS; W 364
A5 Mule of A4 obverse and A2 reverse; Co 264NS; W 365

Cat.No.	Date	Description	VG-8	F-12	VF-20	EF-40	AU-50	AU-55	MS-60
NS-2A1	1824	Four upper leaves	50.	85.	160.	325.	600.	—	—
NS-2A2	1824	Three thin upper leaves	9.	22.	50.	175.	450.	—	—
NS-2A3	1824	Three thick upper leaves	18.	35.	75.	175.	525.	—	—
NS-2A4	1824	Upper leaf touching "F"	9.	22.	50.	175.	450.	—	—
NS-2A5	1824	Mule	22.	45.	115.	250.	575.	—	—

NS-2B   *GEORGE IV PENNY TOKEN 1832*

The mintage of 1832 was 200,000 pennies.

Composition: Copper
Weight: 17.0 to 17.1 g
Diameter: 33.7 to 34.3 mm

Die Axis: ↑↓
Edge: Engrailed
Ref.Nos.: Br 870 (R-1);
              Lr 418-420 (R-3);
              Lr 421 (R-4); McL 339;
              See below

Bow far from head **(B1)**   Bow near head **(B-2)**   Bow touching head
                                                            (B3)

Varieties: Obverse
B1 Bow far from head; Ribbon ends square, equal length; Co 284NS; W 381
B2 Bow near head; Left ribbon longer; Co 285NS; W 382
B3 Bow touching head; Co 285aNS; W 383

Cat.No.	Date	Description	VG-8	F-12	VF-20	EF-40	AU-50	AU-55	MS-60
NS-2B1	1832	Bow far from head	9.	18.	40.	100.	300.	500.	600.
NS-2B2	1832	Bow near head	9.	18.	40.	100.	300.	500.	600.
NS-2B3	1832	Bow touching head	35.	55.	125.	225.	450.	625.	750.

NS-2C ***VICTORIA ONE PENNY TOKEN 1840***

This issue consisted of 150,000 pennies. Crude cast forgeries are known.

Composition: Copper
Weight: 16.4 to 17.4 g
Diameter: 34.0 to 34.5 mm

Die Axis: ↑↑, ↑↓
Edge: Engrailed
Ref.Nos.: Br 873 (R-1); Lr 427 (R-3);
McL 349-350, 354;
See below

Seven fringes **(C1)**   Five fringes **(C2)**   Four fringes **(C3)**

Varieties: Obverse, Die axis
   C1 Seven fringes of hair, Coinage; Co 311NS; W 417
   C2 Five fringes of hair, Coinage; Co 309NS; W 415
   C3 Four fringes of hair, Medal; Co 310NS; W 416

Cat.No.	Date	Description	VG-8	F-12	VF-20	EF-40	AU-50	AU-55	MS-60
NS-2C1	1840	Seven fringes, ↑↓	7.	15.	40.	115.	375.	575.	750.
NS-2C2	1840	Five fringes, ↑↓	15.	30.	75.	200.	450.	700.	900.
NS-2C3	1840	Four fringes, ↑↑	35.	70.	160.	350.	750.	1,150.	1,500.

NS-2D   *VICTORIA ONE PENNY TOKEN 1843*

In 1843 another 150,000 pennies were issued.

Composition: Copper
Weight: 16.4 to 17.2 g
Diameter: 34.3 to 34.5 mm

Die Axis: ↑↑, ↑↓
Edge: Engrailed
Ref.Nos.: Br 873 (R-1); Lr 427 (R-3):
McL 349-350, 354;
See below

Varieties: Obverse
D1 Seven fringes of hair; Co 314NS; W 420
D2 Four fringes of hair; Co 312NS; W 418
D3 Four fringes of hair, 3 over 0; Co 313NS; W 419

Cat.No.	Date	Description	VG-8	F-12	VF-20	EF-40	AU-50	AU-55	MS-60
NS-2D1	1843	Seven fringes	9.	20.	45.	115.	375.	575.	750.
NS-2D2	1843	Four finges	20.	35.	95.	200.	450.	700.	900.
NS-2D3	1843	Four fringes; 3 over 0	100.	165.	450.	—	—	—	—

THE COUNTERFEIT THISTLE TOKENS OF 1832

About 1835, large numbers of counterfeit tokens were struck in Montreal and shipped to Nova Scotia. They were sent to Saint John, New Brunswick, taken across the Bay of Fundy, and used to pay fishermen of the outports of Nova Scotia for their catch. In spite of their light weight and impure metal, the false coins were freely used because Nova Scotia was once again short of copper by 1835.

Both halfpenny and penny tokens were counterfeited, struck and cast forgeries exist of each denomination.

NS-3   *HALFPENNY TOKEN 1832 —*
                    PROVINCE OF NOVA SCOTIA

NS-3A   *GEORGE IV HALFPENNY TOKEN 1832*

Composition: Brass, copper
Weight: 6.2 to 7.5 g
Diameter: 28.2 to 28.6 mm
Die Axis: ↑↓, ↑↑
Edge: Engrailed, plain
Ref.Nos.: Br 871 (R-0); See below

Laurel Crown touches "F"   Hair touches "O"
(A1)   **(A2 and 3)**

Varieties: Obverse, Composition
     A1 Upper right side of the laurel crown touches "F" of OF, Copper; Co 277NS, W386
     A2 Upper lock of hair touches "O" of OF, Copper; Co 278NS; W 384
     A3 Upper lock of hair touches "O" of OF, Brass; Co 279NS; W 384

Variations: NS-3A3 exists struck from clashed dies, the reverse "token" showing under the obverse Scotia

Cat.No.	Date	Description	VG-8	F-12	VF-20	EF-40	AU-50	AU-55	MS-60
NS-3A1	1832	Laurel crown touches "F", Copper,	18.	35.	85.	200.	—	—	—
NS-3A2	1832	Hair touches "O"; Copper, ↑↓	7.	18.	60.	165.	—	—	—
NS-3A2a	1832	Hair Touches "O"; Copper; ↑↑			Extremely Rare				
NS-3A3	1832	Hair touches "O"; Brass	15.	30.	85.	200.	—	—	—

NS-3B *GEORGE IV HALFPENNY TOKEN 1382 (DATE ERROR)*

Composition: Copper
Weight: 6.9 to 7.0 g
Diameter: 28.2 mm
Die Axis: ↑↓
Edge: Engrailed
Ref.Nos.: Br 872 (R-5);
Co 280NS;
Lr 426 (R-6);
McL 348; W 385

1382 **(3B)**

Cat.No.	Date	Description	G-4	VG-8	F-12	VF-20	EF-40	AU-50
NS-3B	1382	Error date	1,000.	2,000.	3,000.	4,000.	6,000.	—

NS-3C *GEORGE IV HALFPENNY TOKEN 1832 (CORRECTED DATE)*

The die used to strike the error date was corrected by sinking an 83 over the 38. The overdating is most noticeable on the 8 over 3. The date at first glance appears to read 1882. The left leaf has sixteen notches.

Composition: Copper
Weight: 5.8 to 7.5 g
Diameter: 28.2 to 28.6 mm
Die Axis: ↑↓
Edge: Engrailed
Ref.Nos.: Br 871 (R-0);
Co 281NS;
W 388

"83" over the "38"
Pointed stem **(3C)**

Cat.No.	Date	Description	VG-8	F-12	VF-20	EF-40	AU-50	AU-55	MS-60
NS-3C	1832	Correct date	18.	35.	95.	250.	—	—	—

NS-3D   *GEORGE IV HALFPENNY TOKEN 1832*

Composition: Copper
Weight: 5.8 to 7.5 g
Diameter: 28.2 to 28.6 mm
Die Axis: ↑↓
Edge: Engrailed
Ref.Nos.: Br 871 (R-0); See below

Fifteen notches,   Thirteen notches,
square stem **(D1)**   square stem **(D2)**

Varieties: Reverse
D1 Left leaf has fifteen notches; Co 282NS; W 389
D2 Left leaf has thirteen notches; Co 283NS; W 390

Cat.No.	Date	Description	VG-8	F-12	VF-20	EF-40	AU-50	AU-55	MS-60
NS-3D1	1832	Fifteen notches	7.	18.	50.	125.	375.	—	—
NS-3D2	1832	Thirteen notches	15.	25.	65.	160.	525.	—	—

NS-4   *ONE PENNY TOKEN 1832 —*
                   PROVINCE OF NOVA SCOTIA

Pennies were counterfeited at the same time and brought to Nova Scotia from the same source as the halfpennies. As with the halfpennies, the counterfeits were a variable copper/brass composition of inferior fabric. Cast forgeries are known.

Composition: Brass, copper
Weight: 12.8 to 16.6 g
Diameter: 33.5 to 34.0 mm

Die Axis: ↑↓
Edge: Engrailed, reeded
Ref.Nos.: Br 870 (R-1);
Lr 418-420 (R-3);
Lr 421 (R-4);
McL 339; See below

Flat top one **(A1)**   Left top one **(A2 and A3)**   Right top one **(A4 and A5)**

Varieties: Reverse, Composition, Edge
A1 Flat top one; Copper; Engrailed; Co 286NS; W 391 *12,0 gr.*
A2 Left top one; Copper; Engrailed, Reeded; Co 287NS; W 392
A3 Left top one; Brass; Engrailed; Co 288NS; W 392
A4 Right top one; Copper; Engrailed; Co 289NS; W 393
A5 Right top one; Brass; Engrailed; Co 289aNS; W 393

Cat.No.	Date	Description	VG-8	F-12	VF-20	EF-40	AU-50	AU-55	MS-60
NS-4A1	1832	Flat top one; Copper	9.	18.	50.	185.	450.	—	—
NS-4A2	1832	Left top one; Copper, Engrailed	9.	18.	50.	185.	450.	—	—
NS-4A2	1832	Left top one; Copper, Reeded	12.	22.	65.	200.	500.	—	—
NS-4A3	1832	Left top one; Brass	22.	45.	125.	250.	525.	—	—
NS-4A4	1832	Right top one; Copper	12.	22.	65.	200.	500.	—	—
NS-4A5	1832	Right top one; Brass	22.	45.	125.	250.	525.	—	—

VICTORIA MAYFLOWER COINAGE

From 1823 to 1843 the government of Nova Scotia imported a series of unauthorized pence and halfpence which collectors have come to call the Thistle series.

In the 1850s, when the British Government was more willing to allow local coinages in the colonies, the Nova Scotia government officially applied for and received a true coinage, its first. These pence and halfpence feature a sprig of mayflower, now the provincial flower, on their reverses and are considered by many to be among the most beautiful coins ever made for North America. They were produced at Heatons Mint in Birmingham (without the H mint mark), but the master tools were made by the Royal Mint.

NS-5 *PROVINCE OF NOVA SCOTIA HALFPENNY TOKEN*
— 1856 VICTORIA D:G:BRITANNIAR:REG:F:D:

This denomination is represented by two obverse varieties, one with and the other without the designers initials (L.C.W.) below the queen's bust. It appears that the variety with" L.C.W." was struck only as a proof. Proofs of the No L.C.W. variety were also struck; it is most interesting that a rare variety of the No L.C.W. proof was struck from a blundered die where an "A" punch was used to repair a defective "V" in PROVINCE in one of the reverse dies, resulting in PRO∀INCE.

A scarce variety of the circulation strikes of the No L.C.W. halfpenny was coined in brass instead of the normal bronze. It can be recognized by its lighter yellow colour.

Composition: Brass, bronze
Weight: 7.6 to 7.9 g
Diameter: 27.7 to 27.8 mm
Die Axis: ↑↑
Edge: Plain
Ref.Nos.: Br 876 (R-0);
Lr 430 (R-4);
McL 360; W 421;
See below

Varieties: Composition
A1 Bronze; Co 315NS
A2 Brass; Co 316NS

Variations: Patterns exist with "L.C.W." Under truncation, Co 317NS.
Minor variations exist in the obverse legend, W 422.

Cat.No.	Date	Description	VG-8	F-12	VF-20	EF-40	AU-50	AU-55	MS-60
NS-5A1	1856	Bronze	5.	7.	15.	40.	115.	225.	300.
NS-5A2	1856	Brass	165.	250.	500.	825.	—	—	—

NS-6   **PROVINCE OF NOVA SCOTIA ONE PENNY TOKEN**
                 — *1856 VICTORIA D:G:BRITANNIAR:REG:F:D:*

With "LCW" **(A1)**	Without "LCW" **(A2)**

Composition: Bronze   **Die Axis:** ↑↑
Weight: 15.1 g   **Edge:** Plain
Diameter: 33.3 mm   **Ref.Nos.:** Br 875 (R-0); Lr 429 (R-4);
                                      W 423; See below

Varieties: Obverse
 A1 With initials "L.C.W." under truncation; Co 319NS
 A2 Without initials "L.C.W."; Co 318NS

Note: Cast counterfeits exist in brass and copper.

Cat.No.	Date	Description	VG-8	F-12	VF-20	EF-40	AU-50	AU-55	MS-60
NS-6A1	1856	With "L.C.W."	6.	12.	22.	75.	225.	400.	525.
NS-6A2	1856	Without "L.C.W."	7.	15.	25.	80.	250.	450.	600.

PRIVATE TOKENS

Most of the local tokens were designed, engraved and struck by Thomas Halliday. The halfpenny inscribed "For The Convenience of Trade" is the work of William Stephen Mossop. A few pieces were struck locally and are very crude in fabric. Most of these are very rare as their crudity made the majority of them unacceptable.

NS-7   *BRITANNIA 1814 — BROKE HALIFAX NOVA SCOTIA*

Captain P.B. Vere Broke, Commander of the H.M.S. Shannon, captured the U.S.S. Chesapeake in 1813 in what was the first British naval victory of the War of 1812. The 'Prize of War' was towed to Halifax and sold. The following year this token was struck honouring both Captain Broke and his victory.

Die preparation was very poor resulting in tokens of inferior quality.

NS-7A   *LONG BUST OF CAPTAIN BROKE*

NS-075

Composition: Copper *8.4*
Weight: 7.7 to 8.1 g
Diameter: 26.8 to 27.1 mm *27.3*
Die Axis: ↑↓
Edge: Reeded |||||
Ref.Nos.: Br 879 (R-1½);
          Co 325NS;
          Lr 435 (R-4);
          McL 308-310; W 313

H

Cat.No.	Date	Description	VG-8	F-12	VF-20	EF-40	AU-50	AU-55	MS-60
NS-7A	1814	Long Bust	12.	22.	65.	200.	450.	—	—

NS-7B   *SHORT BUST OF CAPTAIN BROKE*

Composition: Copper
Weight: 7.1 to 7.3 g
Diameter: 26.6 to 26.8 mm
Die Axis: ↑↑
Edge: Reeded
Ref.Nos.: Br 879 (R-1½);
Lr 435 (R-4);
McL 308-310;
See below

Four buttons **(B1 and 2)**   Three buttons **(B3 and 4)**

Left ship smaller   Two ships of equal
(B2 and 4)   height **(B1 and 2)**

Varieties: Obverse, Reverse
Four buttons — heavy die break through "OTI" in SCOTIA
Three buttons — "S" almost touches "C" in SCOTIA
B1 Four coat buttons, Two ships of equal height; Co 326NS; W 314
B2 Four coat buttons, Left ship smaller; Co 329NS; W 317
B3 Three coat buttons, Two ships of equal height; Co 328NS; W 316
B4 Three coat buttons, Left ship smaller; Co 327NS; W 315

Cat.No.	Date	Description	VG-8	F-12	VF-20	EF-40	AU-50	AU-55	MS-60
NS-7B1	1814	Four; Equal height	22.	44.	100.	250.	525.	—	—
NS-7B2	1814	Four; Left ship smaller	55.	110.	225.	500.	900.	—	—
NS-7B3	1814	Three; Equal height	30.	45.	100.	250.	600.	—	—
NS-7B4	1814	Three; Left ship smaller	8.	150.	40.	125.	300.	—	—

NS-8   *FOR THE CONVENIENCE OF TRADE —*
                1814 HALF PENNY TOKEN

Possibly issued by Carritt and Alport of Halifax, this halfpenny token was struck by William Stephen Mossop of Dublin. The reverse is from an anonymous Irish token of 1804.

Composition: Brass, copper
Weight: 5.4 to 5.8 g
Diameter: 27.7 to 28.8 mm
Die Axis: ↑↓
Edge: Plain
Ref.Nos.: Br 880 (R-2½);
          Lr 436 (R-5); W 318;
          See below

Varieties: Composition
   A1 Copper; Co 333NS
   A2 Brass; Co 334NS

Cat.No.	Date	Description	VG-8	F-12	VF-20	EF-40	AU-50	AU-55	MS-60
NS-8A1	1814	Copper	45.	90.	200.	375.	750.	—	—
NS-8A2	1814	Brass				Very Rare			

NS-9   *PAYABLE BY CARRITT & ALPORT HALIFAX —*
                1814 HALF PENNY TOKEN

The Carritt & Alport tokens were produced by either Peter Wyon or Thomas Wyon the Elder. The reverse type is that of the Gloucester and Berkeley Canal Company halfpenny of 1797, designed by Thomas Wyon the Elder and struck by Peter Kempson, with new inscriptions.

Two different patterns exist of this token. One pattern is in the Bank of Canada Collection (Co 332NS; W 320) and shows the bowsprit pointing directly to the "O" in ALPORT and the other is in the British Museum (W 320a) which shows the obverse legend starting at 9 o'clock and finishing at 3 o'clock. Both are extremely rare.

Composition: Copper
Weight: 6.9 to 7.1 g
Diameter: 28.8 mm to 28.9 mm
Die Axis: ↑↓
Edge: Engrailed
Ref.Nos.: Br 881 (R-1½);
          Co 331NS;
          Lr 447 (R-4);
          McL 311; W 319

Variations: There are two minor edge variations in the engrailing, northwest to southeast and northeast to southwest, the latter being the rarer of the two.

Cat.No.	Date	Description	VG-8	F-12	VF-20	EF-40	AU-50	AU-55	MS-60
NS-9	1814	Carritt & Alport	18.	35.	95.	250.	500.	—	—

NS-10   *PAYABLE BY HOSTERMAN & ETTER HALIFAX —*

Hosterman & Etter were jewellers in Halifax. Their halfpennies are believed to have been produced by Thomas Halliday. Their workmanship is somewhat inferior to what Halliday usually produced, suggesting the halfpennies may have been the work of an apprentice.

NS-10A   *— 1814 HALFPENNY TOKEN*

Composition: Copper
Weight: 8.4 to 8.5 g
Diameter: 27.7 to 27.8 mm
Die Axis: ↑↑
Edge: Plain
Ref.Nos.: Br 882 (R-1½);
         Co 335NS;
         Lr 449 (R-4);
         McL 312; W 321

Cat.No.	Date	Description	VG-8	F-12	VF-20	EF-40	AU-50	AU-55	MS-60
NS-10A	1814	Inner circle	12.	25.	50.	100.	250.	400.	500.

NS-10B   *— 1815 HALFPENNY TOKEN*

Composition: Copper
Weight: 5.7 to 6.5 g
Diameter: 25.8 to 26.0 mm
Die Axis: ↑↓
Edge: Plain
Ref.Nos.: Br 883 (R-1);
         Lr 450 (R-3);
         McL 313; See below

Sashed windows **(B1)**   Plain windows **(B2)**

Varieties: Reverse
    B1 All windows are sashed; Co 336NS; W 322
    B2 Not all windows sashed; Co 337NS: W 323

Note: Contemporary forgeries exist in brass and are very rare.

Cat.No.	Date	Description	VG-8	F-12	VF-20	EF-40	AU-50	AU-55	MS-60
NS-10B1	1815	Sashed windows	8.	18.	40.	95.	225.	350.	450.
NS-10B2	1815	Plain windows	12.	22.	50.	125.	250.	450.	600.

NS-11 **HALFPENNY TOKEN NOVA SCOTIA —**
1815 STARR & SHANNON HALIFAX

Starr and Shannon were hardware merchants whose halfpennies were well known in colonial Nova Scotia. The tokens were produced by John Sheriff of Liverpool, who cut the dies. The designs were probably a suggestion of the issuer.

Composition: Copper
Weight: Thin Flan: 5.8 to 6.0 g
Thick Flan: 7.2 to 7.8 g
Diameter: 27.7 to 28.1 mm
Thickness: Thin Flan: 1.2 mm
Thick Flan: 1.6 mm
Die Axis: ↑↓
Edge: Engrailed, plain
Ref.Nos.: Br 884 (R-1);
Lr 452 (R-3); See below

Varieties: Flan, Edge
A1 Thin flan, Plain; Co 339NS; W 340
A2 Thick flan, Plain
A3 Thick flan, Engrailed; Co 338NS; W 340

Variations: NS-11A1 is found without arrow fletching, NS-11A3 has arrow fletching, NS-11A2 is unknown.

Cat.No.	Date	Description	VG-8	F-12	VF-20	EF-40	AU-50	AU-55	MS-60
NS-11A1	1815	Thin flan, Plain	8.	18.	45.	125.	250.	375.	500.
NS-11A2	1815	Thick flan, Plain	10.	20.	50.	150.	300.	450.	600.
NS-11A3	1815	Thick flan, Engrailed	8.	15.	45.	125.	250.	375.	500.

NS-12 **HALFPENNY TOKEN NOVA SCOTIA —**
1815 COMMERCIAL CHANGE

The obverse die of this token was muled, in worn condition, with an Upper Canada sloop obverse to produce UC-8.

Composition: Copper
Weight: 5.8 g
Diameter: 27.9 to 28.0 mm
Die Axis: ↑↓
Edge: Engrailed
Ref.Nos.: Br 885 (R-1½);
Co 340NS;
Lr 437 (R-4);
McL 319; W 341

Cat.No.	Date	Description	VG-8	F-12	VF-20	EF-40	AU-50	AU-55	MS-60
NS-12	1815	Commerical Change	12.	25.	60.	200.	375.	—	—

NS-13   ***PAYABLE BY MILES W. WHITE HALIFAX NS —***
                1815 HALFPENNY TOKEN

Miles W. White's halfpenny of 1815 was issued in Halifax. White, a hardware merchant in business between 1812 and 1822, issued tokens of full weight, a practice seldom followed by his contemporaries.

Composition: Copper
Weight: 7.3 to 7.9 g.
Diameter: 27.7 to 28.1 mm
Die Axis: ↑↑, ↑↓, ↑→
Edge: Plain
Ref.Nos.: Br 890 (R-1½);
           Co 341NS;
           Lr 453 (R-4);
           McL 320; W 342

Varieties: Die axis
A1 Medal
A2 Ninety degrees east
A3 Coinage

Cat.No.	Date	Description	VG-8	F-12	VF-20	EF-40	AU-50	AU-55	MS-60
NS-13A1	1815	↑↑	12.	22.	75.	185.	450.	525.	750.
NS-13A2	1815	↑→	18.	35.	95.	250	600.	775.	900.
NS-13A3	1815	↑↑	12.	22.	75.	185.	450.	525.	750.

NS-14   *PAYABLE BY JOHN ALEXR. BARRY HALIFAX —*
1815 HALFPENNY TOKEN

John Alexander Barry was a Halifax dry goods merchant who also enjoyed a very stormy political career. He issued a halfpenny token in 1815, the work of Thomas Halliday and his apprentices.

Composition: Brass, copper
Weight: 6.2 to 6.7 g
Diameter: 25.9 to 26.1 mm
Die Axis: ↑↑, ↑↓
Edge: Plain
Ref.Nos.: Br 891 (R-1½);
Lr 444 (R-4);
McL 314-315;
See below

| Large bust, near date, eight leaves (A1) | Slender bust, near date, eight leaves (A2 and 3) | Small bust, far date, seven leaves (A4 and 5) |

Varieties: Obverse, Composition, Die axis
A1 Large bust, 8 Laurel leaves; Co 342NS; W 326
A2 Slender bust, 7 Laurel leaves, Copper; Co 343NS; W 327
A3 Slender bust, 7 Laurel leaves, Brass; Co 344NS; W 327
A4 Small bust, 7 Laurel leaves, Medal; Co 345NS; W 328
A5 Small bust, 7 Laurel leaves, Coinage; Co 345NS; W 328

Cat.No.	Date	Description	VG-8	F-12	VF-20	EF-40	AU-50	AU-55	MS-60
NS-14A1	1815	Large bust, 8 leaves	12.	20.	65.	160.	375.	500.	600.
NS-14A2	1815	Slender bust, 7 leaves, Copper	15.	25.	75.	185.	450.	625.	750.
NS14A3	1815	Slender bust, 7 leaves, Brass			Very Rare				
NS-14A4	1815	Small bust, 7 leaves, ↑↑	9.	18.	45.	125.	300.	475.	600.
NS-14A5	1815	Small bust, 7 leaves, ↑↓	9.	18.	45.	125.	300.	475.	600.

NS-15 — *1816 WHOLESALE & RETAIL HARDWARE STORE*

The Black brothers of Halifax were active merchants in the wholesale and retail trade. The first mention is of a business called Black and Parker in 1809, a year later another Black was added to the business resulting in Black, Parker & Black (1810-1812). In 1812 Parker left and the name now changed to W. A. & S. Black. During the period 1809-1815 they operated as silversmiths and jewellers. In 1816 Samuel left and established an outlet as a hardware merchant called S. Black & Co. The brother rejoined in 1818 under the previously named W. A. & S. Black. These tokens may have been ante-dated.

NS-15A   *HALIFAX NOVA SCOTIA —*

Composition: Copper
Weight: 5.5 to 6.0 g
Diameter: 25.5 to 25.6 mm
Die Axis: ↑↑
Edge: Plain
Ref.Nos.: Br 892 (R-1½);
        Co 358NS;
        Lr 441 (R-4);
        McL 321; W 343

Cat.No.	Date	Description	VG-8	F-12	VF-20	EF-40	AU-50	AU-55	MS-60
NS-15A	1816	Halifax Nova Scotia	22.	40.	95.	185.	450.	575.	675.

NS-15B   *PAYABLE AT W.A. & S. BLACK'S HALIFAX N.S. —*

Composition: Copper
Weight: 5.6 to 6.0 g
Diameter: 25.5 to 25.6 mm
Die Axis: ↑↑
Edge: Plain
Ref.Nos.: Br 893 (R-2);
        Co 357NS;
        Lr 445 (R-5);
        McL 322; W 344

Cat.No.	Date	Description	VG-8	F-12	VF-20	EF-40	AU-50	AU-55	MS-60
NS-15B	1816	W. A. & S. Black's	18.	35.	75.	185.	450.	575.	675.

NS-16   PAYABLE AT THE STORE OF J BROWN —
NEMO ME IMPUNE LACESSIT

John Brown, a Halifax dry goods merchant, issued a halfpenny token with an obverse showing the national motto and flower of Scotland.

Composition: Copper
Weight: 6.1 to 6.5 g
Diameter: 25.9 to 26.0 mm
Die Axis: ↑↑
Edge: Reeded
Ref.Nos.: Br 896 (R-1);
  Co 359NS;
  Lr 446 (R-3);
  McL 314; W 338

Cat.No.	Description	VG-8	F-12	VF-20	EF-40	AU-50	AU-55	MS-60
NS-16	J. Brown	12.	20.	50.	125.	300.	475.	600.

NS-17   W.L. WHITE'S HALIFAX HOUSE HALIFAX CHEAP
DRY GOODS STORE — ONE FARTHING PAYABLE AT
WHITE'S HALIFAX HOUSE HALIFAX

The one farthing token of W. L. White may have been issued after 1830. The fabric of this token is similar to that of tokens issued in Ireland during the coin shortage of 1830-1840.

Composition: Brass, bronze
Weight: 3.9 to 4.2 g
Diameter: 21.8 to 21.9 mm
Die Axis: ↑↓
Edge: Plain
Ref.Nos.: Br 899 (R-2½);
  Lr 454 (R-6);
  McL 323; See below

Varieties: Reverse
A1 The "D" of DRY is to the left of the "C" of CHEAP; Co 362NS; W 349
A2 The "D" of DRY is directly under the "C" of CHEAP; Co 363NS; W 350

Cat.No.	Date	Description	VG-8	F-12	VF-20	EF-40	AU-50	AU-55	MS-60
NS-17A1	(1830)	"D" left of "C"	50.	70.	100.	175.	375.	550.	675.
NS-17A2	(1830)	"D" under "C"	2,000.	3,000.	4,500.	6,000.	—	—	—

ANONYMOUS TOKENS

TRADE AND NAVIGATION TOKENS 1812-1838

The economy of the Atlantic colonies, especially Nova Scotia, was based on trade and navigation. These tokens bear a slogan very popular in that colony.

The reverse inscription clearly reflects the mistrust of paper money. Most of the population of Nova Scotia consisted of Loyalist emigrés from the United States who well recalled the collapse of various issues of paper money in the former colonies prior to 1783.

SEATED COMMERCE TOKENS 1812-1813

The Seated Commerce Issues of 1812 and 1813 were designed by Thomas Halliday and struck over the existing tokens of Samuel Guppy of Bristol. The farthing token was imported into Halifax by a merchant named Haliburton.

NS-18 *PURE COPPER PREFERABLE TO PAPER ONE FARTHING —*
1813 TRADE & NAVIGATION

Composition: Copper
Weight: 3.6 g
Diameter: 22.1 to 22.6 mm
Die Axis: ↑↑, ↑↓
Edge: Plain (Engrailed on original)
Ref.Nos.: Br 964 (R-1½);
Co 5NL; W 301

Cat.No.	Date	Description	VG-8	F-12	VF-20	EF-40	AU-50	AU-55	MS-60
NS-18A	1813	Copper, ↑↑	40.	55.	125.	225.	375.	500.	600.
NS-18B	1813	Copper, ↑↓	55	75.	150.	300.	550.	750.	900.

NS-19   *PURE COPPER PREFERABLE TO*
                 PAPER HALF PENNY TOKEN —

NS-19A   *— 1812 TRADE & NAVIGATION*

Composition: Copper
Weight: 8.8 to 9.2 g
Diameter: 27.6 to 27.8 mm
Die Axis: ↑↑
Edge: Engrailed
Ref.Nos.: Br 963 (R-1); Co 6NL;
Lr 775 (R-4);
McL 565-566; W 302

Variations: Struck on thick or thin flans, some of these pieces are struck over Guppy halfpennies.

Cat.No.	Date	Description	VG-8	F-12	VF-20	EF-40	AU-50	AU-55	MS-60
NS-19A	1812	Trade & Navigation	8.	15.	30.	95.	225.	375.	450.

NS-19B   *— 1813 TRADE & NAVIGATION*

Composition: Copper
Weight: 8.8 to 9.5 g
Diameter: 27.4 to 27.8 mm
Die Axis: ↑↑
Edge: Engrailed, plain
Ref.Nos.: Br 963 (R-1); Co 7NL;
W 302

Varieties: Edge
B1 Plain
B2 Engrailed

Variations: NS-19B exists struck over Bristol halfpennies on thick or thin flans.

Cat.No.	Date	Description	VG-8	F-12	VF-20	EF-40	AU-50	AU-55	MS-60
NS-19B1	1813	Plain	22.	45.	100.	225.	525.	600.	675.
NS-19B2	1813	Engrailed	9.	20.	45.	100.	275.	400.	500.

NS-20 *PURE COPPER PREFERABLE TO PAPER ONE PENNY TOKEN* —

Pennies dated 1812 are reported to have been sold at auction on several occasions in the past and references to their existence in private collections have appeared from time to time. Nevertheless, no specimen has been seen recently. Courteau did not list the date of 1812 in his monograph on non-local tokens. However, a specimen dated 1812 is listed in the catalogue of the sale of his collection in 1944. The "H" mintmark of Thomas Halliday appears on obverse lower right.

NS-20A   — *1813 TRADE & NAVIGATION*

Composition: Copper   **Die Axis:** ↑↑
Weight: 18.8 to 20.3 g   **Edge:** Engrailed
Diameter: 33.5 to 33.8 mm
Ref.Nos.: Br 962 (R-1½); Lr 777 (R-3); McL 563-564; See below

Varieties: Obverse, reverse legend

A1
Large letters, bar ampersand, period in reverse legend high; The "T" in NAVIGATION is found lower than the "I"; Co 8NL; W 304

A2
Large letters, bar ampersand, drapery touches water; The right foot of the "A" in NAVIGATION is in line with the "T"; Co 9NL; W 305

A3
Large letters, bar ampersand, leaves on ground; The "T" in NAVIGATION is higher than the "I"; Co 10NL; W 306

A4   Small letters, round knob ampersand; Co 11NL; W 307

Cat.No.	Date	Description	VG-8	F-12	VF-20	EF-40	AU-50	AU-55	MS-60
NS-20A1	1813	High period	15.	30.	65.	165.	300.	475.	600.
NS-20A2	1813	Drapery	40.	85.	225.	375.	625.	—	—
NS-20A3	1813	Leaves	30.	45.	95.	225.	375.	550.	675.
NS-20A4	1813	Round knob	20.	35.	75.	165.	300.	475.	600.

NS-20B   — 1814 TRADE & NAVIGATION

The one penny token issues of 1814 were struck over many years in imitation of Thomas Hallidays designs. They are of inferior workmanship and lighter in weight than previous issues and the letter "H" does not appear on the obverse.

Composition: Copper
Weight: 15.6 to 17.6 g
Diameter: 33.5 to 33.8 mm
Die Axis: ↑↑, ↑↓
Edge: Engrailed, plain
Ref.Nos.:   Br 962 (R-1½);
Lr 777 (R-3);
McL 563-564;
See below

Second 1 over 0   Plain 1 (**B3**)
(**B1 and 2**)

Varieties: Obverse, Edge, Die axis
B1   1 over 0, Engrailed, Medal; Co 12NL; W 308
B2   1 over 0, Engrailed, Coinage; Co 12NL; W 308
B3   Plain, Coinage; Co 13NL; W 309

Cat.No.	Date	Description	VG-8	F-12	VF-20	EF-40	AU-50	AU-55	MS-60
NS-20B1	1814	1 over 0, Engrailed, ↑↑	35.	65.	160.	300.	600.	—	—
NS-20B2	1814	1 over 0, Engrailed, ↑↓	35.	65.	160.	300.	600.	—	—
NS-20B3	1814	Plain, Coinage, ↑↓	22.	40.	95.	200.	450.	—	—

NS-21
PURE COPPER PREFERABLE TO PAPER
HALF PENNY TOKEN —
1813 TRADE & NAVIGATION

Composition: Copper
Weight: 7.5 to 7.9 g
Diameter: 27.3 to 27.4 mm
Die Axis: ↑↓
Edge: Engrailed, plain, reeded
Ref.Nos.: Br 965 (R-1);
Lr 776 (R-3);
McL 568; See below

Large central wave	Third wave from right	Round right wave **(A4)**
(A1 and 2)	tallest **(A3)**	

Varieties: Obverse, Edge
A1 Large central wave, Plain; Co 15NL; W 310
A2 Large central wave, Engrailed; Co 15NL; W 310
A3 Third wave from right the tallest, Reeded; Co 16NL; W 311
A4 Round right wave, Flaw at date, Plain; Co 17NL; W 312

Variations: NS-21 is found on thin or thick flans resulting in weight variations.

Cat.No.	Date	Description	VG-8	F-12	VF-20	EF-40	AU-50	AU-55	MS-60
NS-21A1	1813	Large wave, Plain	10.	22.	50.	160.	250.	450.	600.
NS-21A2	1813	Large wave, Engrailed	7.	12.	30.	95.	250.	400.	525.
NS-21A3	1813	Third wave tallest, Reeded	7.	12.	30.	95.	250.	400.	525.
NS-21A4	1813	Round wave, Date flaw, Plain	8.	15.	45.	125.	300.	475.	600.

NS-22   **TRADE & NAVIGATION 1838 —**
                  PURE COPPER PREFERABLE TO PAPER

This one penny token was issued for use in British Guiana (modern Guyana). The reverse die is the same as that used to strike the obverse NS-20B except the date was changed from 1814 to 1838. Also, it was struck over a number of years and comes with varying states of reverse rust spots. It is doubtful, even though the legends on this token are similar to ones circulating in Nova Scotia, that it was imported in quantities. It is more likely that collectors imported the token towards the end of the century.

Penny tokens did circulate in Nova Scotia during and after 1838. Trade between the Province and the West Indies was of great importance.

Composition: Copper
Weight: 17.6 to 17.7 g
Diameter: 33.2 to 33.3 mm

Die Axis: ↑↓
Edge: Plain
Ref.Nos.: Br 967 (R-1); Co 14NL;
            Lr 789 (R-3); McL 584;
            W B8

Cat.No.	Date	Description	VG-8	F-12	VF-20	EF-40	AU-50	AU-55	MS-60
NS-22	1838	Trade & Navigation	6.	12.	28.	75.	185.	325.	450.

NS-23   *SUCCESS TO NAVIGATION & TRADE —*
                                 1815 HALFPENNY TOKEN

Nova Scotia depended on shipbuilding and trade with Great Britain, the United States and the West Indies and tokens bearing these legends were readily accepted. Thomas Halliday is credited with the design.

Composition: Copper
Weight: 7.4 to 8.4 g
Diameter: 27.6 to 27.7 mm
Die Axis: ↑↓
Edge: Plain
Ref.Nos.: Br 888 (R-1);
              Lr 439 (R-3); McL 528;
              See below

Large flag **(A1 and 3)**

Small flag **(A2 and 4)**

2 upper leaves
(A1 and 2)

1 upper leaf
(A3 and 4)

Varieties: Obverse and reverse
A1 Laurel crown with 2 upper leaves, Large flag; Co 353NS; W 329
A2 Laurel crown with 2 upper. leaves, Small flag; Co 354NS; W 330
A3 Laurel crown with 1 upper leaf, Large flag; Co 355NS; W 331
A4 Laurel crown with 1 upper leaf, Small flag; Co 356NS; W 332

Cat.No.	Date	Description	VG-8	F-12	VF-20	EF-40	AU-50	AU-55	MS-60
NS-23A1	1815	2 leaves, L flag	12.	22.	65.	160.	375.	500.	600.
NS-23A2	1815	2 leaves, S flag	9.	20.	65.	160.	375.	500.	600.
NS-23A3	1815	1 leaf, L flag	22.	45.	125.	250.	450.	675.	750.
NS-23A4	1815	1 leaf, S flag	8.	18.	45.	115.	250.	450.	600.

NS-24

ONE HALFPENNY TOKEN 1820 —
TRADE & NAVIGATION

In 1817 the government ordered the removal of all halfpenny tokens from circulation by the year 1820. Nothing was done immediately to provide an alternate supply of copper and attempts began once more to do so privately. In 1820, an anonymous halfpenny of Irish design appeared with legends that link it with Nova Scotia. The detail on this token is very poor.

Composition: Brass, copper
Weight: 6.0 to 7.0 g
Diameter: 27.4 to 27.6 mm
Die Axis: ↑↓
Edge: Plain
Ref.Nos.: Br 894 (R-1); Co 3NL; Lr 442 (R-3); McL 533; W 348; See below

Varieties: Composition
A1 Copper
A2 Brass

Cat.No.	Date	Description	VG-8	F-12	VF-20	EF-40	AU-50	AU-55	MS-60
NS-24A1	1820	Copper	12.	22.	65.	200.	450.	—	—
NS-24A2	1820	Brass	18.	35.	95.	250.	600.	—	—

GENUINE BRITISH COPPER TOKENS

Issued anonymously at the peak of private token circulation in Nova Scotia, this token stressed honest copper content and competed against the numerous forgeries which threatened confidence in copper currency. The first token is the work of Thomas Halliday while the others are attributed to his apprentices.

NS-25   *GENUINE BRITISH COPPER — 1815 HALF PENNY TOKEN*

Composition: Copper
Weight: 6.1 to 7.1 g
Diameter: 25.8 to 26.1mm
Die Axis: ↑↓
Edge: Plain
Ref.Nos.: Br 886 (R-1½);
Lr 438 (R-4);
McL 526-537;
See below

Large Bust	Slender Bust	Slender Bust	Small Bust
8 Laurel leaves	7 Laurel leaves	6 Laurel leaves	7 Laurel leaves
(A1)	**(A2)**	**(A3)**	**(A4)**

Varieties: Obverse
A1 Large bust, Laurel crown with 8 leaves; Co 347NS; W 333
A2 Slender bust, Laurel crown with 7 leaves; Co 348NS; W 334
A3 Slender bust, Laurel crown with 6 leaves; Co 349NS; W 335
A4 Small bust, Laurel crown with 7 leaves; Co 350NS; W 336

Cat.No.	Date	Description	VG-8	F-12	VF-20	EF-40	AU-50	AU-55	MS-60
NS-25A1	1815	Large bust, 8 leaves	9.	18.	45.	125.	300.	—	—
NS-25A2	1815	Slender bust, 7 leaves	8.	15.	35.	125.	225.	—	—
NS-25A3	1815	Slender bust, 6 leaves	12.	22.	50.	160.	375.	—	—
NS-25A4	1815	Small bust, 7 leaves	35.	55.	160.	325.	600.	—	—

NS-26   *HALFPENNY — 1815 GENUINE BRITISH COPPER*

Composition: Copper
Weight: 5.5 to 5.8 g
Diameter: 28.1 to 28.2 mm
Die Axis: ↑↓
Edge: Engrailed, reeded
Ref.Nos.: Br 887 (R-2½);
           Lr 784 (R-4); See below

Varieties: Edge
   A1 Reeded; Co 346NS; W 337
   A2 Engrailed; Co 346NS; W 337

Cat.No.	Date	Description	VG-8	F-12	VF-20	EF-40	AU-50	AU-55	MS-60
NS-26A1	1815	Reeded	35.	65.	160.	325.	600.	—	—
NS-26A2	1815	Engrailed	35.	65.	160.	325.	600.	—	—

NS-27   *HALIFAX — 1815 HALFPENNY TOKEN*

The Halifax halfpenny token of 1815 is an anonymous issue possibly designed and produced by Thomas Halliday.

Composition: Copper
Weight: 6.2 to 6.5 g
Diameter: 25.9 to 26.0 mm
Die Axis: ↑↑, ↑↓
Edge: Reeded
Ref.Nos.: Br 889 (R-1½);
           Lr 440 (R-4); McL 316;
           See below

No hair between
two upper leaves
(A1 and 2)

Hair between
upper leaves
(A3)

Varieties: Obverse, Die axis
   A1 No hair between two upper leaves, Medal; Co 351NS; W 324
   A2 No hair between two upper leaves, Coinage; Co 351NS; W 324
   A3 Hair between upper leaves, Medal; Co 352NS; W 325

Cat.No.	Date	Description	VG-8	F-12	VF-20	EF-40	AU-50	AU-55	MS-60
NS-27A1	1815	No hair, ↑↑	9.	18.	45.	125.	300.	475.	600.
NS-27A2	1815	No hair, ↑↓	9.	18.	45.	125.	300.	475.	600.
NS-27A3	1815	Hair, ↑↑	12.	22.	65.	200.	450.	575.	675.

NS-28

HALFPENNY TOKEN —
NOVA SCOTIA AND NEW BRUNSWICK SUCCESS

This undated piece was issued anonymously, the inscription clearly favouring the union of Nova Scotia and New Brunswick.

Composition: Brass, copper
Weight: 5.7 to 6.0 g
Diameter: 27.9 to 28.1 mm
Die Axis: ↑↑
Edge: Reeded
Ref.Nos.: Br 895 (R-3);
Co 330NS;
Lr 443 (R-6); McL 326;
W 339

Varieties: Composition
A1 Copper
A2 Brass

Cat.No.	Description	VG-8	F-12	VF-20	EF-40	AU-50	AU-55	MS-60
NS-28A	Copper	30.	55.	160.	325.	600.	775.	900.
NS-28B	Brass	85.	200.	450.	—	—	—	—

Note: Cast forgeries are known to exist.

NS-29

1816 — HALF PENNY TOKEN

This Canadian colonial token discovered in 1988 was the first significant find in over 75 years. The piece bears a striking resemblance in design and workmanship to other tokens attributed to Halifax, Nova Scotia. The JB Script/Warehouse Token(BL-31), the W. A. & S. Black Token of 1816 (NS-15), and the Anchor and H Token (NS-30) can all be linked to this token either through their obverse or reverse designs.

Composition: Copper
Weight: 4.9 g
Diameter: 26.0 mm
Die Axis: ↑↓
Edge: Plain
Ref.Nos.: Previously unlisted

Cat.No.	Date	Description	AG	G-4	VG-8	F-12	VF-20
NS-29	1816	Half Penny Token			Only one known		

NS-30   *H —1816 HALFPENNY TOKEN*

This token was moved from the Anonymous and Miscellaneous section to the Nova Scotia section because of the discovery piece NS-29. That token certainly confirms the Anchor and H as being struck for the Halifax, Nova Scotia trade.

Composition: Copper
Weight: 3.84 to 5.0 g
Diameter: 26.0 to 26.5 mm
Die Axis: ↑↑
Edge: Plain
Ref.Nos.: Co 35NL; W 154

Note: The Courteau sale of 1944 listed a specimen in very poor condition dated 1814. This piece was probably a worn and misidentified 1816 piece.

Cat.No.	Date	Description	AG	G-4	VG-8	F-12	VF-20
NS-30	1816	Half Penny Token	1,500.	2,000.	2,500.	3,500.	—

IMITATIONS OF NOVA SCOTIA TOKENS "BLACKSMITH STYLE"

For listings of imitations of Nova Scotia tokens see page 219 and 220, BL-29 to BL-31.

TOKENS OF NEW BRUNSWICK

Unlike most other pre-Confederation British American colonies, New Brunswick did not have a serious deficiency of copper currency until the late 1830s and early 1840s.

In 1843 the provincial government obtained copper pence and halfpence from Boulton and Watt, a private mint in England. These pieces are technically tokens because they were obtained without the permission of the British government.

In 1853 a further issue of copper was required. The adoption of a decimal currency was being seriously considered but was still up in the air. Therefore, it was decided to order more coppers in the pounds/shillings/pence system. It was at this time that the British government learned of the "spurious" token issue of 1843. The master tools for the 1843 coppers were sent to the Royal Mint in London where the reverses were modified by substituting CURRENCY for TOKEN. Totally new obverses were prepared.

The actual striking of the 1854 coinage took place at Heaton's Mint in Birmingham, but the coins lack the familiar "H" mint mark.

BRETON CROSS REFERENCE TABLE FOR NEW BRUNSWICK TOKENS

Breton Cat. No.	Charlton Cat. No.	Page No.	Breton Cat. No.	Charlton Cat. No.	Page No.
909	NB-2A	78	912	NB-1B	77
910	NB-1A	77	913	NB-4	79
911	NB-2B	78	914	NB-3	79

SEMI-REGAL TOKENS AND 1854 COINAGE

VICTORIA FRIGATE TOKENS 1843-1854

TOKEN COINAGE OF 1843

After an unsuccessful attempt to circulate British copper the New Brunswick government decided to issue penny and halfpenny tokens and entered into an arrangement with William Hammond of Halifax to procure a coinage. The Colonial Office, on being informed of the plan, was displeased and ordered the New Brunswick authorities to cease at once from proceeding with the proposed coinage. The New Brunswick government then terminated the arrangement with Hammond and informed the Colonial Office. Evidently either Hammond or the New Brunswick government secretly went ahead with the plans as a coinage of pennies and halfpennies was struck by Boulton & Watt and surreptitiously reached circulation. The matrices and punches were sent to New Brunswick after the coinage was completed. It was not known in England that the colonial government had ignored the wishes of the Colonial Office until 1853, when the succeeding governor was corresponding with London concerning the coinage of 1854, and learned to his surprise that there was not supposed to be a coinage of 1843.

COINAGE OF 1854

Under the provisions of the Currency Act of 1852, the government of New Brunswick in June 1853 sought permission to issue a coinage of copper pennies and halfpennies. Imperial sanction was obtained for this coinage and the matrices and punches of the coinage of 1843 were sent to England. The coinage was struck by Ralph Heaton & Co. of Birmingham from modified reverse dies and new obverse dies. The dies were prepared by Leonard Charles Wyon, who used for the obverse the head punch of the contemporary English coinage. These head punches were of the attractive young head designed by William Wyon. The coinage was secured through the agency of John Sears of Saint John and comprised 480,000 pennies and 480,000 halfpennies.

New Brunswick adopted the decimal system in 1860 and had no further need for the pennies and halfpennies of 1843 and 1854.

Pending the arrival of the bronze cents of 1861, New Brunswick imported Canadian cents of 1858 and 1859 to provide a temporary stock of cents. Canada, having difficulty in getting these coins into circulation, was glad to ship some $5,000 worth to New Brunswick. They circulated side by side with the New Brunswick cents of 1861 and 1864 until and after Confederation in 1867.

THE RIGGING OF "H.M.S. NEW BRUNSWICK"

The reverse of the coins shows a frigate with sails furled. There are numerous variations in the rigging of the ship giving rise to many varieties. These varieties are a result of different dies and the polishing as well as retouching of older dies.

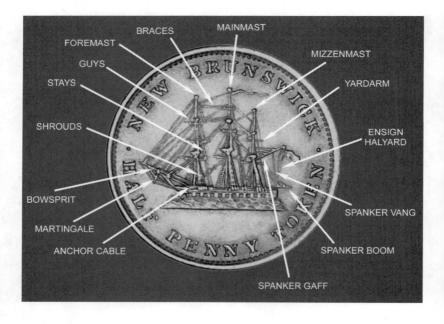

NB-1   *NEW BRUNSWICK HALF PENNY TOKEN/CURRENCY —*
            1843/1854 VICTORIA DEI GRATIA REGINA

NB-1A   *HALF PENNY TOKEN 1843*

Composition: Copper
Weight: 8.6 to 9.0 g
Diameter: 28.2 to 28.3 mm
Die Axis: ↑↑
Edge: Plain
Ref.Nos.: Br 910 (R-1);
               Lr 374 (R-3); McL 386;
               See below

Three complete groups **(A1)**   Two complete groups **(A2)**

Varieties: Obverse
A1 Three complete groupings of Heraldic flowers in the queen's diadem;
       Co 13-20NB; W 458-464
A2 Two complete groupings of Heraldic flowers, the third group has the
       thistle missing; Co 3-12NB; W 453-457

Variations: New dies or the retouching of old dies resulted in minor variations in the
               ship's rigging.

Cat.No.	Date	Description	VG-8	F-12	VF-20	EF-40	AU-50	AU-55	MS-60
NB-1A1	1843	Three complete groups	6.	12.	25.	80.	250.	400.	525.
NB-1A2	1843	Two complete groups	6.	12.	25.	80.	250.	400.	525.

NB-1B   *HALF PENNY CURRENCY 1854*

Composition: Copper
Weight: 7.6 to 8.2 g
Diameter: 28.2 to 28.4 mm
Die Axis: ↑↑
Edge: Plain
Ref.Nos.: Br 912 (R-1);
               Co 30-41NB;
               Lr 376 (R-3); McL 389;
               W 469-473

Variations: New dies or the retouching of old dies resulted in minor variations. On
               the obverse the placement of the 4 in the date varies. On the reverse
               there are four, five or six lines in the mizzenmast.

Cat.No.	Date	Description	VG-8	F-12	VF-20	EF-40	AU-50	AU-55	MS-60
NB-1B	1854	Half Penny Currency	6.	12.	25.	80.	250.	400.	525.

NB-2   *NEW BRUNSWICK ONE PENNY TOKEN/CURRENCY —*
1843/1854 VICTORIA DEI GRATIA REGINA

NB-2A   *ONE PENNY TOKEN 1843*

Composition: Copper
Weight: 17.6 g
Diameter: 34.1 mm
Die Axis: ↑↑
Edge: Plain
Ref.Nos.: Br 909 (R-1);
Co 21-29NB;
Lr 373 (R-4);
McL 387;
W 465-468

Variations: Minor variations exist because of new dies and the retouching of old dies. Reverse variations exist with two, three or four stays to the right of the mizzenmast.

Cat.No.	Date	Description	VG-8	F-12	VF-20	EF-40	AU-50	AU-55	MS-60
NB-2A	1843	Copper	7.	15.	40.	115.	300.	425.	525.

NB-2B   *ONE PENNY CURRENCY 1854*

Composition: Copper
Weight: 15.1 to 15.8 g
Diameter: 34.2 mm
Die Axis: ↑↑
Edge: Plain
Ref.Nos.: Br 911 (R-1);
Lr 375 (R-3);
McL 388;
See below

Complete ensign **(B1)**   Incomplete ensign **(B2)**

Varieties: Reverse
B1 Complete ensign; Co 42-45NB; W 474
B2 Incomplete ensign; Co 46-52NB; W 475

Variations: New dies or the retouching of old dies resulted in minor variations.

Cat.No.	Date	Description	VG-8	F-12	VF-20	EF-40	AU-50	AU-55	MS-60
NB-2B1	1854	Complete ensign	7.	15.	40.	115.	250.	400.	500.
NB-2B2	1854	Incomplete ensign	7.	15.	40.	115.	250.	400.	500.

PRIVATE TOKENS

NB-3 *F. MCDERMOTT IMPORTER OF ENGLISH, FRENCH &*
GERMAN FANCY GOODS, KING ST. SAINT JOHN, N.B. —
DEPOSITORY OF ARTS

This token is a business card and it is doubtful that it circulated as a halfpenny token.

Composition: Brass, copper
Weight: 5.5 g
Diameter: 23.9 mm
Die Axis: ↑↑
Edge: Plain
Ref.Nos.: Br 914 (R-4);
          Co 2NB; Lr 380 (R-6)

Cat.No.	Date	Description	VG-8	F-12	VF-20	EF-40	AU-50	AU-55	MS-60
NB-3	(1845)	F. McDermott	650.	850.	1,250.	1,750.	2,750.	—	—

ANONYMOUS TOKENS

NB-4 *ST. JOHN NEW BRUNSWICK HALF PENNY TOKEN —*
FOR PUBLIC ACCOMMODATION

In New Brunswick the need for currency was never very great because trade across the Bay of Fundy constantly brought Nova Scotia copper into the city and the colony. The first local tokens appeared about 1830.

Composition: Copper
Weight: 5.2 to 5.4 g
Diameter: 27.9 to 28.1 mm
Die Axis: ↑↑
Edge: Reeded
Ref.Nos.: Br 913 (R-2); Co 1NB;
          Lr 379 (R-5); McL 384;
          W 451

Variations: Minor varieties exist because of rusty dies.

Cat.No.	Date	Description	VG-8	F-12	VF-20	EF-40	AU-50	AU-55	MS-60
NB-4	(1830s)	Public Accommodation	12.	25.	65.	160.	375.	—	—

NB-5   *ST. JOHN'S N.B. HALFPENNY TOKEN —*

This extremely rare piece was not known to Breton or Courteau. This token was refused because the city named was rendered as St. John's which is the capital of Newfoundland, not New Brunswick. Minter and Issuer are unknown.

Photograph
not
available
at press time

Composition: Copper
Weight: 6.2 g
Diameter: 28.0 to 28.2 mm
Die Axis: ↑↑
Edge: Reeded
Ref.Nos.: W 452

Cat.No.	Date	Description	AG	G-4	VG-8	F-12	VF-20
NB-5	(1830s)	Copper		Only two known. Extremely Rare			

TOKENS OF LOWER CANADA

New France was in British hands in 1759 and was renamed the Colony of Quebec when British possession was confirmed in 1763. Its territory included the valley of the St. Lawrence River and the Great Lakes Region south to the Ohio River. After 1783 the Great Lakes, the upper St. Lawrence, the forty-fifth parallel and the water-shed between the St. Lawrence and its drainage basins became the southern boundary. In 1791 the colony was divided into Upper and Lower Canada.

English and American merchants entered the colony soon after 1760 and influenced the local currency. The shortage of coined money was beginning to result in the use of cut money in Montreal. Spanish dollars were being cut into aliquot parts and circulated without any countermarking of value. The practice was short-lived for the Ordinance of 1764 expressly forbade it. As time passed the colony became very short of coinage.

After 1764 the cut legal money used in Montreal was taken out of circulation. Some French coins circulated and were augmented by small amounts of English coin. The only legal copper pieces were English and Irish halfpennies which were in insufficient and dwindling supply. After 1797 some shipments of halfpennies of George III were sent from England but not enough for the needs of trade. After 1812 anonymous tokens were imported from England and Ireland. Very soon afterward locally-made tokens appeared. At first the weight was good but in later years it steadily decreased. After 1825 many pieces in circulation were brass. A law forbidding the further import of private tokens was passed in 1825. It was so loosely worded that it was possible to import tokens dated before 1825.

By 1837 anything the size of a halfpenny would pass for a token and the banks, in the absence of action by the government, refused to take any of the so-called copper currency except by weight and issued their own tokens.

BRETON CROSS REFERENCE TABLE FOR LOWER CANADA

Breton Cat. No.	Charlton Cat. No.	Page No.	Breton Cat. No.	Charlton Cat. No.	Page No.
520	LC-1	83	680	LC-21	109
521	LC-9A-D	94, 95, 96	681	LC-22C	110
522	LC-8A-D	91, 92, 93	682	LC-22B	110
523	LC-11A-B	99	683	LC-25	113
524	LC-10A-B	97, 98	684	LC-41	128
525	LC-11C	100	685	LC-30C	118
531	LC-12	100	686	LC-30D	118
532	LC-13A-B	101	687	LC-32A	120
533	LC-14	102	688	LC-31A	119
561	LC-15	102	689	LC-43	129
562	LC-16	103	690	LC-44	130
563	LC-17	104	691	LC-27	114
564	LC-18	104	692	LC-32B	120
565	LC-19	105	693	LC-31B	119
670	LC-45	130	694	LC-31C	119
671	LC-20	106	695	LC-29A	115
672	LC-6	90	696	LC-29B	115
673	LC-7	90	697	LC-29E	116
674	LC-40	127	698	LC-30A	117
675	LC-23A	111	699	LC-30B	117
676	LC-22A	110	700	LC-29C	115
677	LC-23B	111	701	LC-29D	116
678	LC-23C	111	702	LC-28	114
679	LC-24	112	703	LC-30F	118

BRETON CROSS REFERENCE TABLE FOR LOWER CANADA (cont.)

Breton Cat. No.	Charlton Cat. No.	Page No.	Breton Cat. No.	Charlton Cat. No.	Page No.
704	LC-33A	121	960	LC-46	131
705	LC-33C1	121	960	LC-48A-B	138, 139
706	LC-34	122	961	LC-48C	140
707	LC-35	123	982	LC-49	140
708	LC-36	123	989	LC-52	142
709	LC-37	124	990	LC-51	141
710	LC-38A	125	991	LC-50	141
711	LC-39	126	992	LC-53A	142
712	LC-38B	125	994	LC-54A-D	143, 144, 145
713	LC-2	84, 85	1001	LC-55	146
714	LC-3	86, 87	1002	LC-58A-B	149, 150
715	LC-5	89	1004	LC-56A-B	146, 147
716	LC-4	88	1005	LC-56C	147
957	LC-47A	132	1007	LC-59A-B	151
958	LC-47B-C	133, 134	1011	LC-57	148
959	LC-47D	135	1012	LC-60A-F	152 to 157

SEMI-REGAL TOKENS

MAGDALEN ISLAND TOKEN

The Magdalen Islands were settled by the French who gave them the name Îles de la Madeleine. During the French period the islands were governed from Acadia and after 1713 from Isle Royale. The islands were ceded to Great Britain in 1763 and placed under the control of the government of Newfoundland. When the Quebec Act was passed in 1774 the Magdalen Islands were transferred to the colony of Quebec. In 1791 they were included in the territory of Lower Canada.

After the American Revolution the islands were granted to Sir Isaac Coffin as a reward for loyalty during the war. He visited the islands only once, in 1815, with the intent to set up a feudal barony.

One of the privileges claimed by Sir Isaac Coffin was the right to coin money. He ordered a coinage of pennies from Sir Edward Thomason of Birmingham and planned to issue halfpennies as well. He was reputed to have taken a coining press and dies with him in order to set up a mint on the islands.

The coin was struck by Sir Edward Thomason from dies probably cut by Thomas Halliday who produced several dies for Sir Edward.

After a long history of bad relations, the government of Canada bought out the descendants of Sir Isaac Coffin and resold the land to its inhabitants.

LC-1　　　　**SUCCESS TO THE FISHERY ONE PENNY —**
1815 MAGDALEN ISLAND TOKEN

LC-001

Composition: Copper
Weight: 17.1 to 17.4 g
Diameter: 33.4 to 33.6 mm

Die Axis: ↑↑, ↑→
Edge: Engrailed
Ref.Nos: Br 520 (R-2½);
　　　　　　Lr 495 (R-4); McL 23;
　　　　　　W 500

Variations: Examples struck on extra thick planchets of 23.5 grams are known but are very rare.

Cat.No.	Date	Description	G-4	VG-8	F-12	VF-20	EF-40	AU-50	AU-55	MS-60
LC-1	1815	Magdelan Island	50.	100.	200.	425.	900.	2,000.	2,500.	3.000.

BANK OF MONTREAL UN SOUS TOKENS

About 1835, the Bank of Montreal's directors, alarmed at the state of the copper currency, began to issue tokens. In 1836 the bank was permitted to issue sous inscribed with its name. They probably were struck in Birmingham by Boulton and Watt. Their fabric suggests this but nothing has yet been discovered to confirm their place of manufacture. The engravers, in their ignorance of the French language, cut the value to read UN SOUS. Thus the Bank of Montreal sous of both issues carried the value erroneously rendered in the plural. The misspelling was not a hindrance to their circulation but an easy means of identification when numerous imitations were later imported.

LC-2   ***BANK TOKEN MONTREAL UN SOUS —***
                   TRADE & AGRICULTURE LOWER CANADA

This Bank of Montreal token is linked to the Birmingham issue of the bouquet sou LC-37 by the common obverse LC-2A5.

Composition: Copper
Weight: 7.9 to 9.0 g
Diameter: 27.4 to 28.2 mm
Die Axis: ↑↑
Edge: Plain
Ref.Nos.: Br 713 (R-1); See below

La 518

Varieties: Obverse
A1 The stem of the lower left rosebud is nearly straight with a leaf hanging from a short stem; Co 8B; W 678

Lp 520

A2 The stem of the lower left rosebud curves upward with a leaf with no stem; Co 9B; W 679

Cat.No.	Date	Description	VG-8	F-12	VF-20	EF-40	AU-50	AU-55	MS-60
LC-2A1	(1835)	Straight stem	12.	18.	35.	80.	150.	275.	350.
LC-2A2	(1835)	Curved stem	6.	10.	25.	55.	125.	225.	275.

007
008

8 VARIETIES

LC-2   **BANK TOKEN MONTREAL UN SOUS —**
                    TRADE & AGRICULTURE LOWER CANADA

Le 522

A3   The bow on the bouquet is doubled; Co 10B; W 680

A4   The stem of the lower left rosebud is broken; Co 11B; W 681

A5   The stem of the lower left rosebud does not connect directly to the
         bouquet; Co 12B; W 682

A6   The stem of the lower left rosebud originates from a leaf, large
         ampersand; Co 13B; W 683

Cat.No.	Date	Description	VG-8	F-12	VF-20	EF-40	AU-50	AU-55	MS-60
LC-2A3	(1835)	Double bow	6.	12.	25.	80.	150.	300.	400.
LC-2A4	(1835)	Broken stem	7.	15.	30.	80.	150.	300.	400.
LC-2A5	(1835)	Short stem	7.	15.	30.	80.	150.	300.	400.
LC-2A6	(1835)	Large ampersand	12.	22.	50.	100.	175.	350.	475.

LC-3

BANK OF MONTREAL TOKEN UN SOUS —
TRADE & AGRICULTURE LOWER CANADA

Composition: Copper
Weight: 7.9 to 8.6 g
Diameter: 27.5 to 28.2 mm
Die Axis: ↑↑
Edge: Plain
Ref.Nos.: Br 714 (R-1); See below

LR 517

Varieties: Obverse and reverse
A1 Obverse: Similar to LC-2A1
Reverse: The first palm leaf under the second letter "S" in SOUS is forked with the left side much shorter that the right one. The three cherry leaves opposite "NK" of BANK have the centre leaf with a short slender stem; Co 3B; W 684

A2 Obverse: The lower left rosebud has a long curved stem
Reverse: The first palm leaf is forked with sides of equal length. The centre leaf of the group has no stem; Co 4B; W 685

002
003

Cat.No.	Date	Description	VG-8	F-12	VF-20	EF-40	AU-50	AU-55	MS-60
LC-3A1	(1836)	Short stem	6.	12.	25.	115.	200.	325.	400.
LC-3A2	(1836)	No stem	6.	12.	25.	115.	200.	325.	400.

LC-3 **BANK OF MONTREAL TOKEN UN SOUS —**
TRADE & AGRICULTURE LOWER CANADA

LR 519

A3 Obverse: Similar to LC-2A2
       Reverse: The first palm leaf is forked with the left side short and
                slender. All three leaves of the group have clear stems;
                Co 5B; W 686

LR 521

A4 Obverse: Similar to LC-2A3
       Reverse: The first palm leaf is forked but the two sides are curved.
                The group of leaves has only one stem; Co 6B; W 687

A5 Obverse: The lower left rosebud has no stem
       Reverse: The group of leaves has three slender long stems; Co 7B;
                W 688

Cat.No.	Date	Description	VG-8	F-12	VF-20	EF-40	AU-50	AU-55	MS-60
LC-3A3	(1836)	Three short stems	6.	12.	20.	75.	225.	325.	400.
LC-3A4	(1836)	One stem	7.	15.	25.	90.	225.	325.	400.
LC-3A5	(1836)	Three long stems	7.	15.	25.	90.	225.	325.	400.

LA BANQUE DU PEUPLE UN SOU TOKENS

The first sous of La Banque du Peuple were issued in 1837. The bank was organized in 1835 by reformists (including French and Scottish) excluded by the conservatives or Tories who dominated the Bank of Montreal's board of directors. La Banque du Peuple never applied for a charter until 1843 and operated as a private bank, Viger, DeWitt & Cie., until it finally was granted a charter in 1844. The bank remained in business until 1895.

The first sou is the famous Rebellion Sou struck by Jean-Marie Arnault, who also cut the dies from designs suggested by the bank. It received its popular name because it was believed that the star and liberty cap were added to the design at the instigation of bank personnel who sympathized with the rebel cause. All the bank's directors were real or suspected rebels late in 1837. (Warrants were issued for their arrest).

Later in 1837 the bank was permitted to issue more sous, and released an issue of bouquet sous struck in Belleville, New Jersey. The dies were cut by John Gibbs, a senior partner of the firm. The bank also participated in the issue of the 1837 "Habitant" tokens.

LC-4   *BANQUE DU PEUPLE MONTREAL UN SOU —*
             AGRICULTURE & COMMERCE BAS-CANADA

ARNAULT ISSUE 1837

Composition: Copper
Weight: 7.0 to 9.0 g
Diameter: 27.2 to 28.1 mm
Die Axis: ↑↑, ↑↓
Edge: Reeded
Ref.Nos.: Br 716 (R-1½); Co 14B; Lr 509 (R-4); McL 102; W 689

Varieties: Die Axis
A1 Medal
A2 Coinage

Note: LC-4 is found on thin and thick flans, resulting in weight variations.

Cat.No.	Date	Description	VG-8	F-12	VF-20	EF-40	AU-50	AU-55	MS-60
LC-4A1	1837	Medal	25.	50.	90.	200.	300.	425.	500.
LC-4A2	1837	Coinage	10.	25.	60.	125.	200.	275.	325.

013-A
013-B

LC-5

BANQUE DU PEUPLE MONTREAL UN SOU —
AGRICULTURE AND COMMERCE BAS CANADA

BELLEVILLE ISSUE 1837

Composition: Brass, copper
Weight: 8.1 to 9.3 g
Diameter: 27.3 to 28.0 mm
Die Axis: ↑↑
Edge: Plain, reeded
Ref.Nos.: Br 715 (R-1); McL 101;
See below

Open Wreath **(A1 and 2)**   Closed Wreath **(A3)**

Varieties: Reverse, Edge
A1 Open wreath, Reeded; Co 15B; Lr 508a (R-5); W 690
A2 Open wreath, Plain; Co 16B; Lr 508a (R-5); W 690
A3 Closed wreath, Reeded; Brass; Co 17B, Lr 508 (R-3); W 691

Notes:
1. The open wreath variety may also be identified by a heavy die break joining the "T" and "U" at the top in 'AGRICULTURE.' Many other varieties are described by Geo. Thomson; see Reference Works p.xxiii.
2. The open wreath, plain edge variety is probably the result of light, undersized planchets. Care must be exercised in identification for the reeding may be so weak as to be almost undetectable.
3. The closed wreath variety is the result of a die break joining the two upper leaves of the reverse wreath.

Cat.No.	Date	Description	VG-8	F-12	VF-20	EF-40	AU-50	AU-55	MS-60
LC-5A1	(1838)	Open wreath, Reeded	50.	120.	200.	400.	550.	—	—
LC-5A2	(1838)	Open wreath, Plain	200.	350.	675.	900.	—	—	—
LC-5A3	(1838)	Closed wreath, Reeded	5.	7.	12.	35.	100.	—	—

CITY BANK HALF PENNY TOKENS

The City Bank was organized in 1833 for the benefit of businessmen denied the services of the Bank of Montreal because of their political views. The City Bank prospered until 1873 when it suffered a severe strain owing to an unfavourable court decision.

In 1876 the City Bank merged with the Royal Canadian Bank. The combined firm was known as the Consolidated Bank of Canada. The bank collapsed during the financial depression of 1879.

The sous attributed to the City Bank were struck by Jean-Marie Arnault from dies cut by him.

LC-6   *PRO BONO PUBLICO MONTREAL ½ PENNY TOKEN 1837 —*
TRADE & AGRICULTURE LOWER CANADA

Composition: Copper
Weight: N/A
Diameter: 26.9 to 27.1 mm
Die Axis: ↑↑
Edge: Plain
Ref.Nos.: Br 672 (R-6); Co 1B;
Lr 534 (R-9); W 692

Cat.No.	Date	Description	VG-8	F-12	VF-20	EF-40	AU-50	AU-55	MS-60
LC-6	1837	Copper			Unique. Bank of Canada Collection				

LC-7   *BANK TOKEN MONTREAL ½ PENNY —*
TRADE & AGRICULTURE LOWER CANADA

Composition: Copper
Weight: 7.8 g
Diameter: 26.9 to 27.1 mm
Die Axis: ↑↑
Edge: Plain
Ref.Nos.: Br 673 (R-5); Co 2B;
Lr 535 (R-8); McL 59;
W 693

Cat.No.	Date	Description	AG	G-4	VG-8	F-12	VF-20
LC-7	(1837)	Copper			Very Rare		

PROVINCE DU BAS CANADA "HABITANT TOKENS"

In 1837 the Bank of Montreal applied for permission to import halfpennies and pennies. Permission was granted provided the City Bank, Quebec Bank and the Banque du Peuple would also participate. Tokens were ordered through Albert Furniss of Montreal and struck by Boulton & Watt. The obverse design depicted a Canadian Habitant standing in traditional winter costume. The reverse carried the arms of the City of Montreal with the name of the participating bank appearing on the ribbon.

LC-8
BANK TOKEN HALF PENNY 1837 —
PROVINCE DU BAS CANADA UN SOU

LC-8A *– 105 ♂*
106
CITY BANK ON RIBBON

Composition: Copper
Weight: 9.2 to 9.5 g
Diameter: 28.2 to 28.3 mm
Die Axis: ↑↑, ↑↓
Edge: Plain
Ref.Nos.: Br 522 (R-1);
Lr 529 (R-3); McL 105;
See below

"V" and "I" in line **(A1)**   "V" lower than top of "I" **(A2)**

Varieties: Obverse
105 **A1** The right seriph of "V" and the top of "I" in PROVINCE are in line;
Co 1-1oH; W 736-739
106 **A2** The right seriph of "V" is lower than the top of the "I" in PROVINCE;
Co 2-2IH; W 740-744

Variations: LC-8A2 exists (Co 2e) with a coinage axis and is very rare.

Cat.No.	Date	Description	VG-8	F-12	VF-20	EF-40	AU-50	AU-55	MS-60
LC-8A1	1837	In line	5.	7.	15.	50.	150.	225.	250.
LC-8A2	1837	Lower, Medal	7.	10.	20.	65.	150.	225.	275.

LC-8B – $|0^7 \, d\, |0\, \&$ **QUEBEC BANK ON RIBBON**

Composition: Copper
Weight: 9.0 to 9.4 g
Diameter: 28.2 to 28.3 mm
Die Axis: ↑↑
Edge: Plain
Ref.Nos.: Br 522 (R-1);
Lr 531 (R-3); McL 110;
See below

Varieties: Obverse
$|0^7$ – **B1** The right seriph of "V" and the top of "I" in PROVINCE are in line; Co 3-3gH; W 749-751
$|0\,\&$ – **B2** The right seriph of "V" is lower than the top of the "I" in PROVINCE; Co 4-4iH; W 752-756

Variations: LC-8B2, Co4c, is without a period after "half penny." These tokens are priced identical to LC-8B2.

Note: For variety illustration see page No. 91

Cat.No.	Date	Description	VG-8	F-12	VF-20	EF-40	AU-50	AU-55	MS-60
LC-8B1	1837	In Line	5.	7.	15.	50.	150.	225.	275.
LC-8B2	1837	Lower	6.	10.	20.	65.	150.	225.	275.

LC-8C – $|0^9 \, d\, |^{|0}$ **LA BANQUE DU PEUPLE ON RIBBON**

Composition: Copper
Weight: 9.5 g
Diameter: 28.2 to 28.3 mm
Die Axis: ↑↑
Edge: Plain
Ref.Nos.: Br 522 (R-1);
Lr 506 (R-3); McL 108;
See below

Varieties: Obverse
$|0^9$ – **C1** The right seriph of "V" and the top of "I" in PROVINCE are in line; Co 6-6eH; W 760-762
$||\,0$ – **C2** The right seriph of "V" is lower than the top of the "I" in PROVINCE; Co 7-7bH; W 763

Note: For variety illustration see page No. 91.

Cat.No.	Date	Description	VG-8	F-12	VF-20	EF-40	AU-50	AU-55	MS-60
LC-8C1	1837	In line	7.	15.	30.	90.	200.	250.	300.
LC-8C2	1837	Lower	8.	18.	35.	110.	225.	300.	375.

LC-8D -111 d 112   **BANK OF MONTREAL ON RIBBON**

Composition: Copper
Weight: 9.5 gm
Diameter: 28.2 to 28.3 mm
Die Axis: ↑↑
Edge: Plain
Ref.Nos.: Br 522 (R-1);
Lr 512 (R-3); McL 104;
See below

Varieties: Obverse

111 — **D1** The right seriph of "V" and the top of "I" in PROVINCE are in line;
Co 20 10b and 23BM and H; W 766-769

112 — **D2** The right seriph of "V" is lower than the top of the "I" in PROVINCE;
Co 20-22BM; W 770-771
Co 14 - 19b

Note: For variety illustration see page 91. Proofs exist for LC-8D2.

Cat.No.	Date	Description	VG-8	F-12	VF-20	EF-40	AU-50	AU-55	MS-60
LC-8D1	1837	In line	7.	15.	30.	65.	150.	225.	275.
LC-8D2	1837	Lower	7.	15.	30.	65.	150.	225.	275.

LC-9 BANK TOKEN ONE PENNY 1837 —
PROVINCE DU BAS CANADA DEUX SOUS

LC-9A *113, 114,* CITY BANK ON RIBBON

115,

Composition: Copper
Weight: 18.7 to 19.0 g
Diameter: 34.0 to 34.1 mm

Die Axis: ↑↑, ↑↓
Edge: Plain
Ref.Nos.: Br 521 (R-1); McL 104;
See below

Far button; Left
collar below

Near button; Left
collar at shoulder

Period
(A1, 3 / A4)

No period (A2)

Strong or large
ground (A1 / A2)

Weak or small
ground (A3 / A4)

Varieties: Obverse, Die axis
Large ground — Left collar below shoulder
Small ground — Left collar at shoulder

113 — **A1** Strong ground, Period after Canada, Medal; Co 8-8cH; Lr 528 (R-4);
W 745

114 — **A2** Strong ground, No period after Canada, Medal; Co 9-9iH;
Lr 528a (R-4); W 746

115 — **A3** Weak ground, Period after Canada, Medal; Co 10-10dH;
Lr 528 (R-4); W 747, 748

116 — **A4** Weak ground, Period after Canada, Coinage; Co 11H; Lr 528a (R-4)

Note: Proofs exist for LC-9A1.

Cat.No.	Date	Description	VG-8	F-12	VF-20	EF-40	AU-50	AU-55	MS-60
LC-9A1	1837	Strong, Period, ↑↑	6.	12.	30.	65.	150.	275.	350.
LC-9A2	1837	Strong, No period, ↑↑	5.	9.	22.	60.	150.	275.	350.
LC-9A3	1837	Weak, Period, ↑↑	7.	15.	35.	65.	150.	275.	375.
LC-9A4	1837	Weak, Period, ↑↓	12.	22.	50.	95.	200.	350.	425.

LC-9B 117, 118, 119, 120 *QUEBEC BANK ON RIBBON*

Composition: Copper
Weight: 19.0 g
Diameter: 34.1 mm
Die Axis: ↑↑, ↑↓
Edge: Plain
Ref.Nos.: Br 521 (R-1); McL 109; See below

Varieties: Obverse, Die axis
- **B1** Strong ground, Period after Canada, Medal; Co 12-12bH; Lr 530 (R-3); W 757
- **B2** Strong ground, No period after Canada, Medal; Co 13-13f and 13hH; Lr 530a (R-3)
- **B3** Strong ground, No period after Canada, Coinage; Co 13-13hH; Lr 530a (R-3); W 758
- **B4** Weak ground, Period after Canada, Medal; Co 14-14bH; Lr 530 (R-3); W 759

Note: For variety illustration see page 94.

Cat.No.	Date	Description	VG-8	F-12	VF-20	EF-40	AU-50	AU-55	MS-60
LC-9B1	1837	Strong, Period, ↑↑	5.	8.	20.	65.	150.	250.	325.
LC-9B2	1837	Strong, No period, ↑↑	6.	12.	22.	75.	150.	250.	325.
LC-9B3	1837	Strong, No period, ↑↓	18.	35.	65.	125.	225.	350.	425.
LC-9B4	1837	Weak, Period, ↑↑	18.	35.	65.	125.	225.	350.	425.

LC-9C 121, 122 *BANQUE DU PEUPLE ON RIBBON*

Composition: Copper
Weight: 19.0 g
Diameter: 34.1 mm
Die Axis: ↑↑
Edge: Plain
Ref.Nos.: Br 521 (R-1); Lr 505 (R-3); McL 107; See below

Varieties: Obverse
- **C1** Strong ground, Period after Canada; Co 16, 16aH; W 764
- **C2** Weak ground, Period after Canada; Co 17-17dH; W 765

Note: For variety illustration see page 94.

Cat.No.	Date	Description	VG-8	F-12	VF-20	EF-40	AU-50	AU-55	MS-60
LC-9C1	1837	Strong, Period	20.	35.	75.	160.	275.	375.	450.
LC-9C2	1837	Weak, Period	18.	22.	65.	160.	250.	375.	450.

LC-9D   *BANK OF MONTREAL ON RIBBON*

123, 124, 125

Composition: Copper
Weight: 19.0 g
Diameter: 34.1 mm

Die Axis: ↑↑
Edge: Plain
Ref.Nos.: Br 521 (R-1); McL 103;
See below

Varieties: Obverse

123 — **D1** Strong ground, No period after Canada; Co 29BM and H;
Lr 511 (R-4); W 775

124 — **D2** Weak ground, Period after Canada; Co 24-27BM and H;
Lr 510 (R-3); W 772, 773

125 — **D3** Weak ground, No period after Canada; Co 28BM and H;
Lr 511 (R-4); W 774

Note: For variety illustration see page 94.
The strong ground, LC-9D1, does not appear in Courteau under Bank of
Montreal pennies, however there is a Courteau variety, 29BM, which is listed as
an extended ground. Willey classified this example as W 775.

Cat.No.	Date	Description	VG-8	F-12	VF-20	EF-40	AU-50	AU-55	MS-60
LC-9D1	1837	Strong, No period	8.	18.	35.	85.	200.	300.	375.
LC-9D2	1837	Weak, Period	8.	18.	35.	85.	200.	300.	375.
LC-9D3	1837	Weak, No period	8.	18.	35.	85.	200.	300.	375.

BANK OF MONTREAL "SIDE VIEW" TOKENS

LC-10   *BANK TOKEN HALF PENNY —*
                   1838/1839 BANK OF MONTREAL

In 1838 the Bank of Montreal replaced the Habitant tokens with a new issue showing a corner or side view of the bank building on the obverse. The tokens were procured by Cotterill, Hill & Co. of Walsall, Staffordshire and arrived in Montreal in June of 1839. They were short-lived because the manager of the bank did not like their workmanship or weight, and the shipment was returned to England for melting.

LC-10A   *HALF PENNY DATED 1838 BANK OF MONTREAL ON RIBBON*

Composition: Brass, copper
Weight: 9.9 to 10.4 g
Diameter: 28.0 to 28.3 mm
Die Axis: ↑↑
Edge: Plain
Ref.Nos.: Br 524 (R-4);
Lr 514 (R-6); McL 115;
See below

| 13 Palings, 8 Left of tree **(A1 and A2)** | 11 Palings, 6 Left of tree **(A3)** | 8 Palings, 3 Left of tree **(A4)** |

Varieties: Obverse
A1 Left fence has thirteen palings, eight to left of tree, Copper; Co 30BM; W 776
A2 Left fence has thirteen palings, eight to left of tree, Brass; Co 30BM; W 776
A3 Left fence has eleven palings, six to left of tree, Copper; Co 31BM; W 777; Also reported in brass.
A4 Right fence has eight palings, three to left of tree, Copper; Co 32BM; W 778

Cat.No.	Date	Description	VG-8	F-12	VF-20	EF-40	AU-50	AU-55	MS-60
LC-10A1	1838	Thirteen palings, Copper	625.	950.	1,500.	2,250.	3,000.	—	—
LC-10A2	1838	Thirteen palings, Brass	750.	1,000.	1,750.	2,500.	3,500.	—	—
LC-10A3	1838	Eleven palings, Copper	625.	950.	1,500.	2,250.	3,000.	—	—
LC-10A3	1838	Eleven palings, Brass			Extremely Rare				
LC-10A4	1838	Eight palings, Copper	625.	950.	1,500.	2,250.	3,000.	—	—

LC-10B   HALF PENNY DATED 1839 BANK OF MONTREAL ON RIBBON

In 1839 the bank asked that the order of 1838 be refilled in the same amount as originally requested. The coinage of 1839 was again procured by Cotterill, Hill & Co., but this time in better copper and in more proper weight. This coinage was refused as well by the bank's manager who considered its quality even worse than that of the 1838 issues.

Composition: Copper
Weight: 8.8 g
Diameter: 28.3 mm
Die Axis: ↑↑
Edge: Plain
Ref.Nos.: Br 524 (R-4);
Lr 514 (R-6); McL 115;
See below

15 Palings (**B1**)   14 Palings (**B2**)

Tail touches garter (**B1**)

Varieties: Obverse and reverse
B1 Left fence has fifteen palings; Beaver's tail touches garter; Co 33BM; W 781
B2 Left fence has fourteen palings; Beaver's tail does not touch garter; Co 34BM; W 782
B3 Mule of B1 and B2, Left fence has fifteen palings; Beaver's tail does not touch garter; Co 35BM; W 783

Cat.No.	Date	Description	VG-8	F-12	VF-20	EF-40	AU-50	AU-55	MS-60
LC-10B1	1839	Fifteen palings	625.	950.	1,400.	1,850.	3,000.	—	—
LC-10B2	1839	Fourteen palings	625.	950.	1,400.	1,850.	3,000.	—	—
LC-10B3	1839	Mule	1,250.	1,750.	2,500.	3,000.	—	—	—

LC-11   *BANK TOKEN ONE PENNY —*
                1838/1839 BANK OF MONTREAL

LC-11A   *ONE PENNY DATED 1838 BANK OF MONTREAL ON RIBBON*

Composition: Brass, copper
Weight: 19.2 to 19.8 g
Diameter: 33.8 mm
Die Axis: ↑↑
Edge: Plain
Ref.Nos.:   Br 523 (R-4½);
                Lr 513 (R-7);
                See below

Tail almost touches "M" **(A1)**   Tail points to left foot of "M"
                                          (A2)

Varieties: Reverse
  A1 Narrow tail beaver almost touches "M"; Co 36BM; W 779
  A2 Wide tail beaver points to left foot of "M"; Co 37BM; W 780

Cat.No.	Date	Description	VG-8	F-12	VF-20	EF-40	AU-50	AU-55	MS-60
LC-11A1	1838	Narrow tail almost touches	950.	1,250.	1,750.	3,000.	4,500.	—	—
LC-11A2	1838	Wide tail does not touch	950.	1,250.	1,750.	3,000.	4,500.	—	—

LC-11B   *ONE PENNY BATED 1839 BANK OF MONTREAL ON RIBBON*

Composition: Copper
Weight: 18.7 g
Diameter: 34.2 mm
Die Axis: ↑↑
Edge: Plain
Ref.Nos.:   Br 523 (R-4);
                Co 38BM;
                Lr 513 (R-7);
                W 784

Cat.No.	Date	Description	VG-8	F-12	VF-20	EF-40	AU-50	AU-55	MS-60
LC-11B	1839	Thirteen palings	950.	1,250.	1,750.	3,000.	4,500.	—	—

LC-11C   ONE PENNY DATED 1839 BANQUE DU PEUPLE ON RIBBON

This was once considered an error. It is now thought that the manufacturer struck it deliberately, either at the bank's suggestion or to show to the bank as an example of their work. Either way, nothing came of it as there are fewer than eight examples known today.

Composition: Copper
Weight: 18.7 g
Diameter: 33.8 mm
Die Axis: ↑↑
Edge: Plain
Ref.Nos.: Br 525 (R-4½);
Co 39BM;
Lr 507 (R-8);
McL 116; W 785

Cat.No.	Date	Description	AG	G-4	VG-8	F-12	VF-20
LC-11C	1839	Copper	—	—	4,000.	5,000.	6,000.

PRIVATE TOKENS
LC-12   MONTREAL — 1816 HALF PENNY TOKEN

Composition: Copper
Weight: 5.2 to 5.7 g
Diameter: 27.9 to 28.2 mm
Die Axis: ↑↑
Edge: Plain
Ref.Nos.: Br 531 (R-1);
Co 47W; Lr 502 (R-3);
McL 24; W 541

Variations: Varying degrees of rust areas, especially on the reverse, are in evidence on most pieces. Very shallow die engraving resulted in poor detail in the struck token.

Cat.No.	Date	Description	VG-8	F-12	VF-20	EF-40	AU-50	AU-55	MS-60
LC-12	1816	Montreal	7.	15	45.	160.	300.	425.	500.

104

also WE-62

LC-13   *HALF PENNY — 1830/1841 CANADA*

These tokens were issued by Duncan & Co., a Montreal hardware firm. Specimens were put into circulation in Prince Edward Island by James Duncan, brother of the owner, who later issued his own tokens.

LC-13A   *— 1830 CANADA*

Composition: Copper
Weight: 5.8 g
Diameter: 25.7 to 26.1 mm
Die Axis: ↑↑
Edge: Plain
Ref.Nos.: Br 532 (R1½);
          Lr 503 (R-4); McL 30;
          W 575

Cat.No.	Date	Description	VG-8	F-12	VF-20	EF-40	AU-50	AU-55	MS-60
LC-13A	1830	Half Penny	8.	18.	40.	125.	250.	325.	400.

LC-13B   *— 1841 CANADA*

Composition: Copper
Weight: 5.3 to 5.8 g
Diameter: 25.7 to 26.1 mm
Die Axis: ↑↑
Edge: Plain
Ref.Nos.: Br 532 (R-1½);
          Lr 503 (R-4); McL 30;
          W 575

Cat.No.	Date	Description	VG-8	F-12	VF-20	EF-40	AU-50	AU-55	MS-60
LC-13B	1841	Half Penny	8.	18.	40.	125.	250.	325.	400.

LC-14

CANADA HALF PENNY TOKEN —
FOR PUBLIC ACCOMMODATION

This token was issued around 1830.

Composition: Copper
Weight: 6.5 to 7.2 g
Diameter: 27.6 to 28.0 mm
Die Axis: ↑↑, ↑↓
Edge: Plain, reeded
Ref.Nos.: Br 533 (R-1½);
Lr 504 (R-4); McL 27;
W 574

Variations: The obverse comes with large or small periods. This token was struck with rusted dies.

Cat.No.	Date	Description	VG-8	F-12	VF-20	EF-40	AU-50	AU-55	MS-60
LC-14A	(1830)	Copper, ↑↑	8.	15.	35.	100.	175.	275.	350.
LC-14B	(1830)	Copper, ↑↓	20.	30.	50.	125.	250.	350.	450.

LC-15

T.S. BROWN & CO.
IMPORTERS OF HARDWARES MONTREAL —

These halfpennies were issued by Thomas Storrow Brown, a Montreal hardware merchant. He led the Fils de la Liberte in the rebellion of 1837 and fled to the United States when the rebellion was put down, remaining there until amnesty was granted in 1844. His coppers were condemned by "Le Populaire" as a profiteering scheme, but are better than the brass pieces then in circulation. The tokens were struck in Birmingham. The obverse was also used for a Louisville, Kentucky, business card issued in 1845, and for a Green and Wetmore card, New York.

Composition: Copper
Weight: 7.1 to 7.6 g
Diameter: 27.9 to 28.3 mm
Die Axis: ↑↑
Edge: Plain, reeded
Ref.Nos.: Br 561 (R-1½);
Lr 573 (R-4);
McL 47-48; See below

"S" Close to "Co"
Period under "o"
(A1)

"S" Far from "Co"
No period under "o"
(A2)

Varieties: Reverse legends
A1 "S" of Importers close to "Co"; W 576
A2 "S" of Importers far from "Co"; W 577
Variations: The reverse exists with a far "S", and a period under the "o" of "Co."

Cat.No.	Date	Description	VG-8	F-12	VF-20	EF-40	AU-50	AU-55	MS-60
LC-15A1	(1832)	Close "S"; Period	8.	18.	45.	125.	250.	350.	425.
LC-15A2	(1832)	Far "S", No period	8.	18.	45.	135.	265.	375.	475.

LC-16   *CASH PAID FOR ALL SORTS OF GRAIN 1837 —*
             THS & WM MOLSON MONTREAL BREWERS
             DISTILLERS &&& UN SOU

The dies, which are still owned by the firm, were cut by Jean-Marie Arnault who also struck the coins. Evidently the firm supplied a specimen of a Perthshire halfpenny token of 1797 as a model for the distillery. The reverse of the Molson token is an exact copy, in reverse, of the Perthshire piece.

Composition: Copper, silver
Weight: Thick flan, 11.0 to 11.3 g
       Thin flan, 8.8 to 9.8 g
Thickness: Thick flan, 2.1 to 2.3mm
       Thin flan, 1.7 to 1.9mm

Diameter: 28.2 to 29.4 mm
Die Axis: ↑↑
Edge: Plain, reeded
Ref.Nos.: Br 562 (R-3);
       Lr 576 (R-5); McL 51;
       W 579

Varieties: Flan, Edge
       A1 Thick flan, Reeded
       A2 Thick flan, Plain
       A3 Thin flan, Reeded
       A4 Thin flan, Plain

Note: A few specimens were struck in silver for presentation purposes.

Cat.No.	Date	Description	VG-8	F-12	VF-20	EF-40	AU-50	AU-55	MS-60
LC-16A1	1837	Thick flan, Reeded	350.	525.	750.	1,100.	2,000.	2,500.	3,000.
LC-16A2	1837	Thick flan, Plain	400.	600.	1,000.	1,500.	2,250.	3,000.	3,500.
LC-16A3	1837	Thin flan, Reeded	350.	525.	750.	1,100.	2,000.	2,500.	3,000.
LC-16A4	1837	Thin flan, Plain	400.	600.	1,000.	1,500.	2,250.	3,000.	3,500.

LC-17   FRANCIS MULLINS & SON MONTREAL IMPORTERS OF SHIP
CHANDLERY &C. — COMMERCE TOKEN

Francis Mullins, a ship chandler in Montreal, imported these tokens in 1828.

Composition: Brass, copper
Weight: 4.8 to 5.4 g
Diameter: 26.6 to 26.8 mm
Die Axis: ↑↓
Edge: Plain
Ref.Nos.: Br 563 (R-2);
Lr 577 (R-4); McL 52;
W 573

Varieties: Composition
A1 Copper
A2 Brass

095

Cat.No.	Date	Description	VG-8	F-12	VF-20	EF-40	AU-50	AU-55	MS-60
LC-17A1	(1828)	Copper	18.	30.	65.	165.	325.	425.	500.
LC-17A2	(1828)	Brass	600.	800.	1,000.	—	—	—	—

LC-18   R.W. OWEN MONTREAL ROPERY — (SAILING SHIP DESIGN)

This token was issued in 1824 shortly before R.W. Owen sold out to J.A. Converse, against whose larger, steam-powered ropery he could not compete successfully. As a result very few of these tokens circulated. Forgeries exist.

Composition: Copper
Weight: 7.7 to 7.8 g
Diameter: 26.7 mm
Die Axis: ↑↑
Edge: Engrailed
Ref.Nos.: Br 564 (R-5);
Lr 578 (R-8); McL 50;
W 572

Cat.No.	Date	Description	AG	G-4	VG-8	F-12	VF-20
LC-18	(1824)	Montreal Ropery	—	—	10,000.	15,000.	20,000.

Note: Less than 10 examples are known to exist.

LC-19   *J. SHAW & CO. IMPORTERS OF HARDWARES*
              UPPER TOWN QUEBEC —

This token was issued in 1837 by John Shaw. It was denounced as a profiteering fraud by the newspaper "Le Canadien." Shaw at once replied that his halfpennies were issued to provide some supply of small change at a time of a great dearth of copper and that they were redeemable on demand. When the Habitant coppers of the Quebec Bank were released in 1838, Shaw attempted to withdraw his halfpennies.

Composition: Copper
Weight: 6.4 to 7.6 g
Diameter: 27.9 to 28.3 mm
Die Axis: ↑↑
Edge: Reeded
Ref.Nos.: Br 565 (R-1½);
              Lr 580 (R-4);
              McL 49; W 578

Cat.No.	Date	Description	VG-8	F-12	VF-20	EF-40	AU-50	AU-55	MS-60
LC-19	(1837)	J. Shaw & Co.	12.	22.	60.	125.	250.	350.	425.

LC-20   *J. ROY MONTREAL UN SOU —*
COMMERCE BAS-CANADA

Mr. Joseph Roy was a dry goods merchant who operated a business at 70 St. Paul Street in Montreal. During September of 1837 he issued tokens, probably designed by Jean-Marie Arnault.

The shipment to Roy contained tokens of mixed weights even though he had instructed the minter to produce his pieces at the weight of 51 tokens to the pound (which equalled the weight of the current bank tokens.)

A newspaper article published in "Le Populaire" on November 17, 1837, condemned Roy for his lightweight tokens. After a second attempt to have Arnault produce tokens of proper weight, Roy cancelled the order.

Composition: Copper
Weight: Thick flan, 8.9 to 9.2 g
          Thin flan, 6.2 to 6.8 g
Thickness: Thick flan, 2.1 to 2.3mm
          Thin flan, 1.7 to 1.9mm

Diameter: 27.1 to 28.0 mm
Die Axis: ↑↑
Edge: Plain
Ref.Nos.: Br 671 (R-2); Co 72B;
          Lr 579 (R-5); McL 57;
          W 580

Varieties: Flan
     A1 Thick flan
     A2 Thin flan

Cat.No.	Date	Description	VG-8	F-12	VF-20	EF-40	AU-50	AU-55	MS-60
LC-20A1	(1837)	Thick flan	50.	100.	200.	600.	1,500.	2,350.	3,000.
LC-20A2	(1837)	Thin flan	50.	100.	200.	600.	1,500.	2,350.	3,000.

088
088a

THE "BOUQUET SOUS"

These tokens feature a bouquet of the heraldic flowers on the obverse. Because of their popularity with the mainly French-speaking opponents of the government of the day they were called the "Sous des Patriotes."

These Patriotes began to boycott English goods and refused English money, relying on the meagre supply of old French coins remaining from the French regime. They also accepted the tokens of the Bank of Montreal, Banque du Peuple and City Bank because they were inscribed in French.

To fill the void caused by this action, a Montreal exchange broker named Dexter Chapin imported a large shipment of sous imitating the design of the sous of the Bank of Montreal from Belleville, New Jersey. Their circulation was very profitable to Chapin because of their lighter weight. Similar imports came from Birmingham and a few were struck in Montreal. By 1837 the Bouquet sous were so numerous that they, in turn, were refused by the banks.

IDENTIFICATION OF "BOUQUET SOUS" TOKENS

The bouquet sous tokens are listed by the number of cherry leaves in the reverse wreath with sublistings according to the number of shamrocks and the position of the bow in the obverse bouquet.

REVERSE

Reverse bow No reverse bow

OBVERSE

BELLEVILLE ISSUES

Cat. Number	Leaves in Rev. Wreath	Shamrocks in Obv. Wreath	Position Obverse Bow	Breton Number	Courteau Number	LeRoux Number	Willey Number
LC-21	16	2	Right	680	53B	539	700
LC-22A,B	16	3	Left	676, 682	57, 59B	558, 559	695, 702
LC-22C	16	3	None	681	60B	565	701
LC-23	16	4	Left	675, 677-678	56, 58, 61-62B	548, 554, 555	694, 696, 697, 698
LC-24	16	7	Left	679	54-55B	557	699
LC-25	17	2	Right	683	51-52B	536	703
LC-26	17	3	None	—	—		704
LC-27	18	0	None	691	43-44B	563	710
LC-28	18	1	None	702	29B	561	721
LC-29A-D	18	2	Right	695-696, 700-701	31-32B, 45-46B	537, 538, 543, 544	714-715 719-720
LC-29E	18	2	None	697	33-34B	564	716
LC-30A,B	18	3	Left	698-699	35-36B	550, 551	717-718
LC-30C-F	18	3	None	685-686, 703	30, 47, 48B	562, 566, 567	705-706 708, 722
LC-31A,B,C	18	5	Right	688, 693-694	37-38, 41B	540-542	709, 712, 713
LC-32A,B	18	7	Left	687, 692	39, 42B	552, 556	707, 711
LC-33A,B	20	2	Left	704	27-28B	560	723-724
LC-33C	20	2	None	705	25-26B	546	725

BIRMINGHAM ISSUES

Cat. Number	Leaves in Rev. Wreath	Shamrocks in Obv. Wreath	Position Obverse Bow	Breton Number	Courteau Number	LeRoux Number	Willey Number
LC-34	32	1	None	706	23B	572	726
LC-35	32	2	None	707	22B	571	727
LC-36	32	3	None	708	20B	570	728
LC-37	32	3	Left	709	21B	525	729
LC-38A	39	3	None	710	19B	569	730
LC-38B	39	3	Double	712	—	548a	G3
LC-39	39	6	None	711	18B	568	731

MONTREAL ISSUES

Cat. Number	Leaves in Rev. Wreath	Shamrocks in Obv. Wreath	Position Obverse Bow	Breton Number	Courteau Number	LeRoux Number	Willey Number
LC-40	16	5	Left	674	63-70B	547	734
LC-41	17	6	Right	684	49-50B	545	732
LC-42	18	2	None	—	—	—	735
LC-43	21	0	None	689	24B	549	733

MISCELLANEOUS ISSUES

Cat. Number	Leaves in Rev. Wreath	Shamrocks in Obv. Wreath	Position Obverse Bow	Breton Number	Courteau Number	LeRoux Number	Willey Number
LC-44	18	7	Left	690	40B	553	G2
LC-45	—	3	None	670	71B	574	C28

BELLEVILLE ISSUES

TOKEN MONTREAL UN SOU —
AGRICULTURE & COMMERCE BAS-CANADA

These pieces were struck at the Belleville Mint, New Jersey, from dies cut by John Gibbs in imitation of the Bank of Montreal sous.

LC-21   *REVERSE WREATH WITH SIXTEEN CHERRY LEAVES*

OBVERSE BOUQUET WITH TWO SHAMROCKS

Composition: Copper
Weight: 6.9 to 7.5 g
Diameter: 26.9 to 27.1 mm
Die Axis: ↑↑
Edge: Plain
Ref.Nos.: Br 680 (R-1½);
Co 53B; Lr 539 (R-4);
McL 66; W 700

Cat.No.	Description	VG-8	F-12	VF-20	EF-40	AU-50	AU-55	MS-60
LC-21	16 CHerry Leaves	18.	35.	100.	175.	—	—	—

LC-22   *REVERSE WREATH WITH SIXTEEN CHERRY LEAVES*

OBVERSE BOUQUET WITH THREE SHAMROCKS

Composition: Copper
Weight: 6.9 to 7.5 g
Diameter: 27.0 to 27.1 mm
Die Axis: ↑↑
Edge: Plain
Ref.Nos.: See below

Varieties: Obverse
    A Small bow to left; Br 676 (R-2½); Co 57B; Lr 559 (R-5);
       McL 62; W 695

    B Small heavy bow to left; Br 682 (R-2½); Co 59B; Lr 558 (R-4);
       McL 68; W 702

    C No bow; Br 681 (R-4); Co 60B; Lr 565 (R-4); McL 67; W 701

Cat.No.	Description	VG-8	F-12	VF-20	EF-40	AU-50	AU-55	MS-60
LC-22A	Small bow	18.	35.	75.	135.	—	—	—
LC-22B	Small heavy bow	12.	30.	60.	115.	—	—	—
LC-22C	No bow	125.	250.	500.	750.	—	—	—

LC-23   ***REVERSE WREATH WITH SIXTEEN CHERRY LEAVES***

OBVERSE BOUQUET WITH FOUR SHAMROCKS

Composition: Brass, copper
Weight: 5.7 to 7.3 g
Diameter: 26.8 to 27.1 mm
Die Axis: ↑↑
Edge: Plain
Ref.Nos.: See below

Varieties: Obverse, reverse and composition
    A No stalk between thistles; Br 675 (R-5); Co 61B; Lr 548 (R-8);
       McL 61; W 694

    B Stalk between thistles; Br 677 (R-4); Co 58B; Lr 555 (R-6);
       McL 63; W 696

    C No berry left of bow; Br 678 (R-1½); Co 56B; Lr 554 (R-3);
       McL 64; W 697

Note: LC-23C ordinarily comes in copper.

Cat.No.	Description	VG-8	F-12	VF-20	EF-40	AU-50	AU-55	MS-60
LC-23A	No stalk between thistles	1,000.	1,500.	2,000.	—	—	—	—
LC-23B	Stalk between thistles	500.	750.	1,000.	—	—	—	—
LC-23C	No berry left of bow	7.	15.	40.	125.	250.	300.	400.

(handwritten left margin: 85, 86, 20)

LC-23 cont'd overleaf

LC-23   *REVERSE WREATH WITH SIXTEEN CHERRY LEAVES*

OBVERSE BOUQUET WITH FOUR SHAMROCKS

D   Mule with the obverse of LC-23A and the reverse of LC-23C; Co 62B; W 698

Cat.No.	Description	VG-8	F-12	VF-20	EF-40	AU-50	AU-55	MS-60
LC-23D	Mule				Extremely Rare			

084

LC-24   *REVERSE WREATH WITH SIXTEEN CHERRY LEAVES*

OBVERSE BOUQUET WITH SEVEN SHAMROCKS

Composition: Brass, copper
Weight: 6.4 to 7.5 g
Diameter: 27.0 to 27.4 mm
Die Axis: ↑↑
Edge: Plain
Ref.Nos.: Br 679 (R-1½);
Lr 557 (R-3); W 699;
McL 65; See below

Varieties: Composition
    A1 Copper; Co 54B
    A2 Brass; Co 55B

Cat.No.	Description	VG-8	F-12	VF-20	EF-40	AU-50	AU-55	MS-60
LC-24A1	Copper	6.	12.	18.	45.	80.	125.	150.
LC-24A2	Brass	250.	500.	750.	—	—	—	—

021
022

LC-25   *REVERSE WREATH WITH SEVENTEEN CHERRY LEAVES*

OBVERSE BOUQUET WITH TWO SHAMROCKS

Composition: Brass, copper
Weight: 5.7 to 6.9 g
Diameter: 27.0 to 27.1 mm
Die Axis: ↑↑
Edge: Plain
Ref.Nos.: Br 683 (R-2);
Lr 536 (R-4); W 703;
McL 69; See below

Variations: Composition
A1 Copper; Co 51B
A2 Brass; Co 52B

Cat.No.	Description	VG-8	F-12	VF-20	EF-40	AU-50	AU-55	MS-60
LC-25A1	Copper	9.	18.	45.	115.	250.	—	—
LC-25A2	Brass	250.	500.	750.	—	—	—	—

23 (handwritten)

LC-26   *REVERSE WREATH WITH SEVENTEEN CHERRY LEAVES*

OBVERSE BOUQUET WITH THREE SHAMROCKS

Composition: Copper
Weight: 5.7 to 6.9 g
Diameter: 27.0 to 27.1 mm
Die Axis: ↑↑
Edge: Plain
Ref.Nos.: W 704

Note: This is a muling of the LC-22C obverse with the LC-25 reverse.

Cat.No.	Description	VG-8	F-12	VF-20	EF-40	AU-50	AU-55	MS-60
LC-26	Copper			Extremely Rare				

23 (handwritten)

LC-27 *REVERSE WREATH WITH EIGHTEEN CHERRY LEAVES*

OBVERSE BOUQUET WITH NO SHAMROCKS

Composition: Brass, copper
Weight: 5.9 to 7.4 g
Diameter: 26.9 to 27.2 mm
Die Axis: ↑↑
Edge: Plain
Ref.Nos.: Br 691 (R-1);
Lr 563 (R-3); W 710;
McL 77; See below

Variations: Composition
A1 Copper, Thin or thick flans; Co 43B
A2 Brass; Co 44B

Cat.No.	Description	VG-8	F-12	VF-20	EF-40	AU-50	AU-55	MS-60
LC-27A1	Copper	5.	7.	15.	45.	100.	150.	200.
LC-27A2	Brass	250.	500.	750.	—	—	—	—

025
026

LC-28 *REVERSE WREATH WITH EIGHTEEN CHERRY LEAVES*

OBVERSE BOUQUET WITH ONE SHAMROCK

Composition: Copper
Weight: 7.2 to 7.8 g
Diameter: 27.0 to 27.1 mm
Die Axis: ↑↑
Edge: Plain
Ref.Nos.: Br 702 (R-1½); Co 29B;
Lr 561 (R-4); McL 88;
W 721

Cat.No.	Description	VG-8	F-12	VF-20	EF-40	AU-50	AU-55	MS-60
LC-28	Copper	6.	12.	18.	55.	125.	200.	250.

027

LC-29   *REVERSE WREATH WITH EIGHTEEN CHERRY LEAVES*

OBVERSE BOUQUET WITH TWO SHAMROCKS

Composition: Brass, copper
Weight: 6.4 to 8.6 g
Diameter: 26.9 to 27.2 mm
Die Axis: ↑↑
Edge: Plain
Ref.Nos.: See below

Varieties: The first four varieties have the obverse bow positioned right.
 A Small reverse bow flanked by cherries; Br 695 (R-1½); Co 46B;
 Lr 538 (R-4); McL 81; W 714

 B Small reverse bow, without flanking cherries; Br 696 (R-2½); Co 45B;
 Lr 537 (R-5); McL 82; W 715

 C Obverse bouquet points to "CA" of Canada, Large reverse bow without
 flanking cherries; Br 700 (R-1½); Co 32B; Lr 543 (R-4); McL 86;
 W 719

Cat.No.	Description	VG-8	F-12	VF-20	EF-40	AU-50	AU-55	MS-60
LC-29A	Small bow, Cherries	12.	30.	65.	125.	225.	—	—
LC-29B	Small bow, No cherries	22.	45.	110.	225.	425.	—	—
LC-29C	Large reverse bow, "CA"	6.	12.	35.	85.	160.	—	—

LC-29 cont'd overleaf

LC-29   *REVERSE WREATH WITH EIGHTEEN CHERRY LEAVES*

OBVERSE BOUQUET WITH TWO SHAMROCKS

D   Obverse bouquet points to "N" of Canada, Large reverse bow without flanking cherries; Br 701 (R-2½); Co 31B; Lr 544 (R-4); McL 87; W 720

E1   No obverse bow, Copper; Br 697 (R-2); Co 33B; Lr 564 (R-4); McL 83; W 716

E2   No obverse bow, Brass; Br 697 (R-2); Co 34B; Lr 564 (R-4); McL 83; W 716

Cat.No.	Description	VG-8	F-12	VF-20	EF-40	AU-50	AU-55	MS-60
LC-29D	Large reverse bow, "N"	15.	30.	55.	125.	250.	—	—
LC-29E1	No obverse bow, Copper	12.	18.	30.	65.	125.	—	—
LC-29E2	No obverse bow, Brass	250.	500.	750.	—	—	—	—

031
032
033

LC-30   *REVERSE WREATH WITH EIGHTEEN CHERRY LEAVES*

OBVERSE BOUQUET WITH THREE SHAMROCKS
OBVERSE BOW POSITIONED LEFT

Composition: Copper
Weight: Bow, 6.2 to 7.1 g
No bow, 5.6 to 6.6 g
Diameter: Bow, 26.9 to 27.1 mm
. No bow, 27.0 to
27.1 mm
Die Axis: ↑↑
Edge: Plain
Ref.Nos.: See below

Varieties: Obverse and reverse
A Obverse bow position left; small reverse bow; Br 698 (R-2½); Co 36B;
Lr 551 (R-5); McL 85; W 717

B Obverse bow positioned left; large reverse bow; Br 699 (R-2); Co 35B;
Lr 550 (R-5); McL 84; W 718

Cat.No.	Description	VG-8	F-12	VF-20	EF-40	AU-50	AU-55	MS-60
LC-30A	Small bow	18.	30.	60.	125.	250.	—	—
LC-30B	Large bow	8.	18.	35.	75.	135.	—	—

LC-30, No obverse bow cont'd overleaf

LC-30   *REVERSE WREATH WITH EIGHTEEN CHERRY LEAVES*

OBVERSE BOUQUET WITH THREE SHAMROCKS
NO OBVERSE BOW

C   No obverse or reverse bows; Open wreath; Br 685 (R-2½); Co 47B; Lr 566 (R-5); McL 72; W 705

D   No obverse or reverse bows; Normal wreath; Br 686 (R-1½); Co 48B; Lr 567 (R-4); McL 71; W 706

E   No obverse or reverse bows; Closed wreath; W 708

F   No obverse bow; Reverse bow; Normal wreath; Br 703 (R-4½); Co 30B; Lr 562 (R-8); W 722

Cat.No.	Description	VG-8	F-12	VF-20	EF-40	AU-50	AU-55	MS-60
LC-30C	No bow, Open wreath	8.	22.	55.	150.	250.	—	—
LC-30D	No bow, Normal wreath	8.	18.	40.	125.	250.	—	—
LC-30E	No bow, Closed wreath			Extremely Rare				
LC-30F	Reverse bow	2,000.	3,000.	5,000.	—	—	—	—

LC-31 *REVERSE WREATH WITH EIGHTEEN CHERRY LEAVES*

OBVERSE BOUQUET WITH FIVE SHAMROCKS

Varieties: Reverse and composition
All varieties have obverse bow positioned right.

Composition: Brass, copper
Weight: 6.0 to 7.1 g
Diameter: 27.1 to 27.4 mm
Die Axis: ↑↑
Edge: Plain
Ref.Nos.: See below

A Obverse with three blades of wheat; Reverse, leaves instead of a
bow; Br 688 (R-1); Co 41B; Lr 542 (R-4); McL 74; W 709

B1 Obverse with three blades of wheat; Reverse, a bow; Copper;
Br 693 (R-1); Co 37B; Lr 541 (R-4); McL 79; W 712
B2 As above, Brass; Br 693 (R-1); Co 37B; Lr 541 (R-4); McL 79; W 712

C Obverse with two blades of wheat; Reverse, a bow; Br 694 (R-1),
Co 38B; Lr 540 (R-3); McL 80; W 713

Cat.No.	Description	VG-8	F-12	VF-20	EF-40	AU-50	AU-55	MS-60
LC-31A	Leaves instead of bow	12.	22.	65.	185.	300.	—	—
LC-31B1	Bow, Three blades, Copper	12.	22.	50.	110.	200.	—	—
LC-31B2	Bow, Three blades, Brass			Very Rare				
LC-31C	Bow, Two blades	5.	7.	15.	75.	150.	—	—

239
40
41
42

LC-32   *REVERSE WREATH WITH EIGHTEEN CHERRY LEAVES*

OBVERSE BOUQUET WITH SEVEN SHAMROCKS

Composition: Copper
Weight: 6.3 to 7.3 g
Diameter: 27.0 to 27.2 mm
Die Axis: ↑↑
Edge: Plain
Ref.Nos.: See below

Varieties: Reverse, and all varieties have obverse bow positioned left

A   No reverse bow; Br 687 (R-1); Co 42B; Lr 552 (R-4); McL 73; W 707

B   Reverse bow; Br 692 (R-1); Co 39B; Lr 556 (R-3); McL 78; W 711

Cat.No.	Description	VG-8	F-12	VF-20	EF-40	AU-50	AU-55	MS-60
LC-32A	No reverse bow	8.	15.	40.	150.	225.	350.	450.
LC-32B	Bow	5.	7.	18.	45.	110.	200.	250.

O43

O44

O45 - LC-32B - BRASS - VERY RARE - UNREPORTED SO FAR BY ANY RESEARCHER

LC-33 *REVERSE WREATH WITH TWENTY CHERRY LEAVES*

OBVERSE BOUQUET WITH TWO SHAMROCKS

Composition: Brass, copper
Weight: 6.6 to 7.8 g
Diameter: 26.9 to 27.1 mm
Die Axis: ↑↑
Edge: Plain
Ref.Nos.: McL 89-90; See below

Varieties: Reverse and composition
  A1 Small flat reverse bow, Copper; Br 704 (R-1½); Co 27B; Lr 560 (R-3); W 723
  A2 Small flat reverse bow, Brass; Br 704 (R-1½); Co 28B; Lr 560 (R-3); W 723

  B Large flat reverse bow, Mule, obverse of LC-33A1, and reverse of LC-33C1; W 724

  C1 Without obverse bow, No blade of wheat; Hart variety; Br 705 (R-1½); Co 26B; Lr 546 (R-4); W 725
  C2 Without obverse bow, Blade of wheat between thistles; Co 25B; W 725

Cat.No.	Description	VG-8	F-12	VF-20	EF-40	AU-50	AU-55	MS-60
LC-33A1	Flat bow, Copper	5.	9.	30.	85.	125.	225.	300.
LC-33A2	Flat bow, Brass	400.	600.	900.	—	—	—	—
LC-33B	Large flat bow, Mule			Extremely Rare				
LC-33C1	Without bow, No wheat, Hart	7.	15.	25.	100.	150.	250.	300.
LC-33C2	Without bow	7.	15.	25.	100.	150.	250.	300.

BIRMINGHAM ISSUES

OBVERSE FRENCH LEGEND

TOKEN MONTREAL UN SOU —
AGRICULTURE & COMMERCE BAS-CANADA

As the popularity of the Bouquet sous increased further importations were made anonymously from England, these pieces being struck by the same Birmingham firm that struck the sous of the Bank of Montreal.

LC-34   *REVERSE WREATH WITH THIRTY TWO LAUREL LEAVES*

OBVERSE BOUQUET WITH ONE SHAMROCK

Composition: Brass, copper
Weight: 7.1 to 8.1 g
Diameter: 27.0 to 27.1 mm
Die Axis: ↑↑
Edge: Plain
Ref.Nos.: Br 706 (R-2½); Co 23B;
Lr 572 (R-4); McL 91;
W 726

Variations: Composition
A1 Copper
A2 Brass

Cat.No.	Description	VG-8	F-12	VF-20	EF-40	AU-50	AU-55	MS-60
LC-34A1	Copper	18.	45.	100.	175.	250.	375.	450.
LC-34A2	Brass	18.	45.	100.	175.	250.	375.	450.

050
051

LC-35 *REVERSE WREATH WITH THIRTY TWO LAUREL LEAVES*

OBVERSE BOUQUET WITH TWO SHAMROCKS

Composition: Brass, copper
Weight: 7.1 to 8.1 g
Diameter: 27.0 to 27.2 mm
Die Axis: ↑↑
Edge: Plain
Ref.Nos.: Br 707 (R-1½);
Lr 571 (R-4); McL 92;
See below

Varieties: Composition
A1 Copper; Co 22B; W 727
A2 Brass; Co 22B

Cat.No.	Description	VG-8	F-12	VF-20	EF-40	AU-50	AU-55	MS-60
LC-35A1	Copper	6.	12.	18.	55.	110.	200.	250.
LC-35A2	Brass	7.	15.	22.	90.	175.	275.	350.

LC-36 *REVERSE WREATH WITH THIRTY TWO LAUREL LEAVES*

OBVERSE BOUQUET WITH THREE SHAMROCKS

Composition: Copper
Weight: 7.1 to 8.1 g
Diameter: 27.0 to 27.1 mm
Die Axis: ↑↑
Edge: Plain
Ref.Nos.: Br 708 (R-1½); Co 20B;
Lr 570 (R-4); McL 93;
W 728

Cat.No.	Description	VG-8	F-12	VF-20	EF-40	AU-50	AU-55	MS-60
LC-36	Copper	18.	30.	40.	100.	200.	325.	400.

OBVERSE ENGLISH LEGEND

LC-37

TOKEN MONTREAL UN SOU —
TRADE & AGRICULTURE LOWER CANADA

REVERSE WREATH WITH THIRTY TWO LAUREL LEAVES
OBVERSE WITH THREE SHAMROCKS

The obverse of this token is the same as that of the Bank of Montreal token (LC-2A5). The obverse die was retouched and mated with the thirty-two-leaf reverse, thus linking the Birmingham issues to the Bank of Montreal tokens.

Composition: Copper
Weight: 7.1 to 7.8 g
Diameter: 27.0 mm
Die Axis: ↑↑
Edge: Plain
Ref.Nos.: Br 709 (R-2); Co 21B;
Lr 525 (R-4); McL 94;
W 729

Cat.No.	Description	VG-8	F-12	VF-20	EF-40	AU-50	AU-55	MS-60
LC-37	Three shamrocks	22.	40	60.	110.	275.	400.	500.

O 55

OBVERSE FRENCH LEGEND

LC-38

TOKEN MONTREAL UN SOU —
AGRICULTURE & COMMERCE BAS-CANADA

REVERSE WREATH WITH THIRTY NINE LAUREL LEAVES

OBVERSE BOUQUET WITH THREE SHAMROCKS

Composition: Copper
Weight: 7.4 to 7.8 g
Diameter: 26.9 to 27.0 mm
Die Axis: ↑↑
Edge: Plain
Ref.Nos.: McL 95; See below

Varieties: Obverse
A No obverse bow; Br 710 (R-1½); Co 19B; Lr 569 (R-4); W 730

B Obverse bow; Br 712 (R-5); Lr 548a (R-8); W G3

Note: McLachlan, in a paper presented before the American Numismatic Association in 1912, illustrated how the two copper examples of this token (LC-38B) were considered by him to be fraudulent.

Cat.No.	Description	VG-8	F-12	VF-20	EF-40	AU-50	AU-55	MS-60
LC-38A	No bow	22.	40.	85.	150.	—	—	—
LC-38B	Bow		Possibly three or four known. Very Rare					

56
80

LC-39   *REVERSE WREATH WITH THIRTY NINE LAUREL LEAVES*

OBVERSE BOUQUET WITH SIX SHAMROCKS

Composition: Copper
Weight: 7.5 to 7.8 g
Diameter: 26.9 to 27.0 mm
Die Axis: ↑↑
Edge: Plain
Ref.Nos.: Br 711 (R-1½); Co 18B;
Lr 568 (R-4); McL 96;
W 731

Cat.No.	Description	VG-8	F-12	VF-20	EF-40	AU-50	AU-55	MS-60
LC-39	Six shamrocks	18.	30.	45.	100.	225.	350.	450.

057

MONTREAL ISSUES

Some varieties were produced in Montreal as the demand for sous continued. These pieces vary considerably in fabric, size and weight. All have the bouquet of the heraldic flowers shown in various ways, with the usual reverse design. Jean-Marie Arnault cut the dies and struck the token LC-40.

LC-40 **TOKEN MONTREAL UN SOU**
— AGRICULTURE & COMMERCE BAS CANADA

REVERSE WREATH WITH SIXTEEN CHERRY LEAVES
OBVERSE BOUQUET WITH FIVE SHAMROCKS

All varieties have the obverse bow positioned to the left and are found struck over the following pieces.

Copper: Various Blacksmith Tokens, The Sloop Tokens of Upper Canada, The Ships Colonies & Commerce Halfpennies of Lower Canada and The Commercial Change Farthing Token

Brass: Various Blacksmith Tokens, Bust & Harp Tokens and Tiffin Tokens

Composition: Brass, copper
Weight: 5.0 to 5.3 g
Diameter: 26.4 to 27.1 mm
Die Axis: ↑↑
Edge: See below
Ref.Nos.: Br 674 (R-1½);
Lr 547 (R-4); McL 60;
W 734; See below

Varieties: Composition, Edge

A1	Copper, Coarsely reeded; Co 63B	**A6**	Brass, Coarsely reeded; Co 67B
A2	Copper, Finely reeded; Co 64B	**A7**	Brass, Finely reeded; Co 68B
A3	Copper, Plain; Co 65B	**A8**	Brass, Plain; Co 69B
A4	Copper, Thin flan, Reeded; Co 66B	**A9**	Brass, Thin flan, Reeded; Co 70B
A5	Copper, Overstruck on various tokens	**A10**	Brass, Overstruck on various tokens

Cat.No.	Description	VG-8	F-12	VF-20	EF-40	AU-50	AU-55	MS-60
LC-40A1	Copper, Coarsely reeded	15.	30.	65.	150.	—	—	—
LC-40A2	Copper, Finely reeded	9.	18.	50.	125.	—	—	—
LC-40A3	Copper, Plain	9.	18.	50.	125.	—	—	—
LC-40A4	Copper, Thin flan, Reeded	12.	22.	55.	125.	—	—	—
LC-40A5	Copper, Overstruck	30.	55.	85.	175.	—	—	—
LC-40A6	Brass, Coarsely reeded	12.	22.	65.	150.	—	—	—
LC-40A7	Brass, Finely reeded	12.	22.	65.	150.	—	—	—
LC-40A8	Brass, Plain	12.	22.	65.	150.	—	—	—
LC-40A9	Brass, Thin flan, Reeded	12.	22.	65.	150.	—	—	—
LC-40A10	Brass, Overstruck	30.	55.	85.	175.	—	—	—

LC-41   *REVERSE WREATH WITH SEVENTEEN CHERRY LEAVES*

OBVERSE BOUQUET WITH SIX SHAMROCKS

Composition: Brass, copper
Weight: 5.9 to 6.7 g
Diameter: 27.6 to 28.3 mm
Die Axis: ↑↑, ↑↓
Edge: Plain
Ref.Nos.: Br 684 (R-2);
Lr 545 (R-4); McL 70;
W 732; See below

Varieties: Composition and die axis
All varieties have obverse bow positioned right
A1   Copper, Medal; Co 49B
A2   Copper, Coinage; Co 49B
A3   Brass, Medal; Co 50B
A4   Brass, Coinage; Co 50B

Cat.No.	Description	VG-8	F-12	VF-20	EF-40	AU-50	AU-55	MS-60
LC-41A1	Copper, ↑↑	7.	15.	40.	100.	225.	350.	450.
LC-41A2	Copper, ↑↓	12.	22.	55.	125.	275.	400.	500.
LC-41A3	Brass, ↑↑				Rare			
LC-41A4	Brass, ↑↓				Rare			

068
069
070
079

LC-42   *REVERSE WREATH WITH EIGHTEEN CHERRY LEAVES*

OBVERSE BOUQUET WITH TWO SHAMROCKS

This token is only known struck over UC-12B. The undertype obscures much of the design. The striking appears to be the work of Jean-Marie Arnault.

Photograph not
available
at press time

Composition: Copper
Weight: 6.5 g
Diameter: 27.6 mm
Die Axis: ↑↑
Edge: Plain
Ref.Nos.: W 735

Cat.No.	Description	AG	G-4	VG-8	F-12	VF-20
LC-42	Copper			Unique		

078

LC-43   *REVERSE WREATH WITH TWENTY ONE CHERRY LEAVES*

OBVERSE BOUQUET WITH NO SHAMROCKS

The dies for this sou were found in Montreal in 1863 and presented to the Antiquarian and Numismatic Society of Montreal which struck a few specimens and then had the dies turned down to receive a collar. Later restrikes were struck with a collar and exist in copper, brass and lead. A few were struck on square flans and over American cents.

Composition: Brass, copper, lead
Weight: Variable
Diameter: 28.3 to 28.5 mm
Die Axis: ↑↑
Edge: Plain, reeded
Ref.Nos.: Br 689 (R-3); Co 24B;
Lr 549 (R-10); McL 75;
W 733

Varieties: Composition, Edge
A1 Original: Brass, Reeded
A2 Restrike: Brass, copper or lead, Without collar
A3 Restrike: Brass or copper, With collar, Plain

Cat.No.	Description	VG-8	F-12	VF-20	EF-40	AU-50	AU-55	MS-60
LC-43A1	Original, Brass, Reeded			Extremely Rare				
LC-43A2	Restrike, Brass, copper or lead, Without collar			Rare				
LC-43A3	Restrike, Brass or copper, With collar, plain	100.	200.	300.	500.	750.	900.	1,000.

77
76
71

MISCELLANEOUS ISSUES

LC-44   *REVERSE WREATH WITH EIGHTEEN CHERRY LEAVES*

OBVERSE BOUQUET WITH SEVEN SHAMROCKS

Composition: Brass, copper
Weight: 6.8 to 7.0 g
Diameter: 27.5 to 27.7 mm
Die Axis: ↑↓
Edge: Plain
Ref.Nos.: Br 690 (R-4); Co 40B;
        Lr 553 (R-6); McL 76;
        W G2

o72
o73

Cat.No.	Description	VG-8	F-12	VF-20	EF-40	AU-50	AU-55	MS-60
LC-44A	Copper	100.	150.	175.	275.	350.	425.	500.
LC-44B	Brass	200.	300.	400.	500.	—	—	—

LC-45   *T. DUSEAMAN BUTCHER BELLEVILLE*

OBVERSE BOUQUET WITH THREE SHAMROCKS

This token was prepared on order for Tobias Seaman, a butcher and hotelier of Belleville, New Jersey, as his business card. After being rejected by him it seems the "U" was added later to create the name Duseaman. This mule of a bouquet and store card die is as heavy as an American Large Cent.

Composition: Copper
Weight: 10.8 to 11.1 g
Diameter: 27.9 to 28.2 mm
Die Axis: ↑↑
Edge: Plain
Ref.Nos.: Br 670 (R-2); Co 71B;
        Lr 574 (R-4); McL 58;
        W C28

o74

Cat.No.	Description	VG-8	F-12	VF-20	EF-40	AU-50	AU-55	MS-60
LC-45	Copper	20.	40.	75.	175.	300.	400.	475.

ANONYMOUS TOKENS OF LOWER CANADA

Most tokens imported into Lower Canada or manufactured in the colony were anonymous. They were usually produced with good weight but as their weight decreased the profit potential for the issuer increased. After 1825, imported tokens were antedated or bore no date whatsoever.

THOMAS HALLIDAY TOKENS 1812-1814

These are an extensive series of anonymous English tokens struck by Thomas Halliday in 1812 and 1813. They are of good weight and were designed by Halliday who also cut the dies. They saw extensive use in England until 1817, when copper tokens were ordered to be withdrawn from circulation, and then circulated in Canada.

LC-46   *HALFPENNY TOKEN*

HALFPENNY TOKEN 1812 — (BUST DESIGN)

The Halliday mintmark "H" must appear on this token.

Composition: Copper
Weight: 8.2 to 8.6 g
Diameter: 28.3 to 28.9 mm
Die Axis: ↑↓
Edge: Engrailed
Ref.Nos: Br 960 (R-0);
LR 770-772 (R-3);
McL 550; See below

"H" right of bust	"H" centre of bust	"H" left of bust
Rosette with four dots (**A1**)	Rosette with six dots (**A2**)	Rosette with four dots (**A3**)

Varieties: Obverse
A1 "H" to right of bust, rosette with four dots; Co 25T; TF-25; W C14
A2 "H" in centre of bust, rosette with six dots; Co 27T; TF-27; W C15
A3 "H" to left of bust, rosette with four dots; Co 26T; TF-26; W C16

Cat.No.	Date	Description	VG-8	F-12	VF-20	EF-40	AU-50	AU-55	MS-60
LC-46A1	1812	"H" Right; rosette wiith four dots	7.	15.	22.	55.	150.	250.	300.
LC-46A2	1812	"H" Centre; rosette with six dots	7.	15.	22.	55.	150.	250.	300.
LC-46A3	1812	"H" Left; rosette with four dots	7.	15.	22.	55.	150.	250.	300.

LC-47   **ONE PENNY TOKEN**

LC-47A   **ONE PENNY TOKEN 1812 — 1812**

Composition: Copper
Weight: 18.2 g
Diameter: 34.4 mm

Die Axis: ↑↓
Edge: Engrailed
Ref.Nos.: Br 957 (R-2); Lr 767 (R-5);
McL 545; See below

Closed wreath **(A1)**   Open wreath **(A2)**

Varieties: Obverse
A1 Closed wreath at top; Co 39T; TF-39; W C26
A2 Open wreath at top; Co 40T, TF-40; W C27

Cat.No.	Date	Description	VG-8	F-12	VF-20	EF-40	AU-50	AU-55	MS-60
LC-47A1	1812	Closed wreath	15.	30.	55.	125.	250.	—	—
LC-47A2	1812	Open wreath	15.	30.	55.	125.	250.	—	—

LC-47B   *ONE PENNY TOKEN — 1812*

Composition: Copper
Weight: 17.1 to 18.2 g
Diameter: 34.2 to 34.6 mm

Die Axis: ↑↓
Edge: Engrailed
Ref.Nos.: Br 958 (R-1½);
Lr 768 (R-3); McL 546-547;
See below

Small ship **(B-1)**   Large ship **(B-2)**

Four leaves in cornucopia **(B1)**

Varieties: Reverse
B1 Small ship, Four leaves in cornucopia; Co 34T; TF-34; W C22
B2 Large ship, Two leaves in cornucopia; Co 35T; TF-35; W C23

Cat.No.	Date	Description	VG-8	F-12	VF-20	EF-40	AU-50	AU-55	MS-60
LC-47B1	1812	Small ship	12.	22.	45.	100.	200.	275.	350.
LC-47B2	1812	Large ship	200.	250.	300.	400.	—	—	—

LC-47C   *ONE PENNY TOKEN — 1813*

Composition: Copper   **Die Axis:** ↑↑, ↑↓
Weight: 17.1 to 18.2 g   **Edge:** Engrailed
Diameter: 34.2 to 34.6 mm   **Ref.Nos.:** Br 958 (R-1½); See below

Leaves **(C1)**   Acorns **(C2)**

Varieties: Obverse, Die axis
C1 Oak wreath begins with leaves, Medal; Co 37T; TF-37; W C25
C2 Oak wreath begins with acorns, Coinage; Co 38T; TF-38; W C24

Cat.No.	Date	Description	VG-8	F-12	VF-20	EF-40	AU-50	AU-55	MS-60
LC-47C1	1813	Leaves, ↑↑	22.	35.	65.	175.	300.	375.	450.
LC-47C2	1813	Acorns, ↑↓	22.	35.	65.	175.	300.	375.	450.

LC-47D   *ONE PENNY TOKEN 1812 —*

Composition: Copper
Weight: 16.5 to 18.2 g
Diameter: 34.1-34.3 mm
Die Axis: ↑↓
Edge: Engrailed, reeded (diagonally)
Ref.Nos.: Br 959 (R 1½); Lr 769 (R-3); See below

Twelve leaves (**D1**)

Nine leaves (**D3**)

Eight leaves (**D4**)

Seven leaves (**D5 and 6**)

Varieties: Obverse, Edge
D1 Laurel crown with twelve leaves, Engrailed; Co 33T; TF-33; W C21
D2 Laurel crown with eleven leaves, Engrailed; Co 32T; TF-32; W C20
D3 Laurel crown with nine leaves, Engrailed; Co 31T; W; TF-31; C19
D4 Laurel crown with eight leaves, Engrailed; Co 29T; TF-29; W C18
D5 Laurel crown with seven leaves, Engrailed; Co 28T; TF-28
D6 Laurel crown with seven leaves, Reeded diagonally ; Co 28T; TF-28; W C17

Cat.No.	Date	Description	VG-8	F-12	VF-20	EF-40	AU-50	AU-55	MS-60
LC-47D1	1812	Twelve leaves	15.	30.	65.	175.	300.	375.	450.
LC-47D2	1812	Eleven leaves	12.	22.	45.	125.	225.	300.	350.
LC-47D3	1812	Nine leaves	15.	30.	55.	150.	250.	325.	400.
LC-47D4	1812	Eight leaves			Very Rare				
LC-47D5	1812	Seven leaves, Engrailed	22.	35.	65.	175.	300.	375.	450.
LC-47D6	1812	Seven leaves, Reeded	22.	35.	65.	175.	300.	375.	450.

LC-47E ONE PENNY TOKEN — 1812 BON POUR DEUX SOUS

This pattern was struck by Halliday possibly as a salesmans sample for the Tiffin series in Canada. The legends giving the value in both English and French were certainly appealing to Lower Canada.

Composition: Copper
Weight: 17.54 g
Diameter: 34.6 mm
Ref.Nos: C 36T; TF-36; W A1

Die Axis: ↑↓
Edge: Engrailed
Thickness: 2.5 mm

Cat.No.	Date	Description	AG	G-4	VG-8	F-12	VF-20
LC-47E	1812	Copper	Only three known, two of which are with the Bank of Canada Collection, and one in a private collection.				

The following two tokens, while produced by Halliday, are English penny tokens. Breton did not recognise these tokens as Canadian, while Courteau in his Tiffin Token monograph listed them because of their die linkage to other Halliday tokens that circulated in Canada.

LC-47F COMMERCE 1814 —

Composition: Copper
Weight: 16.5 to 18.2 g
Diameter: 34.1-34.3 mm

Die Axis: ↑↓
Edge: Engrailed, reeded
Ref.Nos.: Co 30T; TF-30; W C12

Varieties: Edge
E1 Engrailed
E2 Reeded

Cat.No.	Date	Description	VG-8	F-12	VF-20	EF-40	AU-50	AU-55	MS-60
LC-47F1	1814	Engrailed	35.	65.	110.	225.	400.	—	—
LC-47F2	1814	Reeded	35.	65.	110.	225.	400.	—	—

LC-47G   *COMMERCE —*

Composition: Copper
Weight: 16.5 g
Diameter: 34.1 to 34.3 mm

Die Axis: ↑↓
Edge: Engrailed
Ref.Nos.: Co 41T; TF-41; W C13

Cat.No.	Description	VG-8	F-12	VF-20	EF-40	AU-50	AU-55	MS-60
LC-47G	Engrailed	45.	90.	165.	275.	450.	—	—

TIFFIN TOKENS

About 1832, Joseph Tiffin, a Montreal grocer, imported a quantity of lightweight halfpenny copper tokens from England. These were copies of an anonymous English halfpenny struck in 1812 from dies cut by Thomas Halliday (LC-46). Tiffin's tokens bore the date 1812 in order to evade the laws forbidding the importation of tokens into Canada. Eventually the banks refused to accept any of these pieces as currency and accepted them only for their scrap metal value.

LC-48   *TIFFIN COPPER ORIGINALS*

Halliday's "H" does not appear on this token. Courteau listed a brass specimen (23T) among the copper originals.

LC-48A   *HALFPENNY TOKEN 1812 —*

Composition: Brass, copper
Weight: 5.3 to 6.6 g
Diameter: 27.3 to 27.7 mm
Die Axis: ↑↓
Edge: Plain
Ref.Nos.: Br 960 (R-0);
Lr 770-771 (R-3);
McL 550; See below

Two leaves	Three daisies	Two daisies
(A3 and A4)	**(A2, A3 and A4)**	**(A3)**

Varieties: Obverse, Reverse, Composition

    A1 Laurel crown with four upper leaves, Three daisies crown the cornucopia; Co 24T; TF-24; W 608

    A2 Laurel crown with two upper leaves, Three daisies crown the cornucopia, Copper; Co 22T; TF-22; W 607

    A3 Laurel crown with two upper leaves, Three daisies crown the cornucopia, Brass; Co 23T; TF-23; W 607

    A4 Laurel crown with two upper leaves, Two daisies crown the cornucopia; Co 21T; TF-21; W 606

Variations: **A1** was struck on thick or thin flans.

Cat.No.	Date	Description	VG-8	F-12	VF-20	EF-40	AU-50	AU-55	MS-60
LC-48A1	1812	4 leaves, 3 daisies	5.	9.	15.	30.	65.	115.	150.
LC-48A2	1812	2 leaves, 3 daisies, Copper	5.	9.	15.	30.	65.	115.	150.
LC-48A3	1812	2 leaves, 3 daisies, Brass	12.	22.	35.	55.	110.	175.	225.
LC-48A4	1812	2 leaves, 2 daisies	7.	15.	22.	45.	90.	150.	200.

IMITATION TIFFIN TOKENS

Imitations of the Tiffin Tokens appeared in copper and brass from 1832 to 1836. They are of variable workmanship and composition and some varieties are extremely rare.

LC-48B   *HALFPENNY TOKEN 1812 —*

Composition: Brass
Weight: 5.0 to 5.9 g
Diameter: 27.4 to 27.7 mm
Die Axis: ↑↓
Edge: Plain
Ref.Nos.: Br 960 (R-0);
Lr 772 (R-3); McL 554;
See below

Counter-clockwise   Clockwise wreath
wreath **(B1)**   **(B2)**

Varieties: Obverse
B1 Counter-clockwise wreath; Co 10-16, 18-20T; TF-10-16;
TF-18-20; W 610-616, 618-620
B2 Clockwise wreath; Co 9, 17T; TF-09, 17; W 609, 617

Variations: Obverse variations exist in the size, shape and style of the head.

Cat.No.	Date	Description	VG-8	F-12	VF-20	EF-40	AU-50	AU-55	MS-60
LC-48B1	1812	Counter-clockwise, Brass	5.	9.	15.	35.	55.	95.	125.
LC-48B2	1812	Clockwise, Brass	5.	9.	15.	35.	55.	95.	125.

LC-48C   *1812 —*

Composition: Brass, copper
Weight: 5.1 to 5.9 g
Diameter: 27.4 to 27.7 mm
Die Axis: ↑↓
Edge: Plain
Ref.Nos.: Br 961 (R-1);
           Lr 773 (R-4); McL 556;
           See below

Counter-clockwise
wreath **(C1)**

Clockwise wreath
(C2 and C3)

Varieties: Obverse, Composition
C1 Counter-clockwise wreath; Brass; Co 5, 6 and 8T; TF-05, 06, 08;
     W 622-625
C2 Clockwise wreath; Brass; Co 1-4, 7T; TF-01-04, 07; W 621, 626-628
C3 Clockwise wreath, Copper; Co 4T, TF-42; W 621, 626-628

Variations: Obverse variations exist in the size, shape and style of the bust.

Cat.No.	Date	Description	VG-8	F-12	VF-20	EF-40	AU-50	AU-55	MS-60
LC-48C1	1812	Counter-clockwise	7.	15.	30.	50.	100.	150.	200.
LC-48C2	1812	Clockwise, brass	6.	12.	22.	40.	80.	125.	165.
LC-48C3	1812	Clockwise, copper	12.	25.	45.	85.	165.	275.	350.

IMITATIONS OF TIFFIN TOKENS "BLACKSMITH STYLE"

For the listings of these crude Imitations of Tiffin Tokens see page 220 and 221, Cat. Nos. BL-32 and BL-33.

LC-49   *HALFPENNY TOKEN — VICTORIA NOBIS EST*

This token was usually struck over Guppy halfpennies and possibly other tokens. The portrait is one of the "mysterious busts" discussed by McLachlan, Heal and other numismatists writing at the turn of the century. The portrait has never been satisfactorily identified.

Composition: Copper
Weight: 8.5 to 9.0 g
Diameter: 28.0 to 28.3 mm
Die Axis: ↑↓
Edge: Engrailed
Ref.Nos.: Br 982 (R-1); Co 40NL;
           Lr 809 (R-4); W 542

Cat.No.	Description	VG-8	F-12	VF-20	EF-40	AU-50	AU-55	MS-60
LC-49A1	Overstruck	7.	15.	30.	55.	150.	—	—
LC-49A2	Not overstruck	8.	18.	35.	65.	175.	—	—

201
201 a + b

RH TOKENS 1812-1814

Thomas Halliday designed this series of tokens for use in England. The farthing and penny did not circulate in Canada but were imported by collectors after 1870. Of the halfpenny denomination only the plain edge, light weight specimens were imported by Richard Hurd, a Montreal merchant, for use in Canada.

LC-50   *RH (RICHARD HURD) — 1812 FARTHING TOKEN*

Composition: Copper
Weight: 4.0 to 4.1 g
Diameter: 22.2 to 22.4 mm
Die Axis: ↑↓
Edge: Engrailed
Ref.Nos.: Br 991 (R-3); Co 32NL;
            Lr 778 (R-4); W C2

Cat.No.	Date	Description	VG-8	F-12	VF-20	EF-40	AU-50	AU-55	MS-60
LC-50	1812	Engrailed	40.	65.	110.	165.	275.	375.	450.

94

LC-51   *RH (RICHARD HURD) — 1814 HALF PENNY TOKEN*

Composition: Copper
Weight: See below
Diameter: 28.0 to 28.2 mm
Die Axis: ↑↓
Edge: Engrailed, plain
Ref.Nos.: Br 990 (R-1½);
            Co 33NL; Lr 779 (R-4);
            McL 582; See below

Varieties: Flan, Edge
A1 Thick flan: 8.5 g, Engrailed; W C3
A2 Thin flan: 5.5 g, Plain; W 571

Cat.No.	Date	Description	VG-8	F-12	VF-20	EF-40	AU-50	AU-55	MS-60
LC-51A1	1814	Thick flan, Engrailed	15.	30.	45.	110.	225.	325.	400.
LC-51A2	1814	Thin flan, Plain	20.	40.	80.	165.	275.	375.	450.

95
96

LC-52   *RH (RICHARD HURD) — 1814 ONE PENNY TOKEN*

Composition: Copper
Weight: 16.2 g
Diameter: 34.2 to 34.4 mm
Die Axis: ↑↓
Edge: Engrailed
Ref.Nos.: Br 989 (R-2½);
Co 34NL;
Lr 780 (R-4);
McL 581; W C4

Cat.No.	Date	Description	VG-8	F-12	VF-20	EF-40	AU-50	AU-55	MS-60
LC-52	1814	Engrailed	35.	75.	150.	275.	600.	—	—

197

LC-53   *TO FACILITATE TRADE 1825 —*

These two tokens are believed to portray Col. de Salaberry, who repelled the Americans at Chateauguay and Crysler's Farm during the War of 1812, saving Montreal from the fate of York in Upper Canada. The clothing of the bust resembles that seen in a well-known painting of de Salaberry which undoubtedly led early writers to assume that the colonel's features appear on the tokens.

LC-53A   *— (MILITARY BUST OF SALABERRY)*

Composition: Copper
Weight: 6.2 to 6.8 g
Diameter: 27.8 to 28.1 mm
Die Axis: ↑↓
Edge: Plain
Ref.Nos.: Br 992 (R-1);
Lr 787 (R-3); McL 595;
See below

Open sleeve
(A1)

Closed sleeve
(A2)

Varieties: Obverse
     A1   Open sleeve; Co 47NL; W 561
     A2   Closed sleeve; Co 48NL; W 562

Cat.No.	Date	Description	VG-8	F-12	VF-20	EF-40	AU-50	AU-55	MS-60
LC-53A1	1825	Open sleeve	7.	15.	40.	100.	175.	225.	275.
LC-53A2	1825	Closed sleeve	100.	175.	350.	500.	650.	—	—

208
209

LC-53B   — *UNIDENTIFIED (CIVILIAN BUST)*

Composition: Copper
Weight: 6.8 g
Diameter: 27.6 to 27.8 mm
Die Axis: ↑↓
Edge: Plain
Ref.Nos.: Co 49NL; W 563

Note: Mule, Obverse of LC-58A1, Reverse of LC-53A.

Cat.No.	Date	Description	AG	G-4	VG-8	F-12	VF-20
LC-53B	1825	Mule			Extremely Rare		

LC-54   ***SPREAD EAGLE TOKENS 1813-1815***

The eagle was not a popular symbol for a coin design in 1813. The war of 1812-14 was at its height and during this period with the Canadian colonies in the midst of an American invasion, the original issue was not well received.

ORIGINALS OF 1813

The tokens dated 1813 and struck over the Samuel Guppy tokens of Bristol are the original issue by a Boston merchant named Nye, who settled in Phillipsburg during 1812.

LC-54A   *HALFPENNY TOKEN 1813* —

Composition: Copper
Weight: 8.8 g
Diameter: 27.9 mm
Die Axis: ↑↓
Edge: Engrailed
Ref.Nos.: Br 994 (R-1); Co 25NL;
Lr 781 (R-3);
McL 558-560; W 543

Cat.No.	Date	Description	VG-8	F-12	VF-20	EF-40	AU-50	AU-55	MS-60
LC-54A	1813	Copper	8.	15.	30.	55.	125.	175.	225.

IMITATIONS OF 1813-1815

The imitations of the Spread Eagle Token appeared after 1825 and were antedated. They are lighter and cruder in design. The reverse lettering on the imitations is larger than the originals.

These tokens were not struck over Samuel Guppy tokens of Bristol, England.

LC-54B   *HALFPENNY TOKEN 1813 —*

Composition: Brass, copper
Weight: 5.5 to 6.5 g
Diameter: 27.3 mm
Die Axis: ↑↓
Edge: Engrailed
Ref.Nos.: Br 994 (R-1);
Lr 781 (R-3);
McL 558-560;
W 544; See below

Varieties: Composition
B1 Copper; Co 26NL
B2 Brass; Co 27NL

Cat.No.	Date	Description	VG-8	F-12	VF-20	EF-40	AU-50	AU-55	MS-60
LC-54B1	1813	Copper	9.	20.	40.	85.	200.	300.	350.
LC-54B2	1813	Brass				Extremely Rare			

LC-54C   *HALFPENNY TOKEN 1814 —*

Composition: Copper
Weight: 6.5 to 7.0 g
Diameter: 27.5 to 27.6 mm
Die Axis: ↑↓
Edge: Engrailed
Ref.Nos.: Br 994 (R-1);
Lr 781 (R-3);
McL 558-560;
See below

Large shield with
drapery between
shield and trident
handle (**C1**)

Small shield with
drapery left of trident
handle (**C2**)

Varieties: Reverse
C1 Large shield; Co 28NL; W 545
C2 Small shield; Co 29NL; W 546

Cat.No.	Date	Description	VG-8	F-12	VF-20	EF-40	AU-50	AU-55	MS-60
LC-54C1	1814	Large shield	8.	18.	35.	65.	175.	275.	350.
LC-54C2	1814	Small shield	8.	18.	35.	65.	175.	275.	350.

LC-54D   *HALFPENNY TOKEN 1815 —*

Around 1920 a hoard of tokens, in "new" condition, was discovered in the estate of the Nye family.
This hoard when examined yielded a series of varieties for this token. The varieties are simply one of die wear:

1. A small sailing ship to the left of Britannia
2. A partial ship to the left of Britannia
3. Three lines where the ship should be
4. Clear field with a very weak definition of the design.

Currently, we have made no attempt to catalogue these varieties.

Composition: Copper
Weight: 6.1 to 6.5 g
Diameter: 27.5 to 27.7 mm
Die Axis: ↑↓
Edge: Engrailed
Ref.Nos.: Br 994 (R-1);
        Lr 782 (R-4); McL 562;
        See below

Counter-clockwise   Clockwise wreath
wreath **(D1)**   **(D2)**

Varieties: Obverse
  D1 Counter-clockwise wreath; Co 30NL; W 547
  D2 Clockwise wreath; Co 31NL; W 548

Cat.No.	Date	Description	VG-8	F-12	VF-20	EF-40	AU-50	AU-55	MS-60
LC-54D1	1815	Counter-clockwise	12.	18.	30.	55.	150.	225.	275.
LC-54D2	1815	Clockwise	7.	15.	20.	35.	100.	150.	200.

THE SEATED JUSTICE TOKENS

The "Seated Justice" tokens have been found in Lower Canadian hoards. They are derived from a token designed by Thomas Halliday and struck by Sir Edward Thomason for Shaw, Jobson & Co. of Roscoe Mills in Sheffield, England.

LC-55 *(SEATED JUSTICE DESIGN) — (SAILING SHIP DESIGN)*

This token has a Ships, Colonies & Commerce obverse and Seated Justice (LC-57) reverse. This token has passed through several famous collections over the last 100 years: likely Courteau, Wickham, Fargeon, (via a 1947 Schulman Sale), through Nadin-Davis to Hughes, and sold by Hoare in 1995. Considered by many to be a fake, it was listed by Breton as number 1001.

Composition: Copper
Weight: 5.3 g
Diameter: 25.5 mm
Die Axis: ↑↑
Edge: Plain
Ref.Nos.: Br 1001 (R-3½); W 567

Cat.No.	Description	AG	G-4	VG-8	F-12	VF-20
LC-55	No legend	—	—	—	10,000.	—

186

LC-56 *HALFPENNY TOKEN — (SAILING SHIP DESIGN)*

LC-56A *HALFPENNY TOKEN 1812 — BALE MARKED S.J. & Co.*

Composition: Brass, copper
Weight: 5.3 to 6.2 g
Diameter: 28.3 to 28.7 mm
Die Axis: ↑↑, ↑↓
Edge: Plain
Ref.Nos.: Br 1004 (R-1½);
Lr 774 (R-3);
McL 571-572;
See below

Short pennant
(A1 and A2)

No pennant
(A3 and A4)

Varieties:	Obverse, Composition, Die Axis
A1	Short pennant on foremast, Copper; Co 20NL; W 569
A2	Short pennant on foremast, Brass; Co 20NL; W 569
A3	No pennant on foremast, Copper; Co 21NL; W 570
A4	No pennant on foremast, Brass; Co 22NL; W 570

Cat.No.	Date	Description	VG-8	F-12	VF-20	EF-40	AU-50	AU-55	MS-60
LC-56A1	1812	Short pennant, Copper	200.	350.	500.	—	—	—	—
LC-56A2	1812	Short pennant, Brass	9.	18.	35.	65.	150.	225.	275.
LC-56A3	1812	No pennant, Copper		Very Rare					
LC-56A4	1812	No pennant, Brass	22.	45.	65.	150.	—	—	—

180
181
182
183

LC-56B   *HALFPENNY TOKEN 1815 — BALE MARKED S.J. & CO*

Composition: Brass, copper
Weight: 5.3 to 6.4 g
Diameter: 28.3 to 28.9 mm
Die Axis: ↑↓, ↑↓
Edge: Reeded
Ref.Nos.: Br 1004 (R-1½);
Lr 774 (R-3); W 570;
McL 571-572;
See below

Varieties: Composition
B1 Copper; Co 23NL
B2 Brass; Co 24NL

Cat.No.	Date	Description	VG-8	F-12	VF-20	EF-40	AU-50	AU-55	MS-60
LC-56B1	1815	Copper	9.	15.	30.	65.	165.	275.	350.
LC-56B2	1815	Brass	18.	45.	150.	275.	550.	—	—

(handwritten: 84, 85)

LC-56C   *HALFPENNY TOKEN —*

Composition: Brass, copper
Weight: 5.1 to 5.2 g
Diameter: 27.7 to 28.0 mm
Die Axis: ↑↑, ↑↓
Edge: Reeded
Ref.Nos.: Br 1005 (R-2½);
Co 19NL; Lr 774a (R-5);
McL 570; W 568

Varieties: Composition
C1 Copper
C2 Brass

Cat.No.	Description	VG-8	F-12	VF-20	EF-40	AU-50	AU-55	MS-60
LC-56C1	Copper	22.	45.	110.	225.	450.	—	—
LC-56C2	Brass				Very Rare			

(handwritten: 78, 79)

LC-57 *(SEATED JUSTICE DESIGN)* — *1820 (BUST OF GEORGE III)*

Fine head obverse
(A1)

Composition: Brass, copper
Weight: 5.2 to 7.5 g
Diameter: 27.5 to 27.7 mm
Die Axis: ↑↑, ↑↓
Edge: Plain
Ref.Nos.: Br 1011 (R-1);
Lr 785 (R-3);
McL 594;
See below

Crude head obverse
(A2 and A3)

Varieties: Obverse, Composition, Die axis
A1 Fine head design, Coinage; Co 37NL; W 564
A2 Crude head design, Copper, Coinage; Co 38NL; W 565
A3 Crude head design, Brass, Medal; Co 39NL; W 565

Variations: Issued on thick and thin flans. Willey, referring to Davis, lists another variety without a date W566.

Cat.No.	Date	Description	VG-8	F-12	VF-20	EF-40	AU-50	AU-55	MS-60
LC-57A1	1820	Fine head, ↑↓	9.	18.	35.	100.	200.	300.	350.
LC-57A2	1820	Crude head, Copper, ↑↓	22.	45.	90.	175.	—	—	—
LC-57A3	1820	Crude head, Brass, ↑↑			Very Rare				

198
199
200

LC-58   *SHIPS COLONIES & COMMERCE — (BUST DESIGN)*

The busts on the following coins have never been identified. The halfpennies bear a bust once identified as that of British Prime Minister Canning but this was an error, as Canning was bald, and the bust on the coin shows plenty of hair. It was identified by McLachlan as a portrait of Papineau but this cannot be substantiated. It is die-linked with the LC-53B "Salaberry" token.

LC-58A   *— (LARGE BUST DESIGN)*

Composition: Copper
Weight: 4.6 to 5.4 g
Diameter: 26.0 to 26.5 mm
Die Axis: ↑↑
Edge: Plain
Ref.Nos.: Br 1002 (R-2);
                  Lr 813 (R-5); See below

Open sleeve (A1)   Closed sleeve (A2)

"S" points to left of "O"   "S" points to right of "O"
(A1)   (A2)

Varieties: Obverse, Reverse
A1 Open sleeve, Lower seriph of the first "S" in SHIPS points to the left of the first "O" in COLONIES; Co 41NL; W 549
A2 Closed sleeve, Lower seriph of the first "S" in SHIPS points to the right of the first "O" in COLONIES; Co 42NL; W 550
A3 Mule with obverse A1 and reverse A2; Co 43NL; W 551

Cat.No.	Description	VG-8	F-12	VF-20	EF-40	AU-50	AU-55	MS-60
LC-58A1	Open sleeve	12.	22.	40.	85.	175.	275.	350.
LC-58A2	Closed sleeve	45.	85.	165.	350.	—	—	—
LC-58A3	Mule			Extremely Rare				

LC-58B   *— (SMALL BUST DESIGN)*

This wide rim variety is a mule of LC-59B and LC-58A1. The obverse die was built up to match the diameter of the reverse die, resulting in a wide rim.

Composition: Copper
Weight: 4.9 to 5.4 g
Diameter: 26.0 to 26.3 mm
Die Axis: ↑↑
Edge: Plain
Ref.Nos: Br 1002 (R-2),
Co 44NL, Lr 813 (R-5);
W 552

Cat.No.	Description	VG-8	F-12	VF-20	EF-40	AU-50	AU-55	MS-60
LC-58B	Small bust design	125.	200.	350.	550.	—	—	—

205

LC-59   COMMERCIAL CHANGE — (BUST DESIGN)

The obverse die of token number LC-58 was combined with a new reverse die to produce the Commercial Change token. It is clear that both pieces were produced by the same manufacturer.

LC-59A   *— (LARGE BUST DESIGN)*

Composition: Copper
Weight: 4.7 to 4.9 g
Diameter: 23.9 to 24.1 mm
Die Axis: ↑↓
Edge: Plain
Ref.Nos.: Br 1007 (R-1½);
             Co 45NL; Lr 808 (R-4);
             W 554

Cat.No.	Description	AG	G-4	VG-8	F-12	VF-20
LC-59A	Large bust design	—	—	1,000.	2,000.	3,000.

06 (handwritten)

LC-59B   *— (SMALL BUST DESIGN)*

Composition: Copper
Weight: 4.7 to 4.9 g
Diameter: 23.9 to 24.1 mm
Die Axis: ↑↓
Edge: Plain
Ref.Nos.: Br 1007 (R-1½);
             Co 46NL; Lr 808 (R-4);
             W 553

Variations: Struck on thick or thin flans.

Cat.No.	Description	VG-8	F-12	VF-20	EF-40	AU-50	AU-55	MS-60
LC-59B	Small bust design	9.	18.	35.	85.	200.	—	—

07 (handwritten)

a + b (handwritten)
↓ THICK (handwritten)
THIN (handwritten)

BUST AND HARP TOKENS

In 1825 a halfpenny token was struck in Great Britain on Canadian order. It was learned that currency regulations enacted in 1825 forbade the further importation of private tokens into Canada. However, nothing in the regulations interfered with importing tokens dated before 1825. The tokens struck in 1825 are known as the "Bust & Harp" tokens because of their design. They became very popular among the Irish immigrants of Lower Canada. They soon were widely imitated in brass and competed with legitimate colonial coinage for twenty years. The obverse portrays a bust of George IV in a cuirass, a piece of body armour covering the chest and shoulders. Over the shoulders it is divided into several flaps for freedom of movement. The reverse bears a harp with a frame incorporating the body of a winged female facing left.

LC-60   *BUST AND HARP COPPER ORIGINALS*

The originals were struck in 1825 on copper flans. There is a great variation in workmanship and weight.

LC-60A   *(HARP DESIGN) 1820 — (BUST DESIGN)*

REVERSE DATED 1825 —
and 1820 OVER 5

Composition: Copper
Weight: 4.7 to 6.8 g
Diameter: 26.3 to 27.9 mm
Die Axis: ↑↓
Edge: Plain
Ref.Nos.: Br 1012 (R-4);
Lr 786 (R-3); McL 1-24;
See below

0 over 5 **(A2)**

Seven flaps **(A2)**   1820/5 **(A2)**

Varieties: Obverse, Reverse
A1 Dated 1825, Six flaps in the cuirass; BH-21; Co 21BH; W 581
A2 Dated 1820/5, Seven flaps in the cuirass; BH-22; Co 22BH; W 582

Cat.No.	Date	Description	VG-8	F-12	VF-20	EF-40	AU-50	AU-55	MS-60
LC-60A1	1825	Six flaps	2,000.	3,000.	4,000.	6,000.	—	—	—
LC-60A2	1825	"1820/5", Seven flaps	4,500.	8,500.	12,000.	15,000.	—	—	—

LC-60B   *DATED 1820*

Composition: Copper
Weight: 4.7 to 6.8 g
Diameter: 27.4 to 27.7 mm
Die Axis: ↑↓
Edge: Plain
Ref.Nos.: BH-23; Br 1012 (R-0);
Co 23BH; Lr 786 (R-3);
McL 1-24; W 583

Cat.No.	Date	Description	VG-8	F-12	VF-20	EF-40	AU-50	AU-55	MS-60
LC-60B	1820	Seven flaps	30.	55.	110.	225.	—	—	—

BUST AND HARP BRASS IMITATIONS

These brass imitations are all dated 1820 and vary greatly in workmanship. Following McLachlan's example, these tokens are divided into four categories depending on the workmanship.

From 1825 to 1837 the quality of tokens circulating in Lower Canada decreased and the blacksmith style was the only piece circulating by the end of this period. See BL-35 and BL-36.

Throughout this series slight obverse variations exist in the size and number of ruffles under the portrait's chin and the number of flaps in the cuirass.

Reverse variations exist in the style of the female's hair and in the top, foot and placement of the leaves of the harp.

LC-60C   *IMITATIONS ISSUED 1826-1827, DATED 1820*

This group is of good quality and style. The bust of George IV is large.

Composition: Brass, copper
Weight: 4.7 to 6.0 g
Diameter: 27.3 to 28.0 mm
Die Axis: ↑↓
Edge: Plain
Ref.Nos.: Br 1012 (R-0);
Lr 786 (R-3); McL 1-24;
See below

Varieties: Reverse
C1 Ten strings on harp; BH-9-10; Co 9, 10BH; W 584, 585

C2 Nine strings on harp; BH-11-13; Co 11-13BH; W 586-588

C3 Eight strings on harp; BH-24; Co 24-26BH; W 589

Cat.No.	Date	Description	VG-8	F-12	VF-20	EF-40	AU-50	AU-55	MS-60
LC-60C1	1820	Ten strings	6.	12.	18.	35.	65.	85.	110.
LC-60C2	1820	Nine strings	6.	12.	18.	35.	65.	85.	110.
LC-60C3	1820	Eight strings	12.	22.	35.	65.	110.	135.	165.

LC-60D   *IMITATIONS ISSUED 1828-1829, DATED 1820*

This group while slightly inferior in workmanship is also lighter in weight. The bust of George IV is smaller than LC-60B.

Composition: Brass, copper
Weight: 5.0 to 5.5 g
Diameter: 27.4 to 27.8 mm
Die Axis: ↑↓
Edge: Plain
Ref.Nos.: Br 1012 (R-0);
Lr 786 (R-3); McL 1-24;
See below

$8 = 218$

Varieties: Reverse, Composition
D1 Ten strings on harp, Copper; BH-8; Co 8BH; W 593

$4 = 214$
$5 = 215$
$6 = 216$
$7 = 217$
$18 = 228$

D2 Ten strings on harp, Brass; BH-4-7; Co 4-7BH; W 590-593

D3 Nine strings on harp, Brass; BH-18; Co 18BH; W 594

Cat.No.	Date	Description	VG-8	F-12	VF-20	EF-40	AU-50	AU-55	MS-60
LC-60D1	1820	Ten strings, Copper	22.	45.	110.	225.	—	—	—
LC-60D2	1820	Ten strings, Brass	6.	12.	22.	45.	80.	125.	150.
LC-60D3	1820	Nine strings, Brass	6.	12.	22.	45.	80.	125.	150.

$4 \ (COPPER) \bullet BH \ 35 = 239$

LC-60E   IMITATIONS ISSUED Ca 1830, DATED 1820

The workmanship of these tokens was significantly inferior. They are lighter in weight than other tokens of the series and show a larger bust.

Composition: Brass, copper
Weight: 4.2 to 5.2 g
Diameter: 27.5 to 27.8 mm
Die Axis: ↑↓
Edge: Plain
Ref.Nos.: Br 1012 (R-0);
              Lr 786 (R-3); McL 1-24;
              See below

Varieties: Reverse
E1   Ten strings on harp, Brass; BH-01, 03; Co 1, 3BH; W 595, 597

E2   Nine strings on harp, Brass; BH-14-17; Co 14-17BH; W 596, 598-600

Photograph not available at press time

E3   Nine strings on harp, Copper; BH-36; Co 14BH

E4   Nine strings on harp, Brass; BH-19; Co 19BH; W 601

Cat.No.	Date	Description	VG-8	F-12	VF-20	EF-40	AU-50	AU-55	MS-60
LC-60E1	1820	Ten strings, Brass	7.	15.	22.	35.	65.	85.	100.
LC-60E2	1820	Nine strings, Brass	7.	15.	30.	45.	85.	125.	175.
LC-60E3	1820	Nine Strings, Copper	7.	15.	30.	45.	85.	135.	175.
LC-60E4	1820	Nine strings, Brass				Very Rare			

LC-60F   *IMITATIONS ISSUED 1830-1835, DATED 1820*

This group is the poorest in workmanship.

Composition: Brass, copper
Weight: 5.2 to 5.3 g
Diameter: 27.5 to 27.8 mm
Die Axis: ↑↓
Edge: Plain
Ref.Nos: BH-2; Br 1012 (R-0);
           Co 2BH; Lr 786 (R-3);
           McL 1-24; W 602

Cat.No.	Date	Description	VG-8	F-12	VF-20	EF-40	AU-50	AU-55	MS-60
LC-60F	1820	Ten strings, Brass	7.	15.	22.	45.	90.	150.	200.
LC-60F2	1820	Ten strings, Copper	10.	20.	30.	50.	100.	175.	250.

IMITATIONS OF BUST AND HARP TOKENS "BLACKSMITH STYLE"

For the listing of Imitations of Bust and Harp Tokens see page 221 and 222; Cat. Nos. BL-34 to BL-36

GEORGE ORDS TOKEN

LC-61   *(HARP DESIGN) — (BUST DESIGN)*

This is an Irish halfpenny token struck in 1834 in Dublin. The dies were not deeply cut, resulting in coins of low relief. The legends wore rapidly, making possible the striking of pieces without legend for export to Canada. Large numbers of these were found in the famous hoard of obsolete tokens sent for safety to Quebec from Montreal in the weeks before the rebellion of 1837.

The originals have the obverse legend "George Ords Token" and reverse legend "Ireland 1834."

To qualify as a Canadian example the legends should not be legible.

Composition: Brass, copper
Weight: 7.3 to 7.7 g
Diameter: 28.0 mm
Die Axis: ↑↓
Edge: Plain
Ref.Nos.: W 605; See below

Varieties: Composition
 A Brass; BH-33
 B Copper; BH-34

Cat.No.	Description	VG-8	F-12	VF-20	EF-40	AU-50	AU-55	MS-60
LC-61A	Brass	22.	40.	80.	225.	—	—	—
LC-61B	Copper	50.	100.	200.	450.	—	—	—

IMITATIONS OF LOWER CANADA TOKENS "BLACKSMITH STYLE"

For the listings of Lower Canada Tokens see page 230; Cat.Nos. BL-51 and BL-52.

WELLINGTON TOKENS

During the Peninsular Campaign of the Napoleonic War, a series of copper tokens appeared in Yorkshire and elsewhere in England to remedy a shortage of copper. These pieces showed a bust of the Duke of Wellington. They were withdrawn from circulation in England because they became too plentiful. Some pieces were later brought to the Canadian colonies. The famous "Battle Tokens" were struck for J. Picard of Hull in Yorkshire by Sir Edward Thomason, the dies being cut by Thomas Halliday. Picard had specimens struck in silver for presentation at court and ordered a specimen in gold for the Prince Regent. Large numbers of Picard's tokens were later brought to Canada, it is thought, by troops sent out in 1814 to fight the Americans.

Most Wellington pennies had limited circulation in Canada. The halfpennies circulated much more widely, the halfpenny being the basic copper coin in Colonial Canada. The Wellington halfpennies circulated mostly in Lower Canada but found their way in small numbers into Upper Canada. Worn specimens turned up in circulation even after Confederation in remote areas despite the fact that the old Colonial tokens were being taken out of circulation and replaced with cents of the Dominion of Canada.

BRETON CROSS REFERENCE TABLE FOR WELLINGTON TOKENS

Breton Cat. No.	Charlton Cat. No.	Page No.	Breton Cat. No.	Charlton Cat. No.	Page No.
969	WE-1	160	980	WE-9	166
970	WE-4A	162	981	WE-10	166
971	WE-2A	160	984	WE-12	170
972	WE-2B	161	985	WE-13	170
973	WE-2C	161	986	WE-11B, C	168, 169
974	WE-3	162	987	WE-11A	167
976	WE-5	163	988	WE-11D	169
977	WE-6	164	1003	WE-14	171
978	WE-7	164	1006	WE-15	171
979	WE-8	165			

WE-1   *HALFPENNY TOKEN 1813 — FIELD MARSHAL WELLINGTON*

This token was often struck over Guppy halfpennies.

Composition: Copper
Weight: 7.8 to 11.2 g
Diameter: 27.9 to 28.1 mm
Die Axis: ↑↑, ↑↓
Edge: Engrailed, plain
Ref.Nos.: Br 969 (R-1); Co 26W;
Lr 799 (R-3); W 522

Varieties: Flan, Edge, Die axis
 A1 Engrailed, Thin flan, Medal
 A2 Engrailed, Thin flan, Coinage
 A3 Engrailed,Thick flan, Coinage
 A4 Plain,Thick flan, Medal
 A5 Plain,Thick flan, Coinage

Cat.No.	Date	Description	VG-8	F-12	VF-20	EF-40	AU-50	AU-55	MS-60
WE-1A1	1813	Engrailed, Thin, ↑↑	20.	40.	80.	125.	200.	300.	350.
WE-1A2	1813	Engrailed, Thin, ↑↓	8.	15.	30.	60.	125.	200.	250.
WE-1A3	1813	Engrailed, Thick, ↑↓	8.	15.	30.	60.	125.	200.	250.
WE-1A4	1813	Plain, Thick, ↑↑	5.	10.	20.	40.	90.	150.	225.
WE-1A5	1813	Plain, Thick, ↑↓	5.	10.	20.	40.	90.	150.	225.

WE-2   *HALFPENNY TOKEN — FIELD MARSHAL WELLINGTON*

WE-2A   *LEGENDS IN LARGE BOLD LETTERING*

Composition: Copper
Weight: 7.8 to 9.2 g
Diameter: 27.6 to 28.6 mm
Die Axis: ↑↓
Edge: Engrailed, plain, reeded
Ref.Nos.: Br 971 (R-1); Co 30W;
Lr 807 (R-3); W 526

Varieties: Edge
 A1 Plain
 A2 Engrailed
 A3 Reeded; Not previously listed

Cat.No.	Description	VG-8	F-12	VF-20	EF-40	AU-50	AU-55	MS-60
WE-2A1	Plain	5.	8.	20.	60.	125.	200.	250.
WE-2A2	Engrailed	5.	8.	20.	60.	125.	200.	250.
WE-2A3	Reeded	5.	8.	20.	60.	125.	200.	250.

WE-2B   *LEGENDS IN SMALL LETTERING*

Composition: Copper
Weight: 7.8 to 10.0 g
Diameter: 27.7 to 28.2 mm
Die Axis: ↑↓
Edge: Engrailed, plain
Ref.Nos.: Br 972 (R-1);
Lr 806 (R-3);
See below

Trident **(B1, 2 and 3)**   Spear **(B4)**

Varieties: Reverse, Flan, Edge
B1 Trident, Thick flan, Plain; Co 28W
B2 Trident, Thick flan, Engrailed; Co 28W; W 523
B3 Trident, Thin flan, Engrailed; Co 28W; W 523
B4 Spear, Engrailed; Co 27W; W 524

Cat.No.	Description	VG-8	F-12	VF-20	EF-40	AU-50	AU-55	MS-60
WE-2B1	Trident, Thick flan, Plain	5.	8.	25.	65.	125.	200.	250.
WE-2B2	Trident, Thick flan, Engrailed	5.	8.	25.	65.	125.	200.	250.
WE-2B3	Trident, Thin flan, Engrailed	10.	20.	40.	100.	175.	250.	300.
WE-2B4	Spear, Engrailed	20.	35.	70.	150.	225.	300.	350.

WE-2C   *(CONTINUOUS OAK WREATH REVERSE)*

Courteau and Leroux did not list this token. McLachlan denounced it as a fake.

Composition: Copper
Weight: 6.2 g
Diameter: 26.9 to 27.2 mm
Die Axis: ↑↑, ↑↓
Edge: Engrailed, plain
Ref.Nos.: Br 973 (R-3½);
Lr 807a (R-5); W 528

Varieties: Die axis
C1 Coinage
C2 Medal

Cat.No.	Description	AG	G-4	VG-8	F-12	VF-20
WE-2C1	Coinage			Extremely Rare		
WE-2C2	Medal			Extremely Rare		

WE-3   ONE PENNY TOKEN — 1813 FIELD MARSHAL WELLINGTON

Composition: Copper
Weight: 17.8 to 18.8 g
Diameter: 33.9-35.0 mm

Die Axis: ↑↓
Edge: Engrailed
Ref.Nos.: Br 974 (R-3½); Co 29W;
    Lr 807c (R-6); W 521

Cat.No.	Date	Description	VG-8	F-12	VF-20	EF-40	AU-50	AU-55	MS-60
WE-3	1813	Dated, no wreath	45.	75.	150.	300.	400.	525.	600.

WE-4   ONE PENNY TOKEN — FIELD MARSHAL WELLINGTON

The following two varieties are usually found struck over Bristol pennies.

WE-4A   WITH REVERSE WREATH DESIGN

Composition: Copper
Weight: 16.6 to 18.2 g
Diameter: 33.8-34.0 mm

Die Axis: ↑↓
Edge: Engrailed
Ref.Nos.: Br 970 (R-3); Co 31W;
    Lr 807b (R-5); W 527

Cat.No.	Description	VG-8	F-12	VF-20	EF-40	AU-50	AU-55	MS-60
WE-4A	Obv. and Rev. wreath	40.	55.	125.	175.	275.	375.	450.

WE-4B   *WITHOUT REVERSE WREATH DESIGN*

Composition: Copper
Weight: 17.6 to 18.5 g
Diameter: 33.8-34.0 mm *68*

Die Axis: ↑↓
Edge: Engrailed
Ref.Nos.: Co 32W; W 525 *LR-NOT LISTED*

Cat.No.	Description	VG-8	F-12	VF-20	EF-40	AU-50	AU-55	MS-60
WE-4B	Obv. wreath *R4*	75.	110.	200.	300.	500.	625.	700.

WE-5 *L-794-R4* *HIBERNIA 1805 — FIELD MARSHAL WELLINGTON*

This token is an anonymous Irish piece from the County of Dublin. It is antedated and the engraver is unknown. The token was found only in small quantities in Canada.

Composition: Copper
Weight: 6.4 to 6.7 g
Diameter: 28.2 to 28.4 mm
Die Axis: ↑↑, ↑↓
Edge: Reeded (diagonally)
Ref.Nos.: Br 976 (R-1½);
         Lr 794 (R-4):
         See below

Large letters   Small letters
Double lock **(A1)**   Single lock **(A2 and 3)**

Varieties: Obverse, Die axis
  ✓**A1** Large letters, Double lock, Coinage; Co 1W; W C7 *W + PLAIN EDGE;*
    A2 Small letters, Single lock, Medal; Co 2W; W C8 **
  ✓**A3** Small letters, Single lock, Coinage; Co 2W; W C8 **

Variations: Rusted and unrusted dies caused very minor variations on this token.

Cat.No.	Date	Description	VG-8	F-12	VF-20	EF-40	AU-50	AU-55	MS-60
WE-5A1	1805	Large letters, Coinage	25.	40.	80.	200.	300.	—	—	*R*
WE-5A2	1805	Small letters, Medal	25.	40.	80.	200.	300.	—	—	*RR*
WE-5A3	1805	Small letters, Coinage	25.	40.	80.	200.	300.	—	—	*RR*

FRANK WINTERS HAS A1 STRUCK

WE-6   TRADE & COMMERCE 1811 — (BUST DESIGN)

As with the Hibernia 1805 token, this piece is also of Irish origin.

Composition: Copper
Weight: 8.4 to 8.9 g
Diameter: 28.9 to 29.1 mm
Die Axis: ↑↓
Edge: Reeded (diagonally)
Ref.Nos.: Br 977 (R-3½);
       Co 43W; Lr 795 (R-4);
       W C9

Cat.No.	Date	Description	VG-8	F-12	VF-20	EF-40	AU-50	AU-55	MS-60
WE-6	1811	Bust design	50.	75.	125.	275.	500.	—	—

WE-7   COMMERCE — 1813 MARQUIS WELLINGTON

This Irish token was designed and struck by Isaac Parkes of Dublin. Wellington was promoted to Marquis sometime between August 18, 1812, and the listing in Burke's "Peerage" as at October 3, 1812. Small numbers have been found in Canadian hoards.

Composition: Copper
Weight: 8.2 to 8.6 g
Diameter: 28.4 to 28.5 mm
Die Axis: ↑↓
Edge: Engrailed
Ref.Nos.: Br 978 (R-2); Co 44W;
       Lr 797 (R-4); W C10

Cat.No.	Date	Description	VG-8	F-12	VF-20	EF-40	AU-50	AU-55	MS-60
WE-7	1813	Copper, Coinage	15.	30.	50.	150.	250.	325.	375.

WE-8   *1814 — WELLINGTON HALFPENNY TOKEN*

After 1825, halfpennies began to appear which had been antedated to evade regulations against the import of private tokens. All the lightweight pieces are dated 1814 to 1816 and are clearly antedated.

Composition: Copper
Weight: 5.9 to 6.5 g
Diameter: 27.1 to 27.5 mm
Die Axis: ↑↓
Edge: Engrailed
Ref.Nos.: Br 979 (R-1);
              Lr 800 (R-3); See below

Middle tine longest (A2) — Middle tine shorter (A6)

Square epaulette Eight leaves **(A3)**

Round epaulette Seven leaves **(A6)**

Large trident two tines barbed **(A3)**

Varieties: Obverse, Reverse
A1 Square epaulette, Nine leaves, Ship sails in left background, Cannon balls, Middle tine barbed; Co 33W; W 529
A2 Square epaulette, Nine leaves, No ship, No cannonballs, Middle tine longest; Co 34W; W 530
A3 Square epaulette, Eight leaves, Ship sails in left background, Large trident with two tines barbed; Co 37W; W 533
A4 Round epaulette, Eight leaves, Ship sails in left background, Upper tine longer others equal in size none being barbed; Co 35W; W 531
A5 Mule, Obverse A4, Reverse A2; Co 36W; W 532;
A6 Round epaulette, Seven leaves, Middle tine shorter; Co 38W; W 534

Cat.No.	Date	Description	VG-8	F-12	VF-20	EF-40	AU-50	AU-55	MS-60
WE-8A1	1814	Middle tine barbed	5.	10.	20.	60.	125.	225.	300.
WE-8A2	1814	Middle tine longest	5.	10.	20.	60.	125.	225.	300.
WE-8A3	1814	Trident tine barbed	5.	10.	20.	60.	125.	225.	300.
WE-8A4	1814	Upper tine longer	8.	15.	30.	75.	150.	275.	350.
WE-8A5	1814	Mule	100.	200.	300.	400.	—	—	—
WE-8A6	1814	Middle tine shorter	8.	15.	30.	75.	150.	275.	350.

WE-9 — *WELLINGTON HALFPENNY TOKEN*

Composition: Copper
Weight: 5.4 to 6.2 g
Diameter: 27.1 to 27.5 mm
Die Axis: ↑↓
Edge: Engrailed
Ref.Nos.: Br 980 (R-2); Co 39W;
      Lr 801 (R-4); W 535

Cat.No.	Description	VG-8	F-12	VF-20	EF-40	AU-50	AU-55	MS-60
WE-9	Copper, Coinage 36	85.	175.	400.	—	—	—	—

WE-10 *WATERLOO HALFPENNY 1816 —*
THE ILLUSTRIOUS WELLINGTON

Composition: Copper
Weight: 4.1 to 5.8 g
Diameter: 26.3 to 26.9 mm
Die Axis: ↑↓
Edge: Plain, reeded (Vertically or
      Diagonally)
Ref.Nos.: Br 981 (R-1½);
      Lr 804 (R-3); See below

Wreath with two   Wreath with one
upper leaves **(A2)**   upper leaf **(A3)**

Ten strings **(A1)**   Eight strings **(A2 and 3)**

Varieties: Obverse, Reverse, Edge
  A1 Harp with 10 strings; Plain, reeded; Co 40W; W 538
  A2 Harp with 8 strings, Wreath has two upper leaves, Reeded;   PLAIN
      Co 41W; W 539 $80. — @ EF
  A3 Harp with 8 strings, Wreath has one upper leaf, Reeded;
      Co 42W; W 540

Variations: A1 has diagonal or vertical reeding.

Cat.No.	Date	Description	VG-8	F-12	VF-20	EF-40	AU-50	AU-55	MS-60
WE-10A1	1816	Ten strings	7.	14.	30.	75.	150.	250.	350.
WE-10A2	1816	Eight strings, two leaves	5.	10.	25.	60.	125.	225.	300.
WE-10A3	1816	Eight strings. one leaf	7.	14.	30.	75.	150.	250.	350.

PENINSULAR TOKENS

The Peninsular Tokens were struck for use by Wellington's Army in Portugal and Spain. J.K. Picard of Hull was asked to secure coins of a design distinct from English and Spanish regal copper. The order was placed with Sir Edward Thomason, who secured the services of Thomas Halliday to design the coins and cut the dies. Specimens were brought to Canada by troops sent over to fight the Americans in 1814.

The reverse legends of the halfpennies and the obverse legends of the pennies carry the names of the famous battles Wellington won against Napoleon. Halfpennies circulated to a far greater extent than the penny tokens.

WE-11   *VIMIERA TALAVERA ALMEIDA —*
        HISPANIAM ET LVSITANIAM RESTITVIT WELLINGTON

WE-11A   *L - 811 -R4*   *CUIDAD RODRIGO, BADAJOZ, SALAMANCA —*

Composition: Brass, copper, silver
Weight: 8.1 to 8.9 g
Diameter: 27.2 to 27.7 mm
Die Axis: ↑↑
Edge: Plain, reeded (vertically or diagonal)
Ref.Nos.: Br 987 (R-1);
           Lr 811 (R-4); See below

Varieties: Obverse, Composition, Edge, Thickness

A1   Laurel crown with ten leaves, At the hairline three locks of hair with the centre lock large, Copper, Brass, Silver, Thin and thick flans, Plain, reeded vertically or diagonally; Co 4W; W 502 *////*

A2   Laurel crown with ten leaves, One small lock above two large locks, Copper; Co 5W; Silver, Co 6W; Reeded diagonally; W 503 *////*

A3   Laurel crown with ten leaves, The lower lock below the ribbon knot points to the ear, Copper, Silver, Reeded diagonally; Co 7W; W 504 *////*

A4   Laurel crown with ten leaves, Three short and equal length locks, Copper, Reeded vertically or diagonally; Co 8W; W 505

A5   Laurel crown with ten leaves, Tied with a single bow, Copper, Reeded vertically or diagonally; Co 9W; W 506

A6   Laurel crown with ten leaves, Without coat button, Copper, Reeded vertically or diagonally; Co 10W, W 507

A7   Laurel crown with nine leaves, Without coat button, Brass, Plain; Co 11W; W 508

Variations: A1, A2 and A3 were issued in silver and are rare. They will command a price in excess of $1,000.

Note: WE-11A7 is a brass counterfeit. Other brass forgeries exist.

Cat.No.	Description	VG-8	F-12	VF-20	EF-40	AU-50	AU-55	MS-60
WE-11A1	Ten leaves, Large centre lock	6.	10.	18.	30.	75.	125.	150.
WE-11A2	Ten leaves, Small lock	6.	10.	18.	30.	75.	125.	150.
WE-11A3	Ten leaves, Lock below ribbon	6.	10.	18.	30.	75.	125.	150.
WE-11A4	Ten leaves, Short equal locks	6.	10.	18.	30.	75.	125.	150.
WE-11A5	Ten leaves, Single bow	6.	10.	18.	30.	75.	125.	150.
WE-11A6	Ten leaves, Without button	6.	10.	18.	30.	75.	125.	150.
WE-11A7	Nine leaves, Without button	45.	90.	175.	300.	—	—	—

NEW VARIETIES

WE-11B   *CUIDAD RODRIGO, BADAJOZ, SALAMANCA, MADRID* —

Composition: Brass, copper, silver
Weight: 8.2 to 8.4 g
Diameter: 27.2 to 27.7 mm
Die Axis: ↑↑, ↑↓
Edge: Reeded (diagonally)
Ref.Nos.: Br 986 (R-2);
         Lr 810 (R-4); See below

Varieties: Obverse, Composition, Edge

B1 Laurel crown with ten leaves, Two locks, Copper, Reeded diagonally; Co 12W; W 509

B2 Laurel crown with ten leaves, One small lock above two large locks, Similar to WE-11A2, Copper, Reeded diagonally; Co 13W, W 510

B3 Laurel crown with ten leaves, Three locks of equal length, Similar to WE-11A4, Copper, Reeded diagonally; Co 14W; W 511

B4 Laurel crown with ten leaves, Without coat button, Similar to WE-11A6, Copper, Reeded diagonally; Co 15W; W 512

B5 Laurel crown with ten leaves, Locks are small, Coat button near lapel, Copper, Reeded diagonally; Co 16W; W 513

B6 Laurel crown with nine leaves, Three locks with the centre lock largest, Copper, Reeded diagonally; Co 17W; W 514

B7 Laurel crown with nine leaves, Single upper leaf, Three locks with the centre lock largest, Copper, Silver, Thin or thick flans, Reeded diagonally; Co 18W; W 515

B8 Laurel crown with eight leaves, Copper, Thin or thick flans, Coinage, Reeded; Co 19W; W 516

Variations: B7 was issued in silver and is rare. This token commands a price in excess of $1,000.

Cat.No.	Date	Description	VG-8	F-12	VF-20	EF-40	AU-50	AU-55	MS-60
WE-11B1		10 leaves, 2 locks	8.	18.	30.	65.	150.	250.	300.
WE-11B2	(1812)	10 leaves, 1 small lock	8.	18.	30.	65.	150.	250.	300.
WE-11B3		10 leaves, 3 equal locks	8.	18.	30.	65.	150.	250.	300.
WE-11B4		10 leaves, Without button	8.	18.	30.	65.	175.	275.	375.
WE-11B5		10 leaves, Button near lapel	8.	18.	30.	65.	150.	250.	300.
WE-11B6		9 leaves, large centre lock	8.	18.	30.	65.	175.	300.	375.
WE-11B7		9 leaves, Single upper leaf	8.	18.	30.	65.	175.	300.	375.
WE-11B8		8 leaves	8.	18.	30.	65.	150.	250.	300.

WE-11C   CIUDAD, RODRIGO, BADAJOZ, SALAMANCA, MADRID —

The correct spelling of the Spanish word for city is "Ciudad" not Cuidad. This error on the previous tokens was corrected.

Composition: Copper
Weight: 9.1 g
Diameter: 27.7 to 27.9 mm
Die Axis: ↑↑
Edge: Reeded (diagonally)
Ref.Nos.: Br 986 (R-1); See below

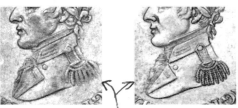

Coat button
near collar (**C1**)

Coat button far
from collar (**C2**)

Varieties: Obverse   *I N C O R R E C T   I L L U S T R A T I O N S* (handwritten)
C1 Coat button near collar; Co 20W; W 517
C2 Coat button far from collar; Co 21W, W 518

Cat.No.	Date	Description	VG-8	F-12	VF-20	EF-40	AU-50	AU-55	MS-60
WE-11C1	(1813)	Button near collar	18.	35.	65.	100.	225.	300.	375.
WE-11C2		Button far from collar	18.	35.	65.	100.	225.	300.	375.

26 (handwritten) ... *27* (handwritten)

28 — W# 1555 - PPP -INCORRECTLY LISTED AS Co 20 (handwritten)

WE-11D   SALAMANCA, MADRID, ST. SEBASTIAN, PAMPLUNO —

Composition: Copper
Weight: 7.6 to 9.7 g
Diameter: 27.2 to 28.1 mm
Die Axis: ↑↑
Edge: Plain, reeded
Ref.Nos.: Br 988 (R-1½);
            Co 22W; Lr 812 (R-5);
            W 519

Varieties: Edge
D1 Plain
D2 Reeded

Variations: Struck on thin or thick flans.

Cat.No.	Date	Description	VG-8	F-12	VF-20	EF-40	AU-50	AU-55	MS-60
WE-11D1	(1813)	Plain	65.	100.	200.	—	—	—	—
WE-11D2		Reeded	15.	35.	65.	150.	375.	450.	525.

30a (handwritten) ... *30* (handwritten)

WE-12   **ONE PENNY TOKEN 1813 —**
VIMIERA TALAVERA BADAJOZ SALAMANCA VITTORIA

Composition: Copper
Weight: 17.3 to 18.8 g
Diameter: 33.9 to 34.0 mm

Die Axis: ↑↑
Edge: Engrailed
Ref.Nos.: Br 984 (R-2½); Co 23W;
Lr 798 (R-4); W 520

62

Cat.No.	Date	Description	VG-8	F-12	VF-20	EF-40	AU-50	AU-55	MS-60
WE-12	1813	Vittoria	25.	50.	85.	150.	250.	375.	450.

WE-13   **COSSACK PENNY TOKEN —**
VIMIERA TALAVERA BUSACO BADAJOZ SALAMANCA

Composition: Copper
Weight: 18.2 to 19.2 g
Diameter: 33.9 to 34.2 mm

Die Axis: ↑↑
Edge: Engrailed
Ref.Nos.: Br 985 (R-2½); Co 24W;
Lr 805 (R-5); W C11

64

Cat.No.	Date	Description	VG-8	F-12	VF-20	EF-40	AU-50	AU-55	MS-60
WE-13	(1813)	Cossack	25.	50.	70.	125.	250.	375.	450.

65 — NEW VARIETY
W#1506

WE-14   *WELLINGTON WATERLOO 1815 — (SAILING SHIP DESIGN)*

Composition: Copper
Weight: 6.4 to 6.5 g
Diameter: 26.4 to 26.6 g
Die Axis: ↑↓
Edge: Plain
Ref.Nos.: Br 1003 (R-1½);
Co 46W; Lr 802 (R-4);
W 537

Note: Forgeries are known in pewter.

Cat.No.	Date	Description	VG-8	F-12	VF-20	EF-40	AU-50	AU-55	MS-60
WE-14	1815	Ship	12.	18.	35.	100.	200.	300.	375.

WE-15   *WELLINGTON WATERLOO 1815 — (LARGE BUST DESIGN)*

Composition: Copper
Weight: 4.5 to 6.5 g
Diameter: 26.1 to 26.4 mm
Die Axis: ↑↓
Edge: Plain
Ref.Nos.: Br 1006 (R-2); Co 45W;
Lr 803 (R-4); W 536

Variations: Struck on thin or thick flans.

Cat.No.	Date	Description	VG-8	F-12	VF-20	EF-40	AU-50	AU-55	MS-60
WE-15	1815	Large bust	15.	30.	50.	125.	225.	300.	350.

TOKENS OF UPPER CANADA

After the American War of Independence the thousands who remained loyal to the British crown were dispossessed of their property and had to leave the territory of the newly-independent United States. Many came to the Great Lakes region from the state of New York and found themselves in the colony of Quebec and under jurisdiction of the Quebec Act of 1774. In 1791 the British government detached the Great Lakes region from the colony of Quebec, organizing it as the colony of Upper Canada.

Since so many Loyalists had come from New York, the popular mode of reckoning in many areas was the standard of New York State known as York currency. In 1809 the ratings of gold coins were adjusted to keep Spanish and French gold from being exported but no changes were made in the values of silver coin. Silver became the standard as there was no discount on lightweight coin.

York currency continued in use until 1821. About that time the government policy stated that no contracts of any kind in York currency would be permitted to bear interest and no contract would be enforceable in the courts unless expressed in Halifax Currency.

BRETON CROSS REFERENCE TABLE FOR UPPER CANADA TOKENS

Breton Cat. No.	Charlton Cat. No.	Page No.	Breton Cat. No.	Charlton Cat. No.	Page No.
717	UC-3	175	727	UC-9	181
718	UC-2	174	728	UC-10	182
721	UC-1	173	729	UC-11	182
723	UC-5	177	730	UC-12A-B	183, 184
724	UC-6	178	731	UC-13	184
725	UC-7	179	732	UC-14	185
726	UC-8	180	1010	UC-4	176

PRIVATE TOKENS

UC-1
COPPER COMPANY OF UPPER CANADA
ONE HALF PENNY — 1794

Governor Simcoe of Upper Canada through intermediaries requested sample coinage from Boulton & Watt for the new colony of Upper Canada. The Soho Mint, using an obverse design by Noel-Alexandre Ponthon and a simple reverse design, submitted a pattern illustrating their capabilities as minters. The proposed coinage for Upper Canada was abandoned. Restrikes appeared in 1894, offered by J. R. Thomas, a British dealer.

Original

Composition	Weight	Diameter	Thickness	Die Axis	Edge
Copper	12.8-13.1	28.9	N/A	↑↓	Plain
White metal	8.3	29.1	N/A	Uniface	Plain

Restrike

Composition	Weight	Diameter	Thickness	Die Axis	Edge
Gold	15.7	28.9	N/A	↑↑	Plain
Silver	12.8	28.9	M/A	↑↑	Plain
Bronze	9.8	28.9	N/A	↑↑	Plain
White metal	NA	28.9	N/A	↑↑	Plain

 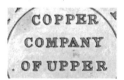

Original: Round "O"
Straight tail "R"(A)

Restrike: Oval "O"
Curved tail "R" (B)

Varieties: Reverse
A Original: All "O" letters are round; All "R" letters have straight tails; Br 721 (R-5); Lr 696 (R-8); W A2
B Restrike: All "O" letters are oval; All "R" letters have curved tails;

Cat.No.	Date	Description	PR-60	PR-63	PR-65
UC-1A1	1794	Original, Copper	4,500.	6,500.	9,000.
UC-1A2	1794	Original, White metal	—	10,000.	—
UC-1B1	(1794)	Restrike, Gold	—	—	20,000.
UC-1B2	(1794)	Restrike, Silver	3,000.	4,500.	6,000.
UC-1B3	(1794)	Restrike, Copper	1,000.	1,750.	2,500.
UC-1B4	(1794)	Restrike, White metal	—	1,500.	—

Note: **1.** A 1796 Myddelton (British Settlement Kentucky) obverse is found muled with the Copper Company of Upper Canada reverse (Lr 697), struck by the Soho Mint.
2. A lead Progress obverse trial exists. The die differs slightly from both the original and the restrike. While it has been termed restrike, it really is not, they are two different dies.

LESSLIE & SONS TOKENS

The firm of Lesslie & Sons, in the drug and book trade, was established in 1820 with branches at York and Dundas. A third branch was opened in Kingston in 1822. From 1820 to 1823, William Lyon MacKenzie was John Lesslie's partner in the firm. James Lesslie was a partner from 1822, and William Lesslie later. The tokens of the firm were struck by Boulton & Watt and the dies were cut by Thomas Wells Ingram.

The twopenny piece bears the name Toronto, even though it was issued before Toronto was incorporated under that name in 1834. Ever since it was founded, York was unofficially called Toronto, popularly thought to be the old Indian name for "meeting place," and in 1822 a petition was circulated asking that the town of York be renamed Toronto. Sir Peregrine Maitland, the governor at the time, chose to ignore the petition altogether and York remained the official name until 1834.

UC-2   ***PROSPERITY TO CANADA LA PRUDENCE***
ET LA CANDEUR TOKEN HALFPENNY —
LESSLIE & SONS YORK KINGSTON & DUNDAS

Composition: Copper
Weight: 7.0 to 7.3 g
Diameter: 27.1 to 28.0 mm
Die Axis: ↑↑
Edge: Plain, reeded
Ref.Nos.: Br 718 (R-1);
Lr 699 (R-4); See below

Lower plough handle
points to "Period" **(A1)**

Lower plough handle points
above "A" **(A2, A3 and A4)**

Lower plough handle
points to "A" **(A5)**

No comma after
York **(A1 and 2)**

Comma after York
(A4 and 5)

Varieties: Obverse, Reverse, Edge
A1 No comma after York, Lower plough handle points to period, Plain; W 824; Mc 26
A2 No comma after York, Lower plough handle points above final "A" of CANADA, Plain; W 825; Mc 27
A3 Weak comma after York, Lower plough handle points above final "A" of CANADA, Plain; W 826; Mc 28
A4 Comma after York, Lower plough handle points above final "A" of CANADA, Reeded; W 827; Mc 29
A5 Comma after York, Lower plough handle points to final "A" of CANADA, Reeded; W 828; Mc 30

Cat.No.	Date	Description	VG-8	F-12	VF-20	EF-40	AU-50	AU-55	MS-60
UC-2A1	(1824)	No comma, To period	12.	22.	65.	175.	300.	375.	450.
UC-2A2	(1824)	No comma, Above "A"	12.	22.	65.	175.	300.	375.	450.
UC-2A3	(1824)	Weak comma, Above "A"	12.	22.	65.	175.	300.	375.	450.
UC-2A4	(1828)	Comma, Above "A"	15.	30.	85.	200.	350.	425.	500.
UC-2A5	(1828)	Comma, To "A"	15.	30.	85.	200.	350.	425.	500.

UC-3 **PROSPERITY TO CANADA LA PRUDENCE ET LA CANDEUR TOKEN 2d CURRENCY — 1822 LESSLIE & SONS TORONTO & DUNDASS**

Composition: Copper
Weight: 27.8 to 28.3 g
Diameter: 40.2 to 40.5 mm

Die Axis: ↑↑
Edge: Plain
Ref.Nos.: Br 717 (R-4); Lr 698 (R-6); W 823; Mc 31

Cat.No.	Date	Description	VG-8	F-12	VF-20	EF-40	AU-50	AU-55	MS-60
UC-3	1822	Copper	125.	200.	350.	600.	1,000.	1,450.	1,750.

UC-4   SPEED THE PLOUGH HALFPENNY TOKEN — NO LABOUR NO BREAD

About 1830 these tokens were imported into Toronto by Perrins Bros., a dry goods firm. Under the act outlawing private tokens the customs seized and ordered the tokens melted. However, most escaped the meltdown and were still in circulation as late as 1837.

5.6

Composition: Copper
Weight: ~~6.0~~ to 6.5 g
Diameter: 26.1 to 26.2 mm
Die Axis: ↑↓
Edge: Plain
Ref.Nos.: Br 1010 (R-1½);
Lr 790 (R-4);
McL 28-29; See below

Varieties: Obverse and reverse

A1 Long threshing floor, Wheat table ends vertically, Ground points to middle of "N", Man far from "H"; W 829

A2 Short threshing floor, Wheat table ends diagonally, Ground points to left seriph of "N", Man near "H"; W 830

A3 Mule, obverse A1, reverse A2

Cat.No.	Date	Description	VG-8	F-12	VF-20	EF-40	AU-50	AU-55	MS-60
UC-4A1	(1830)	Long, Far from "H"	8.	18.	40.	125.	300.	425.	500.
UC-4A2	(1830)	Short, Near "H"	8.	18.	40.	125.	300.	425.	500.
UC-4A3	(1830)	Mule	45.	85.	185.	375.	900.	—	—

ANONYMOUS TOKENS

THE BROCK TOKENS 1812-1816

The Brock Series of halfpenny tokens was struck in memory of General Sir Isaac Brock, Commander of the British forces in Upper Canada. During July 1812, Brock captured Detroit. On October 13th of that same year, he died during the unsuccessful American invasion at Queenstown, Upper Canada.

The tokens first appeared around 1813. A second issue was released in 1816 but these tokens became too plentiful and were discredited by 1820. They were the lightest Canadian coppers and were in use as early as 1814-1816.

UC-5　　　　　　　　*SIR ISAAC BROOK BART.*
　　　　　　　THE HERO OF UPPER CANADA 1812 —

Full legend reads:

Reverse:　"SIR ISAAC BROOK, BART. THE HERO OF UPPER CANADA WHO FELL IN THE GLORIOUS BATTLE OF QUEENSTOWN HEIGHT ON THE 13 OCTR 1812."

Obverse:　"SUCCESS TO THE COMMERCE OF UPPR & LOWR CANADA."

The spelling "Brook" is incorrect, as it should read "Brock."

Composition: Copper
Weight: 4.9 to 5.1 g
Diameter: 26.4 to 26.9 mm
Die Axis: ↑↑
Edge: Plain, reeded (diagonally)
Ref.Nos.: Br 723 (R-1);
　　　　　　Lr 680 (R-4); Mc 10;
　　　　　　W 801

Varieties: Edge
A1 Reeded
A2 Plain

Cat.No.	Date	Description	VG-8	F-12	VF-20	EF-40	AU-50	AU-55	MS-60
UC-5A1	1812	"Brook", Reeded	15.	30.	75.	225.	400.	—	—
UC-5A2	1812	"Brook", Plain	15.	30.	75.	225.	400.	—	—

Note: A modern mule of obverse UC-6 and reverse UC-5 exists, struck by Pobjoy Mint, naturally all are in mint condition.

UC-6

SUCCESS TO COMMERCE & PEACE
TO THE WORLD 1816 — SR. ISAAC BROCK
THE HERO OF UPR CANADA FELL OCT 13 1812

Composition: Copper
Weight: 4.5 to 4.9 g
Diameter: 26.4 to 26.8 mm
Die Axis: ↑↑, ↑↓
Edge: Reeded (diagonally) ⫽⫽⫽
Ref.Nos.: Br 724 (R-1);
Lr 682 (R-4); See below

Varieties: Obverse, Die axis

A1 Cherubs' heads under "T" and "ER", Oval wreath, Base of urn is curved, Large date, Flat top "1's"; W 802; Mc 4

A2 Cherubs' heads under "TH" and "R", Oval wreath, Base of urn is flat, Pedestal has three steps, Flat top "1's"; W 803; Mc 5

A3 Cherubs' heads under "T" and "ER", Circular wreath, Base of urn is flat, Pedestal has two steps, Flat top "1's"; W 804; Mc 6

A4 Cherubs' heads under "T" and "ER", Circular wreath, Base of urn curves upwards, Pedestal has two steps, Flat top "1's"; W 805

A5 Small cherubs' heads under "T" and "R", Circular wreath, Base of urn is flat, Pedestal has two steps, Flat top "1's"; W 806; Mc 7

A6 Cherubs' heads under "TH" and "R", Oval wreath, Base of urn is flat, Pedestal has three steps, Top of "1's" slanted; W 807; Mc 8

A7 Cherubs' heads under "T" and "R", Oval wreath, Base of urn is flat, Pedestal has three steps, Flat top "1's", Coinage; W 808; Mc 9

Cat.No.	Date	Description	VG-8	F-12	VF-20	EF-40	AU-50	AU-55	MS-60
UC-6A1	1816	Under "T"/"ER", Curved	7.	15.	30.	65.	150.	225.	300.
UC-6A2	1816	Under "TH"/"R", Flat	7.	15.	30.	65.	150.	225.	300.
UC-6A3	1816	Under "T"/"ER", Flat	7.	15.	30.	65.	150.	225.	300.
UC-6A4	1816	Under "T"/"ER", Curved	7.	15.	30.	65.	150.	225.	300.
UC-6A5	1816	Under "T"/"R", Flat	7.	15.	30.	65.	150.	225.	300.
UC-6A6	1816	Under "TH"/"R", Flat	7.	15.	30.	65.	150.	225.	300.
UC-6A7	1816	Under "T"/"R", Flat	7.	15.	30.	65.	150.	225.	300.

Note: Gibbs states that "all varieties are diagonally reeded although some are so faint as to appear plain."

UC-7 ***SUCCESS TO COMMERCE AND PEACE***
TO THE WORLD 1816 — SUCCESS TO THE
COMMERCE OF UPPR AND LOWR CANADA

This is a mule of the worn obverse of UC-5 and the well worn reverse of UC-6A7.

4.1

Composition: Copper
Weight: ~~4.9~~ to 5.2 g
Diameter: 26.5 to 26.9 mm
Die Axis: ↑↑
Edge: Reeded (diagonally) ~ *PLAIN*
Ref.Nos.: Br 725 (R-2);
Lr 681 (R-6); Mc 11;
W 809

Cat.No.	Date	Description	VG-8	F-12	VF-20	EF-40	AU-50	AU-55	MS-60
UC-7	1816	Mule	55.	110.	250.	600.	—	—	—

THE SLOOP TOKENS

These tokens appeared after 1825, some being antedated to evade the law of 1825 against private tokens. In time, the law was openly ignored in Upper Canada by many issuers who were secure in the relative isolation of Upper Canada from the commercial and political centre of Lower Canada.

It is believed that sloop tokens were produced by John Sheriff of Liverpool from a design sent from Upper Canada. The sloop was the chief means of transportation on the Great Lakes at the time and far more reliable than any form of land transport. The sloop shown on the tokens was said by Rev. Henry Scadding to be a portrayal of the packet "Duke of Richmond," owned by a man named Oates.

UC-8   *COMMERCIAL CHANGE 1815 —*
            HALFPENNY TOKEN UPPER CANADA

The Commercial Change 1815 obverse of the Starr & Shannon token, NS-12, becomes the reverse of UC-8 and was mated with the Sloop obverse to produce this halfpenny token of Upper Canada.

Composition: Copper
Weight: 5.8 to 6.5 g
Diameter: 27.1 to 27.4 mm
Die Axis: ↑↑, ↑↓
Edge: Reeded
Ref.Nos.: See below

Varieties: Obverse, Die axis
   A1 Bowsprit points above final "A" in CANADA, Coinage; Lr 688 (R-5); McL 22, W 820
   A2 Bowsprit points between "DA" of CANADA, ↑↑; Br 726 (R-2); Lr 683 (R-4); Mc 21; W 819

Cat.No.	Date	Description	VG-8	F-12	VF-20	EF-40	AU-50	AU-55	MS-60
UC-8A1	1815	Points to final "A", ↑↑	45.	85.	300.	—	—	—	—
UC-8A2	1815	Points between "DA", ↑↓	55.	100.	375.	—	—	—	—

24
25

UC-9

COMMERCIAL CHANGE 1820 —
HALFPENNY TOKEN UPPER CANADA

Composition: Copper
Weight: 6.4 to 6.7 g
Diameter: 27.2 to 27.7 mm
Die Axis: ↑↑, ↑↓
Edge: Reeded ⫴⫴
Ref.Nos.: Br 727 (R-1); See below

| Bowsprit points to "A" (A1) | Bowsprit points between "DA" (A2 and A3) | Bowsprit points above "A" (A4) |

Varieties: Obverse, Die axis
   A1 Bowsprit points to final "A" in CANADA, Coinage; Mc 12; W 810
   A2 Bowsprit points between "DA" of CANADA, Medal; Lr 684 (R-3);
       Mc 13; W 811
   A3 Bowsprit points between "DA" of Canada, Coinage; Lr 684 (R-3);
       Mc 13; W 811
   A4 Bowsprit points above final "A" of Canada; Lr 689 (R-3); Mc 14-16;
       W 812-814

Variations: Variety UC-9A4 has minor reverse variations including differences in the
       size of the shovel handle and double punching of the 2nd and 3rd "C" in
       reverse legend. It was struck with rusted obverse dies.

Cat.No.	Date	Description	VG-8	F-12	VF-20	EF-40	AU-50	AU-55	MS-60
UC-9A1	1820	Points to final "A", ↑↓	7.	15.	30.	65.	150.	250.	300.
UC-9A2	1820	Points between "DA", ↑↑	7.	15.	30.	65.	175.	300.	375.
UC-9A3	1820	Points between "DA", ↑↓	7.	15.	30.	65.	175.	300.	375.
UC-9A4	1820	Points above final "A"	7.	15.	30.	65.	175.	300.	375.

[Handwritten annotations in margins:]
-6   27   28   30
SHOVEL HANDLE BELOW "C" IN "COMMERCE"
29 - SHOVEL HANDLE BETWEEN "R & C" → - 9A4a
31
‖‖

UC-10

COMMERCIAL CHANGE 1821 —
HALFPENNY TOKEN UPPER CANADA

CASK MARKED — *UPPER CANADA*

Composition: Copper
Weight: 6.0 to 6.5 g
Diameter: 27.1 to 27.3 mm
Die Axis: ↑↑
Edge: Reeded
Ref.Nos.: Br 728 (R-2½);
Lr 685 (R-4); Mc 17;
W 815

Cat.No.	Date	Description	VG-8	F-12	VF-20	EF-40	AU-50	AU-55	MS-60
UC-10	1821	Upper Canada	85.	150.	275.	500.	675.	—	—

32

UC-11

COMMERCIAL CHANGE 1821 —
HALFPENNY TOKEN UPPER CANADA

CASK MARKED — *JAMAICA*

Composition: Copper
Weight: 6.4 to 6.5 g
Diameter: 27.2 to 27.6 mm
Die Axis: ↑↑
Edge: Reeded
Ref.Nos.: Br 729 (R-4);
Lr 686 (R-5); Mc 18;
W 816

Cat.No.	Date	Description	AG	G-4	VG-8	F-12	VF-20
UC-11	1821	Jamaica	—	400.	800.	1,500.	2,500.

33

UC-12　　　　*TO FACILITATE TRADE 1823/1833 —*
　　　　　　　HALFPENNY TOKEN UPPER CANADA

UC-12A　　　　　*TO FACILITATE TRADE 1823 —*

Composition: Copper
Weight: 6.5 g
Diameter: 27.2 to 27.6 mm
Die Axis: ↑↑, ↑↓
Edge: Reeded
Ref.Nos.: See below

Bowsprit points between　　　　　Bowsprit points above "A" **(A2)**
"DA" of CANADA **(A1)**

Varieties: Obverse, Reverse, Die Axis
　　A1 Bowsprit points between "DA" of CANADA, Medal; Br 730 (R-1½);
　　　　Lr 687 (R-4); Mc 19; W 817
　　A2 Bowsprit points above final "A", Coinage; Lr 690 (R-3); Mc 20; W 818

Cat.No.	Date	Description	VG-8	F-12	VF-20	EF-40	AU-50	AU-55	MS-60
UC-12A1	1823	Between "DA", ↑↑	9.	18.	35.	80.	175.	300.	375.
UC-12A2	1823	Above "A", ↑↓	12.	22.	40.	90.	225.	300.	375.

UC-12B

TO FACILITATE TRADE 1833 —

Composition: Copper
Weight: 6.5 to 7.3 g
Diameter: 27.2 to 27.7 mm
Die Axis: ↑↑, ↑↓
Edge: Reeded
Ref.Nos.: See below

Varieties: Die axis
B1 Bowsprit points between "DA" of CANADA, Medal; Br 730 (R-1);
Lr 687 (R-4); W 821
B2 Bowsprit points above final "A", Coinage; Lr 690 (R-3); Mc 23; W 821

Cat.No.	Date	Description	VG-8	F-12	VF-20	EF-40	AU-50	AU-55	MS-60
UC-12B1	1833	Between "DA", ↑↑	7.	15.	30.	60.	150.	275.	350.
UC-12B2	1833	Above "A", ↑↓	7.	15.	30.	60.	150.	275.	350.

36
37

UC-13

COMMERCIAL CHANGE 1833 —
HALFPENNY TOKEN UPPER CANADA

This piece is attributed to Watkins & Harris, a hardware firm in Toronto.

Composition: Brass
Weight: 4.9 to 5.8 g
Diameter: 27.6 to 27.9 mm
Die Axis: ↑↓
Edge: Plain
Ref.Nos.: Br 731 (R-1);
Lr 691 (R-4); Mc 24

Cat.No.	Date	Description	VG-8	F-12	VF-20	EF-40	AU-50	AU-55	MS-60
UC-13	1833	Plain	12.	22.	45.	125.	275.	350.	425.

38

UC-14

HALFPENNY TOKEN 1832 —
PROVINCE OF UPPER CANADA

This token was procured by John Walker & Co. of Birmingham, and incorrectly bears the bust of George IV that was used by this firm for the 1832 coinage of Nova Scotia. It is not known whether this token is semi-regal or private.

Composition: Copper
Weight: 8.6 g
Diameter: 28.1 to 28.3 mm
Die Axis: ↑↓
Edge: Engrailed 🖾
Ref.Nos.: Br 732 (R-1½);
Lr 692 (R-4); Mc 32;
W 831

Cat.No.	Date	Description	VG-8	F-12	VF-20	EF-40	AU-50	AU-55	MS-60
UC-14	1832	Engrailed	15.	30.	55.	185.	600.	—	—

39

IMITATIONS OF UPPER CANADA TOKENS, "BLACKSMITH STYLE"

For the listings of imitations of Upper Canada Tokens see page No. 229; Cat. Nos. BL-49 and BL-50.

TOKENS OF THE PROVINCE OF CANADA

The rebellions of 1837 in Upper and Lower Canada forced the British government to pay closer attention to conditions in the Canadian colonies. In 1838 Lord Durham was sent out as Governor-in-Chief to inquire into the causes of the revolt and to recommend steps to be taken to ensure that such a breach of the peace would not recur. Among his recommendations was the union of Upper and Lower Canada. Union took place in 1841.

The currency was one of the first problems to be dealt with by the new government. In 1841 a new Currency Act superseded the previous currency legislation of both colonies.

In 1857 the decimal system was adopted and took effect at the beginning of the following year. Decimal coins were in use before the end of 1858.

For decimal coins of Canada see the Charlton Standard Catalogue of Canadian Coins.

BRETON CROSS REFERENCE TABLE FOR PROVINCE OF CANADA TOKENS

Breton Cat. No.	Charlton Cat. No.	Page No.	Breton Cat. No.	Charlton Cat. No.	Page No.
526	PC-2B	190	529	PC-3	191
527	PC-1A-C	187-189	719	PC-6A-D	194-196
528	PC-4	191	720	PC-5A-D	192-194

SEMI-REGAL TOKENS

BANK OF MONTREAL FRONT VIEW TOKENS

In 1842, after Upper and Lower Canada were united as the Province of Canada, the Bank of Montreal was permitted to import 5,000 Pounds Sterling in copper provided that the entire amount was imported before 1845. The Bank issued 1,000 Pounds in pennies and 1,000 Pounds in halfpennies in 1842, 2,000 Pounds in halfpennies in 1844, and 1,000 Pounds in 1845.

The halfpennies issued in 1845 are all dated 1844. The Bank was permitted to issue another 1,200 Pounds in copper in 1845 but did not do so. Dies dated 1845 were prepared but only two halfpennies are known. Proofs exist and are very rare.

PC-1 *BANK TOKEN HALF PENNY 1842/1844/1845 —*
PROVINCE OF CANADA BANK OF MONTREAL

PC-1A *HALFPENNY DATED 1842 BANK OF MONTREAL ON RIBBON*

Composition: Copper
Weight: 9.2 to 9.5 g
Diameter: 28.2 to 28.6 mm
Die Axis: ↑↑
Edge: Plain
Ref.Nos.: Br 527 (R-1);
Lr 516 (R-3);
McL 118-119;
See below

Short nose beaver
(A1, A2 and A3)

Varieties: Obverse, Reverse
A1 1842, Tall trees, Short nose beaver; Co 40BM; W 851
A2 1842, Heavy trees, Short nose beaver; Co 46BM; W 854
A3 1842, Small trees, Short nose beaver; Co 64 and 65BM; W 857

Variations: There are variations in this series caused by the deterioration and reworking of the dies. Courteau gave numbers to die breaks as well as weak areas in the legend and design.

Note: For illustrations of the trees and the long nose beaver see page 188.

Cat.No.	Date	Description	VG-8	F-12	VF-20	EF-40	AU-50	AU-55	MS-60
PC-1A1	1842	Tall trees	175.	250.	400.	—	—	—	—
PC-1A2	1842	Heavy trees	8.	18.	22.	45.	125.	200.	250.
PC-1A3	1842	Small trees	8.	18.	22.	45.	125.	200.	250.

PC-1B HALFPENNY DATED 1844 BANK OF MONTREAL ON RIBBON

Composition: Copper
Weight: 9.4 to 9.5 g
Diameter: 28.2 to 28.7 mm
Die Axis: ↑↑
Edge: Plain
Ref.Nos.: Br 527 (R-1);
Lr 516 (R-3);
McL 118-119;
See below

Tall trees **(B1 and B2)**

Heavy trees **B3 anad B4)**

Small trees **(B5 and B6)**

Long nose beaver
(B2, B4 and B6)

Varieties: Obverse and reverse
B1 Tall trees, Short nose beaver, Co 42-45BM; W 852
B2 Tall trees, Long nose beaver, Co 41BM; W 853
B3 Heavy trees, Short nose beaver, Co 54-63BM; W 855
B4 Heavy trees, Long nose beaver, Co 47-53BM; W 856
B5 Small trees, Short nose beaver, Co 69-70BM; W 858
B6 Small trees, Long nose beaver, Co 66-68BM; W 859

Note: For illustrations of short nose beaver see page 187. For heavy trees, Courteau states "There is a short line from the base of the left fence running upwards."

Cat.No.	Date	Description	VG-8	F-12	VF-20	EF-40	AU-50	AU-55	MS-60
PC-1B1	1844	Tall trees, Short nose	6.	9.	15.	40.	125.	225.	300.
PC-1B2	1844	Tall trees, Long nose	7.	10.	18.	45.	150.	300.	375.
PC-1B3	1844	Heavy trees, Short nose	5.	7.	12.	35.	100.	225.	300.
PC-1B4	1844	Heavy trees, Long nose	5.	7.	15.	40.	100.	225.	300.
PC-1B5	1844	Small trees, Short nose	6.	9.	15.	40.	125.	225.	325.
PC-1B6	1844	Small trees, Long nose	7.	10.	18.	45.	125.	300.	375.

PC-1C   *HALFPENNY DATED 1845 BANK OF MONTREAL ON RIBBON*

Composition: Copper
Weight: 9.5 g
Diameter: 28.7 mm
Die Axis: ↑↑
Edge: Plain
Ref Nos.: Br 527 (R-5);
       Lr 516 (R-8);
       McL 118-119; W 860

Cat.No.	Date	Description	AG	G-4	VG-8	F-12	VF-20
PC-1C1	1845	Halfpenny		Only two known. Extremely rare.			

PC-2   **BANK TOKEN ONE PENNY 1837/1842**
                  PROVINCE OF CANADA BANK OF MONTREAL

PC-2A   *ONE PENNY DATED 1837 CITY BANK ON RIBBON*

    This token has long been considered a mule of the 1842 and the 1837 one penny tokens, having the 1842 obverse of PC-2B (Br 526) and the reverse of LC-9A (Br 521). It was believed by Courteau that PC-2A1 was issued in early 1842, prior to the release of the 1842 (PC-2B) pennies. It is not a mule of the 1842/1837 penny as the obverse die is different from the 1842 obverse die used to mint PC-2B.

    PC-2A1 was possibly struck by W. J. Taylor from the Soho Mint dies.

Composition: Copper
Weight: See below
Diameter: 34.0 mm

Die Axis: ↑↑, ↑↓
Edge: Plain
Ref.Nos.: Co 88BM; Lr 514a (R-6);
       McL 111; W G13

Varieties: Composition
    A1   Weight — 16.1 to 18.9 g; Die axis — Medal; Regular size flan
    A2   Weight — 23.0 to 24.0 g; Die axis — Coinage; Thick flan

Variations: Specimens are known in brass and nickel. They are extremely rare.

Cat.No.	Date	Description	VG-8	F-12	VF-20	EF-40	AU-50	AU-55	MS-60
PC-2A1	(1842)	Copper, ↑↑	165.	225.	275.	400.	500.	700.	875.
PC-2A2	(1870)	Copper, ↑↓, (Taylor)	—	—	—	—	—	1,000.	1,500.

Note: A Taylor example was sold during 2003 in an Ebay auction. It was listed and and certified as silver plated.

PC-2B   ONE PENNY DATED 1842 BANK OF MONTREAL ON RIBBON

Composition: Copper
Weight: 17.7 to 18.9 g
Diameter: 34.0 mm

Die Axis: ↑↑
Edge: Plain
Ref.Nos.: Br 526 (R-2);
        Co 71-87BM; Lr 515 (R-4);
        McL 117; W 861-872

Variations: Extensive varieties exist, caused by the retouching of dies.
        Proofs exist but are very rare.

Cat.No.	Date	Description	VG-8	F-12	VF-20	EF-40	AU-50	AU-55	MS-60
PC-2B	1842	Penny	7.	12.	30.	55.	150.	275.	375.

QUEBEC BANK TOKENS

In 1851 the Quebec Bank asked for permission to import copper because of its shortage in Quebec. This and a further request were refused because the Bank of Upper Canada had already agreed to land some of its copper coinage of 1850 at Quebec. A third request was granted because the promised copper landed at Quebec late and in insufficient amounts.

The tokens were struck by Ralph Heaton & Co. from designs probably suggested by the Quebec Bank but it is not known who cut the dies.

PC-3 *QUEBEC BANK TOKEN HALF PENNY 1852 —*
PROVINCE DU CANADA UN SOU

Composition: Copper
Weight: 9.5 to 9.8 g
Diameter: 28.3 to 28.4 mm
Die Axis: ↑↑
Edge: Plain
Ref.Nos.: Br 529 (R-1);
Co 5-5hH;
Lr 533 (R-3); McL 124;
W 873-876

Variations: Minor varieties exist caused by retouching of the dies.
Proofs exist but are very rare.

Cat.No.	Date	Description	VG-8	F-12	VF-20	EF-40	AU-50	AU-55	MS-60
PC-3	1852	Half Penny	5.	8.	18.	45.	125.	225.	300.

PC-4 *QUEBEC BANK TOKEN ONE PENNY 1852 —*
PROVINCE DU CANADA DEUX SOUS

Composition: Copper
Weight: 18.8 to 19.3 g
Diameter: 34.1 to 34.2 mm

Die Axis: ↑↑
Edge: Plain
Ref.Nos.: Br 528 (R-1); Co 15fH;
Lr 532 (R-3); McL 123;
W 877, 878

Variations: Minor variations exist caused by the retouching of dies.
Proofs exist but are very rare.

Cat.No.	Date	Description	VG-8	F-12	VF-20	EF-40	AU-50	AU-55	MS-60
PC-4	1852	Penny	7.	12.	30.	55.	200.	325.	425.

BANK OF UPPER CANADA TOKENS

The Bank of Upper Canada was organized at York in 1820, usurping the charter of a Kingston institution of the same name which never actually started up.

As the instrument of the Family Compact, the bank steadily opposed the chartering of other banks and dominated the government to the extent of effectively retarding the development of banking in Upper Canada. This situation abruptly changed after 1839 and with the union of Upper and Lower Canada in 1841 the monopoly was broken and the government deposits transferred to Montreal.

Toronto became the capital of Canada in 1849 when the government withdrew from Montreal after the serious riots when the "Rebellion Losses Bill" was passed. The Bank of Upper Canada received government deposits and the right to import copper.

The orders were placed through Rowe, Kentish & Co. of London whose initials appear on the token. The tokens of 1850 were struck at the Royal Mint but did not arrive in Canada until 1851. The Royal Mint also began the coinage of 1852 but was unable to complete the order and contracted the work to Ralph Heaton & Co. of Birmingham. The strikings of the Royal Mint have straight (medal) reverses; the Heaton strikings have upset reverses. The coinages of 1854 and 1857 are the work of the Heaton Mint. The design was suggested by the bank. The dies were cut by John Pinches. Courteau has listed over 300 minor varieties of this token.

PC-5   *BANK TOKEN ONE HALF-PENNY 1850/1852/1854/1857 —*
BANK OF UPPER CANADA

PC-5A   *ONE HALF-PENNY DATED 1850*

Composition: Copper
Weight: 7.9 g
Diameter: 27.6 to 27.9 mm
Die Axis: ↑↑
Edge: Plain
Ref.Nos.: Br 720 (R-0);
          Co 1-75UC;
          Lr 695 (R-3); W 879

Note: Proofs exist but are very rare.

Cat.No.	Date	Description	VG-8	F-12	VF-20	EF-40	AU-50	AU-55	MS-60
PC-5A	1850	Half-penny	5.	7.	10.	20.	75.	175.	225.

PC-5B   **ONE HALF–PENNY DATED 1852**

Composition: Copper
Weight: 7.9 to 8.3 g
Diameter: 27.6 to 27.9 mm
Die Axis: ↑↑, ↑↓
Edge: Plain
Ref.Nos.: Br 720 (R-0);
           Lr 695 (R-3); W 879

Varieties: Die Axis
     B1 Royal Mint, Medal; Co 89-110UC
     B2 Heaton Mint, Coinage; Co 76-88UC

Cat.No.	Date	Description	VG-8	F-12	VF-20	EF-40	AU-50	AU-55	MS-60
PC-5B1	1852	Royal Mint, Medal	5.	7.	10.	20.	75.	175.	225.
PC-5B2	1852	Heaton Mint, Coinage	5.	7.	10.	20.	75.	175.	225.

PC-5C   **ONE HALF–PENNY DATED 1854**

Composition: Copper
Weight: 7.9 to 8.4 g
Diameter: 27.6 to 27.9 mm
Die Axis: ↑↓
Edge: Plain
Ref.Nos.: See below

     Plain "4" **(C1)**   Crosslet "4" **(C2)**

Varieties: Obverse
     C1 Plain "4"; Br 720 (R-0); Co 111-113, 115-158UC; Lr 695 (R-3);
         W 879
     C2 Crosslet "4"; Br 720 (R-1½); Co 114UC; Lr 695 (R-4); W 879

Cat.No.	Date	Description	VG-8	F-12	VF-20	EF-40	AU-50	AU-55	MS-60
PC-5C1	1854	Plain "4"	5.	7.	10.	20.	75.	175.	225.
PC-5C2	1854	Crosslet "4"	18.	30.	45.	90.	200.	300.	375.

PC-5D ONE HALF–PENNY DATED 1857

Composition: Copper
Weight: 7.9 to 8.5 g
Diameter: 27.6 to 27.9 mm
Die Axis: ↑↓
Edge: Plain
Ref.Nos.: Br 720 (R-0);
Co 159-207UC;
Lr 695 (R-3); W 879

Cat.No.	Date	Description	VG-8	F-12	VF-20	EF-40	AU-50	AU-55	MS-60
PC-5D	1857	Halfpenny	5.	6.	10.	18.	75.	150.	200.

PC-6 BANK TOKEN ONE PENNY 1850/1852/1854/1857 —
BANK OF UPPER CANADA

PC-6A ONE PENNY DATED 1850

Composition: Copper
Weight: 15.6 to 15.8 g
Diameter: 33.0 to 33.3 mm

Die Axis: ↑↑
Edge: Plain
Ref.Nos.: Br 719 (R-0); Lr 693 (R-3);
W 880

Without dot (**A1**)   With dot (**A2**)

Varieties: Reverse
A1 Without dot between tips of cornucopia; Co 208-218, 220-232UC
A2 With dot between tips of cornucopia; Co 219, 233UC

Cat.No.	Date	Description	VG-8	F-12	VF-20	EF-40	AU-50	AU-55	MS-60
PC-6A1	1850	Without dot	6.	12.	18.	30.	95.	175.	250.
PC-6A2	1850	With dot	7.	15.	30.	55.	150.	275.	375.

PC-6B   **ONE PENNY DATED 1852**

Composition: Copper
Weight: 15.5 to 15.8 g
Diameter: 33.1 to 33.3 mm

Die Axis: ↑↑, ↑↓
Edge: Plain
Ref.Nos.: Br 719 (R-0); Lr 693 (R-3);
W 880; See below

   **Royal Mint**

Small "2" (**B1**)   Large "2" (**B2**)

Wide "2" (**B3**)

   **Heaton Mint**

Narrow "2" (**B4**)   Large "2" (**B5**)

Varieties: Obverse, Die axis
B1 Small "2", Royal Mint, Medal; Co 234-236UC
B2 Large "2", Royal Mint, Medal; Co 242-246
B3 Wide "2", Royal Mint, Medal; Co 254-257UC
B4 Narrow "2", Heaton Mint, Coinage; Co 237-241UC
B5 Large "2", Heaton Mint, Coinage; Co 247, top of 2 is recut;
248-253UC

Note: Proofs exist and are very rare.

Cat.No.	Date	Description	VG-8	F-12	VF-20	EF-40	AU-50	AU-55	MS-60
PC-6B1	1852	Small "2", Royal, ↑↑	6.	8.	15.	35.	100.	150.	200.
PC-6B2	1852	Large "2", Royal, ↑↑	6.	8.	15.	35.	100.	150.	200.
PC-6B3	1852	Wide "2", Royal, ↑↑	6.	8.	15.	35.	100.	150.	200.
PC-6B4	1852	Narrow "2", Heaton, ↑↓	5.	7.	12.	30.	75.	150.	200.
PC-6B5	1852	Large "2", Heaton, ↑↓	5.	7.	12.	30.	75.	150.	200.

PC-6C   *ONE PENNY DATED 1854*

Composition: Copper
Weight: 15.8 to 16.0 g
Diameter: 33.1 to 33.4 mm

Die Axis: ↑↓
Edge: Plain
Ref.Nos.: W 880

Plain "4" (**C1**)   Crosslet "4" (**C2**)

Varieties: Obverse
    C1   Plain "4"; Br 719 (R-0); Co 258-273UC; Lr 693 (R-3); W 880
    C2   Crosslet "4"; Br 719 (R-1); Co 274UC; Lr 694 (R-3)

Cat.No.	Date	Description	VG-8	F-12	VF-20	EF-40	AU-50	AU-55	MS-60
PC-6C1	1854	Plain "4"	5.	7.	12.	35.	95.	150.	200.
PC-6C2	1854	Crosslet "4"	12.	18.	35.	65.	150.	250.	300.

PC-6D   *ONE PENNY DATED 1857*

Composition: Copper
Weight: 15.8 to 16.0 g
Diameter: 33.1 to 33.3 mm

Die Axis: ↑↓
Edge: Plain
Ref.Nos.: Br 719 (R-0);
            Co 275-319UC;
            Lr 693 (R-3); W 880

Cat.No.	Date	Description	VG-8	F-12	VF-20	EF-40	AU-50	AU-55	MS-60
PC-6D	1857	Penny	5.	7.	15.	22.	75.	150.	200.

ANONYMOUS AND MISCELLANEOUS TOKENS

Most tokens listed by the early numismatists as anonymous or miscellaneous are now attributed to specific colonies, provinces, or geographical regions. Only those yet to be assigned to some definite locale are listed here. Most are of English or Irish origin, having circulated elsewhere before being imported for use in Canada. Some may have been imported by collectors because their legends carried messages common to other issues.

BRETON CROSS REFERENCE TABLE FOR ANONYMOUS AND MISCELLANEOUS TOKENS

Breton Cat. No.	Charlton Cat. No.	Page No.
966	AM-1	197
975	AM-2	198
983	AM-3	198
1009	AM-4	199
1013	AM-5	199

AM-1

PURE COPPER PREFERABLE TO PAPER HALF PENNY TOKEN — FOR GENERAL ACCOMMODATION

This token was designed and engraved by Thomas Halliday with two of the popular slogans of the day. The obverse legend indicates that the reason for issuing this token was to supply small change for everyday business.

Composition: Copper *8.8*
Weight: 7.4 to 8.6 g
Diameter: 27.2 to 27.3 mm
Die Axis: ↑↑, ↑↓
Edge: Engrailed, plain
Ref.Nos.: Br 966 (R-1); Co 18NL; Lr 791 (R-4); McL 569; W 152

Varieties: Edge, Die axis
A1 Plain, Medal
A2 Plain, Coinage
A3 Engrailed, Coinage
A4 Engrailed, Medal

With Dot — Without Dot

Cat.No.	Description	VG-8	F-12	VF-20	EF-40	AU-50	AU-55	MS-60
AM-1A1	Plain, ↑↑	22.	45.	100.	250.	600.	—	—
AM-1A2	Plain, ↑↓	7.	15.	35.	100.	225.	—	—
AM-1A3	Engrailed, ↑↓	7.	15.	35.	100.	225.	—	—
AM-1A3	Without Dot, Engrailed, ↑↓	7.	15.	35.	100.	225.	—	—
AM-1A4	Engrailed, ↑↑	7.	15.	35.	100.	225.	—	—

AM-2   *FOR PUBLIC ACCOMMODATION ONE PENNY —*
1805 HIBERNIA

This token is an anonymous Irish penny used in Dublin. It was designed by Peter Wyon and was antedated. Small quantities were found in Lower Canada.

Composition: Copper
Weight: 17.9 g
Diameter: 34.7 to 34.8 mm

Die Axis: ↑↓
Edge: Engrailed
Ref.Nos.: Br 975 (R-2½); W C1

Cat.No.	Date	Description	VG-8	F-12	VF-20	EF-40	AU-50	AU-55	MS-60
AM-2	1805	One penny	45.	85.	200.	350.	—	—	—

AM-3   *COMMERCE RULES THE MAIN — 1812 SUCCESS TO TRADE*

This is an anonymous piece with altered legends. "Success to Trade" was punched over "George III Rules" and "Commerce" was punched over Britannia. This piece has been ascribed to Halliday, but the workmanship is inferior to Halliday's.

Composition: Copper
Weight: 6.9 to 7.6 g
Diameter: 28.5 to 28.8 mm

Die Axis: ↑↓
Edge: Plain
Ref.Nos.: Br 983 (R-2); Co 36NL;
         W C5

Cat.No.	Date	Description	VG-8	F-12	VF-20	EF-40	AU-50	AU-55	MS-60
AM-3	1812	Halfpenny	35.	65.	200.	375.	750.	—	—

AM-4   *PURE COPPER PREFERABLE TO PAPER* —

Designed and engraved by Thomas Halliday, this token originally circulated in Ireland and later appeared in British North America. Lower Canada saw numerous pieces circulating and small quantities circulated in the United States.

Composition: Copper
Weight: 6.7 to 7.7 g
Diameter: 27.7 to 28.0 mm
Die Axis: ↑↑
Edge: Reeded
Ref.Nos.: Br 1009 (R-1½);
Co 4NL; Lr 792 (R-4)
W 153

Variations: AM-4 is found on thin or thick flans, resulting in weight variations.

Cat.No.	Description	VG-8	F-12	VF-20	EF-40	AU-50	AU-55	MS-60
AM-4	Halfpenny	12.	22.	55.	125.	300.	425.	525.

AM-5   *COMMERCE — 1781 NORTH AMERICAN TOKEN*

This North American token was struck in Dublin around 1825 and antedated to evade the importation laws. The token was struck without a collar to simulate an earlier token. This piece saw limited circulation in the United States.

Composition: Brass, copper
Weight: 7.7 to 7.8 g
Diameter: 27.6 to 27.8 mm
Die Axis: ↑↑
Edge: Plain
Ref.Nos.: Br 1013 (R-1);
Lr 766 (R-4); McL 544;
W 151; See below

Varieties: Composition
A1 Copper; Co 1NL
A2 Brass; Co 2NL

Cat.No.	Date	Description	VG-8	F-12	VF-20	EF-40	AU-50	AU-55	MS-60
AM-5A1	1781	Copper	45.	85.	175.	325.	—	—	—
AM-5A2	1781	Brass	85.	135.	300.	500.	—	—	—

THE VEXATOR CANADIENSIS TOKENS

These crude pieces are among the world's most interesting tokens. They are a threefold evasion, designed to protect their issuers from prosecution for sedition, forgery and importing private tokens. Their types, a bust and a seated female figure, resembled those of the regal copper closely enough to ensure ready acceptance. The blundered legends were designed to protect the issuers from accusations of forgery and sedition. The obverse legend meant, to those who thought the pieces seditious, "The Tormentor of Canada." The issuers, on the other hand, said that it meant, "A Canadian Trapper." To create this double meaning they deliberately made the third letter vague in form, so it could be read as an X or an N. Combined with the shaggy bust, the inscription could be construed as identifying the pieces as medalets honouring the fur trade. The reverse inscription means, "Wouldn't you like to catch them?" and could allude to fur-bearing animals or to the issuers of the tokens. The inscription's original compositions in Latin testify that the issuers were educated men and probably numismatists well acquainted with the methods employed by the makers of the English Bungtowns to evade similar English laws against forgery. The "1811" is an antedate to evade regulations against the import of private tokens. The coins appeared after 1830 and possibly allude to King William IV as the Tormentor of Canada or to some local governor or obnoxious official whose identity is now forgotten.

BRETON CROSS REFERENCE TABLE FOR VEXATOR CANADIENSIS TOKENS

Breton Cat. No.	Charlton Cat. No.	Page No.	Breton Cat. No.	Charlton Cat. No.	Page No.
558	VC-1, 2	201	559	VC-3	201

VC-1   *VEXATOR CANADINSIS 1811*

Composition: Copper
Weight: 2.9 to 6.5 g
Diameter: 25.9 to 26.1 mm
Die Axis: Variable
Edge: Plain
Ref.Nos.: Br 558 (R-3);
Lr 500 (R-5);
McL 21; W 676

Cat.No.	Date	Description	AG	G-4	VG-8	F-12	VF-20
VC-1	1811	Copper			Extremely Rare		

VC-2   *VEXATOR (OR VENATOR) CANADINSIS 1811*

Composition: Brass, copper
Weight: 2.9 to 6.5 g
Diameter: 25.9 to 26.7 mm
Die Axis: Variable
Edge: Plain
Ref.Nos.: Br 558 (R-3);
Lr 500 (R-5);
McL 21; W 675

Varieties: Composition
A1 Copper
A2 Brass

Cat.No.	Date	Description	AG	G-4	VG-8	F-12	VF-20
VC-2A1	1811	Copper	—	300.	600.	900.	1,350.
VC-2A2	1811	Brass	—	500.	1,000.	2,000.	3,000.

VC-3   *VEXATOR (OR VENATOR) CANADIENSIS ML 1811*

Composition: Brass, copper
Weight: 2.6 to 6.5 g
Diameter: 25.6 to 26.1 mm
Die Axis: Variable
Edge: Plain
Ref.Nos.: Br 559 (R-3);
Lr 501 (R-5);
McL 22; W 677

Varieties: Composition
A1 Copper
A2 Brass

Cat.No.	Date	Description	AG	G-4	VG-8	F-12	VF-20
VC-3A1	1811	Copper	—	300.	600.	900.	1,350.
VC-3A2	1811	Brass			Extremely Rare		

BLACKSMITH TOKENS

About 1835, according to McLachlan, a dissolute blacksmith in Montreal began to make his own halfpennies to pay for liquor. He made counterfeits of the battered, worn-out, old English and Irish regal halfpennies of George III. His dies were purposely left unfinished in order to create the appearance of a badly worn coin. His halfpennies were then artifically darkened, probably by overheating, to create the illusion of age. Only a crude outline of the type was cut, without date or legend.

A peculiarity of these pieces is that the types are almost always reversed because the die-sinkers cut the types on the dies to face the same way as on the coins they used as models. These pieces were accepted in trade because of the almost insatiable demand for small change in Lower Canada at that time, particularly in Montreal.

CROSS REFERENCE FOR BLACKSMITH TOKENS

Charlton Cat. No.	Breton No.	Courteau No.	Lees No.	LeRoux No.	Willey No.	Woods No.	Page No.
BL-1	—	Co 4BT	—	—	629	Wo 1	204
BL-2	—	Co 5, 6BT	—	—	630	Wo 2, 3	204
BL-3	—	Co 7BT	—	—	631	Wo 4	205
BL-4	—	Co 10BT	—	—	632	Wo 5	205
BL-5	—	Co 11BT	—	—	633	Wo 6	206
BL-6	—	Co 8BT	—	—	634	Wo 7, 8	206
BL-7	—	Co 13BT	—	—	635	Wo 11	207
BL-8	—	Co 14BT	—	—	636	Wo 12	207
BL-9	—	Co 15BT	—	—	638	Wo 13	208
BL-10	—	Co 16BT	—	—	637	Wo 14	208
BL-11	—	Co 17BT	—	—	639	Wo 16	209
BL-12	—	Co 18BT	—	—	640	Wo 17	209
BL-13	—	Co 19BT	—	—	641	Wo 18	210
BL-14	—	—	—	—	642	Wo 38	210
BL-15	—	—	—	—	—	—	211
BL-16	—	—	—	—	643	Wo 39	211
BL-17	—	—	—	—	644	Wo 40	212
BL-18	—	—	—	—	645	—	212
BL-19	—	—	—	—	646	—	213
BL-20	—	—	—	—	647	Wo 41	213
BL-21A, B	—	—	—	—	648	Wo 43	214
BL-22	—	—	—	—	—	—	214
BL-23	—	—	—	—	—	—	215
BL-24A	997	—	3	793	655	—	215
BL-24B	997	—	4	793	654	—	216
BL-24C	999	—	5a	793	657	—	216
BL-25	—	Co 9BT	—	—	652	Wo 9	217
BL-26	999	—	5	793	653	Wo 9A	217
BL-28	998	Co 12BT	—	—	656	Wo 10	218
BL-29	—	Co 361a NS	—	—	347	—	219

CROSS REFERENCE FOR BLACKSMITH TOKENS

Charlton Cat. No.	Breton No.	Courteau No.	Lees No.	LeRoux No.	Willey No.	Woods No.	Page No.
BL-30	—	Co 361 NS	—	—	346	—	219
BL-31	—	Co 360 NS	—	—	345	—	220
BL-32	1008	Co 1, 1aBT	—	—	649	Wo 19, 20	220
BL-33	—	Co 2BT	—	—	650	Wo 21	221
BL-34	—	Co 3BT	—	—	651	Wo 22	221
BL-35	1012	Co 25, 26	—	786	603	—	222
BL-36	—	Co 20	—	—	604	—	222
BL-37	—	—	—	—	658	Wo 33	223
BL-38	—	—	—	—	659	Wo 34	223
BL-39	—	—	—	—	660	Wo 35	224
BL-40	—	Co 20BT	—	—	661	Wo 23	224
BL-41	—	Co 21BT	—	—	662	Wo 24	225
BL-42	—	Co 22BT	—	—	665	Wo 25	225
BL-43	—	Co 23BT	—	—	663	Wo 26	226
BL-44	—	Co 24BT	—	—	666	Wo 27	226
BL-45	—	Co 25BT	—	—	667	Wo 28	227
BL-46	—	Co 26BT	—	—	669	—	227
BL-47	—	Co 27BT	—	—	668	Wo 29	228
BL-48	—	Co 28BT	—	—	664	Wo 30	228
BL-49	—	—	—	—	—	Wo 31	229
BL-50	—	—	—	—	—	Wo 45	229
BL-51	—	—	—	—	—	—	230
BL-52	—	—	—	—	—	—	230
BL-53	—	—	—	—	670	Wo 32	231
BL-54	—	—	—	—	671	Wo 44	231
BL-55	—	—	—	—	672	Wo 46	232
BL-56	—	—	—	—	673	Wo 36	232
BL-57	—	—	—	—	674	—	232

BLACKSMITH IMITATIONS OF REGAL COINAGE

BUST OF GEORGE III FACING LEFT

BL-1

OBVERSE: Laureate bust of George III facing left, the chaplet being tied in a double bow with loops of equal size. The ends of the ribbon are thin, the upper one curving upwards and the lower one being nearly straight.

REVERSE: A crude Britannia seated to the right with a spear and spray of leaves copied from the English regal halfpenny of 1770-1775. The bust and lap are prominent.

Composition: Copper
Weight: 6.8 to 7.8 g
Diameter: 27.0 mm
Die Axis: ↑↓
Edge: Plain
Ref.Nos.: Co 4BT; W 629; Wo 1

Cat.No.	Description	AG	G-4	VG-8	F-12	VF-20
BL-1	Copper, ↑↓	—	25.	50.	85.	125.

BL-2

OBVERSE: Laureate bust of George III. Similar to BL-1, but the mouth is slightly open, the Adams apple larger and the shoulder humped. The bow is double with the upper loop larger and both ribbon ends pointing upwards.

REVERSE: Britannia seated to the right, as BL-1, from a worn die.

Composition: Brass, copper
Weight: See below
Diameter: 26.3 to 26.7 mm
Die Axis: ↑↑, ↑↓
Edge: Plain
Ref.Nos.: W 630; See below

Varieties: Composition, Weight
    A1 Copper, Thick flan, Early issue, Wt 6.5 to 9.5 g; Wo 2
    A2 Copper, Thin flan, Late issue, Wt. 3.7 to 4.3 g; Co 5BT; Wo 2
    A3 Brass, Wt 4.2 to 5.7 g; Co 6BT; Wo 3

Variations: With and without rusted reverse dies.

Cat.No.	Description	AG	G-4	VG-8	F-12	VF-20
BL-2A1	Copper, Thick, Early	—	20.	40.	50.	60.
BL-2A2	Copper, Thin, Late	—	20.	40.	50.	60.
BL-2A3	Brass	—	200.	375.	450.	525.

BL-3

OBVERSE: Laureate bust of George III as BL-2.
REVERSE: Britannia seated right is poorly designed, with a small head and a long, thin neck. The bust is prominent and the shield is of a simpler design.

Composition: Copper
Weight: 4.2 to 6.7 g
Diameter: 27.3 mm
Die Axis: ↑↓
Edge: Plain
Ref.Nos.: Co 7BT; W 631; Wo 4

Cat.No.	Description	AG	G-4	VG-8	F-12	VF-20
BL-3	Copper, ↑↓	—	25.	50.	75.	90.

BL-4

OBVERSE: Laureate bust of George III as BL-2.
REVERSE: A harp facing left with ten strings. The die is badly cracked, especially parallel to the body of the harp.

Composition: Copper
Weight: 3.6 to 4.5 g
Diameter: 27.3 mm
Die Axis: ↑↓
Edge: Plain
Ref.Nos.: Co 10BT; W 632; Wo 5

Cat.No.	Description	AG	G-4	VG-8	F-12	VF-20
BL-4	Copper, ↑↓	—	20.	35.	55.	75.

BL-5

OBVERSE: Laureate bust of George III as BL-2.
REVERSE: Similar to BL-4 but the angel has a larger breast. This die broke, producing several flaws.

Composition: Copper
Weight: 4.5 to 7.5 g
Diameter: 26.6 to 26.8 mm
Die Axis: ↑↑, ↑↓
Edge: Plain
Ref.Nos.: BH-30; Co 11BT; W 633; Wo 6

Varieties: Die Axis
   A Coinage
   B Medal

Variation: A brass uniface example of the reverse weighing 3.2 g sold as Lot 2437, Torex Auction, Fall 1989.

Cat.No.	Description	AG	G-4	VG-8	F-12	VF-20
BL-5A	Copper, ↑↓	—	20.	35.	55.	75.
BL-5B	Copper, ↑↑	—	20.	35.	55.	75.

BL-6

OBVERSE: As BL-2 but from a rusted die.
REVERSE: Britannia seated right as on English regal copper of 1797-1807. Fine lines, resembling water, fill the exergue. The die is so badly cracked that the centre of the type is obliterated.

Composition: Brass, copper
Weight: 5.0 to 5.4 g
Diameter: 26.7 mm
Die Axis: ↑↓
Edge: Plain
Ref.Nos.: Co 8BT; W 634; See below

Varieties: Composition
   A1 Copper; Wo 7
   A2 Brass; Wo 8

Variation: A brass uniface example of the reverse exists.

Cat.No.	Description	AG	G-4	VG-8	F-12	VF-20
BL-6A1	Copper, ↑↓	—	100.	175.	250.	375.
BL-6A2	Brass, ↑↓	—	1,500.	2,000.	2,500.	3,000.

BL-7

OBVERSE: Laureate bust of George III similar to BL-1 but the eyebrows are flush with the forehead, the neck merges into the chin and the mouth is more open. The back of the head is incomplete. The loops of the bow are small and the ribbons are of equal length.

REVERSE: A tall, thin Britannia seated right copied from the English regal copper of 1770-1775 with a small shield.

Composition: Copper
Weight: 5.0 to 5.4 g
Diameter: 27.4 mm
Die Axis: ↑↓
Edge: Plain
Ref.Nos.: Co 13BT; W 635; Wo 11

Cat.No.	Description	AG	G-4	VG-8	F-12	VF-20
BL-7	Copper, ↑↓	—	25.	40.	60.	90.

BL-8

OBVERSE: Laureate bust of George III as BL-7.
REVERSE: A harp facing left with seven strings. The die is badly cracked.

Composition: Copper
Weight: 4.6 g
Diameter: 27.2 mm
Die Axis: ↑↓
Edge: Plain
Ref.Nos.: BH-31; Co 14BT;
W 636; Wo 12

Cat.No.	Description	AG	G-4	VG-8	F-12	VF-20
BL-8	Copper, ↑↓	—	20.	30.	45.	60.

BL-9

OBVERSE: A large bust facing left with a long nose and pointed chin. The bow is plain. The cuirass has horizontal lines in front.

REVERSE: A large broad-shouldered Britannia seated right with a short left forearm.

Composition: Brass
Weight: 6.0 to 6.3 g
Diameter: 27.3 mm
Die Axis: ↑↓
Edge: Plain
Ref.Nos.: Co 15BT; W 638; Wo 13

Cat.No.	Description	AG	G-4	VG-8	F-12	VF-20
BL-9	Brass, ↑↓	—	20.	35.	55.	75.

BL-10

OBVERSE: A smaller bust facing left with a pointed chin. The lower loop of the bow is angular.

REVERSE: A headless Britannia seated right with a long, thin forearm. The exergue line runs to the shield.

The existence of the token Wo 15, which Wood listed as having a composition of copper, cannot be confirmed. No example of BL-10 (W14 - Brass) has yet surfaced in copper. Courteau, Mabbott and Baker have not seen copper examples and the coins from Wood's collection that are listed as copper upon closer examination were found to be brass.

Composition: Brass
Weight: 5.9 to 6.3 g
Diameter: 27.0 to 27.2 mm
Die Axis: ↑↓
Edge: Plain
Ref.Nos.: Co 16BT; W 637; Wo 14

Cat.No.	Description	AG	G-4	VG-8	F-12	VF-20
BL-10	Brass, ↑↓	—	25.	40.	60.	90.

BL-11

OBVERSE: Bust facing left with a low forehead, large nose and weak chin. The front of the bust has a double outline. The chaplet has short ribbons.

REVERSE: A small Britannia seated right with a small head and short, well-proportioned arms. The spear shows between the arm and the drapery. The exergue line reaches the shield.

Composition: Brass
Weight: 6.2 g
Diameter: 27.2 mm
Die Axis: ↑↓
Edge: Plain
Ref.Nos.: Co 17BT; W 639;Wo 16

Cat.No.	Description	AG	G-4	VG-8	F-12	VF-20
BL-11	Brass, ↑↓	—	25.	35.	55	75.

BL-12

OBVERSE: Bust facing left with a long neck, strong chin, angular forehead and a thin, pointed nose. The ribbon of the chaplet is tied with a long, slender bow.

REVERSE: As BL-11.

Composition: Brass
Weight: 5.8 to 6.5 g
Diameter: N/A
Edge: Plain
Die Axis: ↑↓
Ref.Nos.: Co 18BT; W 640; Wo 17

Cat.No.	Description	AG	G-4	VG-8	F-12	VF-20
BL-12	Brass, ↑↓	—	200.	300.	450.	600.

BL-13

OBVERSE: Bust facing left as BL-12.

REVERSE: A headless Britannia seated right with thick right arm. The drapery under the right arm is large and angular. The exergue line does not reach the shield.

Composition: Brass
Weight: 6.3 to 6.5 g
Diameter: 27.0 mm
Die Axis: ↑↓
Edge: Plain
Ref.Nos.: Co 19BT; W 641; Wo 18

Cat.No.	Description	AG	G-4	VG-8	F-12	VF-20
BL-13	Brass, ↑↓	—	20.	35.	55.	75.

BUST OF GEORGE III FACING RIGHT

BL-14

OBVERSE: A small, faceless head facing right with a broad truncation.

REVERSE: A crowned harp facing left.

Photograph not
available
at press time

Composition: Brass
Weight: N/A
Diameter: N/A
Die Axis: N/A
Edge: N/A
Ref.Nos.: W 642; Wo 38

Cat.No.	Description	AG	G-4	VG-8	F-12	VF-20
BL-14	Brass		Fewer than five known. Extremely Rare			

BL-15 *ONE PENNY*

OBVERSE: Crude bust facing right.
REVERSE: Britannia seated right, crude attempts at lettering.

Composition: Copper
Weight: 23.8 g
Diameter: 34.4 mm

Die Axis: ↑↑
Edge: Plain
Ref.Nos.: Not previously listed

Cat.No.	Description	AG	G-4	VG-8	F-12	VF-20
BL-15	Copper, ↑↑		Two known. Extremely Rare.			

UNIFACE BLACKSMITH TOKENS

The following tokens in this series are uniface, and while a weight is indicated, the weight between examples will vary greatly. All the tokens in this series are extremely rare.

BL-16

OBVERSE: Head facing left with a protruding tongue and a small cross behind the head.
REVERSE: Blank.

Photograph not
available
at press time

Composition: N/A
Weight: N/A
Diameter: N/A
Die Axis: Uniface
Edge: Plain
Ref.Nos.: W 643; Wo 39

Cat.No.	Description	AG	G-4	VG-8	F-12	VF-20
BL-16	Uniface		Fewer than five know. Extremely Rare.			

BL-17

OBVERSE: Large head facing right with a broad truncation. The back of the head is unfinished.

REVERSE: Blank.

Composition: Copper
Weight: 3.2 g
Diameter: N/A
Die Axis: Uniface
Edge: Plain
Ref.Nos.: W 644; Wo 40

Cat.No.	Description	AG	G-4	VG-8	F-12	VF-20
BL-17	Copper, Uniface	Probably unique. Baker Sale 1987, $4,000.				

BL-18

OBVERSE: Large, incomplete head facing right with a broad truncation. There are two ribbons protruding from the back of the neck. A large dot appears below the head. Not listed by Wood.

REVERSE: Blank.

Composition: Copper
Weight: 3.5 g
Diameter: 27.0 mm
Die Axis: Uniface
Edge: Plain
Ref.Nos.: W 645; Not listed by Wood.

Cat.No.	Description	AG	G-4	VG-8	F-12	VF-20
BL-18	Copper, Uniface	Probably unique. Baker Sale 1987, $1,900.				

BL-19

OBVERSE: Crude laureate bust facing right with a long nose, a pointed chin and a flat truncation. The ribbon of the chaplet has short ends and no bow. Two marks, apparently intended to imitate a badly worn inscription, appear be hind the head at the top.

REVERSE: Blank.

Composition: Copper
Weight: 5.9 g
Diameter: 27.0 mm
Die Axis: Uniface
Edge: Plain
Ref.Nos.: W 646; Not listed by Wood

Cat.No.	Description	AG	G-4	VG-8	F-12	VF-20
BL-19	Copper, Uniface		Two known. Extremely Rare.			

BL-20

OBVERSE: Poorly defined, faceless laureate bust facing left. Two marks which suggest a worn inscription show behind the head in the same relative position as those on BL-19, proving the former to be the prototype of this token.

REVERSE: Blank.

Composition: Copper
Weight: 8.0 g
Diameter: 27.0 mm
Die Axis: Uniface
Edge: Plain
Ref.Nos.: W 647; Wo 41

Cat.No.	Description	AG	G-4	VG-8	F-12	VF-20
BL-20	Copper, Uniface		Probably unique. Baker Sale 1987, $3,350.			

BL-21

BL-21A
OBVERSE: Crudely cut head facing right in a border of large dots.
REVERSE: Blank.

BL21-B
OBVERSE: Crudely cut head facing right in a border of large dots.
REVERSE: Same as obverse.

Composition: Copper
Weight: 5.7 g
Diameter: 26.4 mm
Die Axis: Uniface, ↑↑, ↑↓
Edge: Plain
Ref.Nos.: W 648; Wo 43

Varieties: Die Axis
   A Uniface
   B Medal or Coinage

Cat.No.	Description	AG	G-4	VG-8	F-12	VF-20
BL-21A	Blank reverse		Extremely Rare.			
BL-21B	Head / Head	—	1,000.	2,000.	3,000.	—

BL-22

OBVERSE: Tall thin bust facing right.
REVERSE: Blank.

Composition: Copper
Weight: 3.43 g
Diameter: 27.0 mm
Die Axis: Uniface
Edge: Plain
Ref.Nos.: Not previously listed.

Cat.No.	Description	AG	G-4	VG-8	F-12	VF-20
BL-22	Copper, Uniface	—	500.	1,000.	1,500.	—

BL-23

OBVERSE: Horned bust facing left.
REVERSE: Blank.

Composition: Copper
Weight: 4.48 g
Diameter: 27.0 mm
Die Axis: Uniface
Edge: Plain
Ref.Nos.: Not previously listed.

Cat.No.	Description	AG	G-4	VG-8	F-12	VF-20
BL-23	Copper, Uniface	—	1,500.	2,000.	2,500.	—

BL-24   BLACKSMITH IMITATIONS OF SHIPS COLONIES AND COMMERCE TOKENS

This section of the Ships, Colonies and Commerce Tokens derives its title from the crude workmanship of this series. Because these tokens vary in fabric and weight it is impossible to attribute them to any one minter.

Refer to page 22 for cross listings of BL-24, 25 and 26.

BL-24A   SHIPS COLONIES & COMMERCE — (SAILING SHIP DESIGN)

OBVERSE: A frigate sailing to the right flying an ensign drooping almost to the deck.
REVERSE: SHIPS COLONIES & COMMERCE in four lines. The first "S" in SHIPS is over the first "O" in COLONIES. Beading occurs on the obverse and reverse rims.

Composition: Copper
Weight: See below
Diameter: 26.0 to 26.9 mm
Die Axis: ↑↑, ↑↓
Edge: Plain
Ref.Nos.: Br 997 (R-0); Lees 3;
Lr 793 (R-2); W 655;

Varieties: Weight, Die axis
   A1 Weight 6.9 to 7.9 g, Medal
   A2 Weight 4.2 to 4.7 g, Coinage, Medal
   A3 Weight 2.9 to 3.5 g, Coinage
   A4 Weight 2.9 to 3.2 g, Medal

Cat.No.	Description	AG	G-4	VG-8	F-12	VF-20
BL-24A1	Copper, Thick, ↑↑	25.	50.	100.	225.	450.
BL-24A2	Copper, Thin, ↑↓, ↑↑	50.	100.	150.	300.	550.
BL-24A3	Copper, Thin, ↑↓	50.	100.	150.	300.	550.
BL-24A4	Copper, Thin, ↑↑			Rare		

BL-24B   *SHIPS COLONIES & COMMERCE — (SAILING SHIP DESIGN)*

OBVERSE: A frigate sailing to the right flying an ensign drooping almost to the deck. Beading is found on the obverse rim only.

REVERSE: Similar to BL-24A but a flaw usually showing over the "P" of SHIPS. No beading.

Composition: Copper
Weight: 2.4 g
Diameter: N/A
Die Axis: ↑↓
Edge: Plain
Ref.Nos.: Br 997 (R-0); Lees 4; Lr 793 (R-2); W 654

Cat.No.	Description	AG	G-4	VG-8	F-12	VF-20
BL-24B	Copper, ↑↓	1,000.	1,350.	1,800.	3,000.	4,000.

BL-24C   *SHIPS COLONIES & COMMERCE — (SAILING SHIP DESIGN)*

Composition: Copper
Weight: 5.0 to 7.0 g
Diameter: 26.5 mm
Die Axis: Variable
Edge: Plain
Ref.Nos.: Br 999 (R-0); Lees 5A; Lr 793 (R-2); W 657

OBVERSE: A frigate sailing to the right with a short hull curving up to the top of a very high poopdeck. The prow joins the deckrail and the lower part of the open sprit sail joins the hull. The mainmast has no staysail. The ensign is wide with three hollows at the top and flies from a flagstaff set well forward of the stern. The flagstaff is double-cut near the deck and extends high above the ensign. The exergue is small with pointed lines. The border is of straight, square-ended teeth. No obverse beading

REVERSE: SHIPS COLONIES & COMMERCE in four lines of crude lettering, unevenly spaced and misaligned, and varying in size. The ampersand has a thick, blunt upper end. The border is finely saw-toothed. Struck on thin or thick. No reverse beading.

Note: For Lees No. 5 see BL-26 page 217.

Cat.No.	Description	AG	G-4	VG-8	F-12	VF-20
BL-24C	Copper, Variable die axis	J. Hoare Auction, February 1995, Lot 1858, VF - $4,800.				

BL-25 *(SAILING SHIP DESIGN) — (LAUREATE BUST DESIGN)*

OBVERSE: Laureate bust of George III, as BL-1.

REVERSE: A frigate sailing to the right flying a straight, rectangular pennant from the mainmast, with no square hollow next to the mast. There are no balls where the guys join the mainmast and the balls of the other masts are small. A short spike projects from the stern and the afterbrace of the mizzenmast joins the flagstaff. The ensign droops slightly. Similar to BL-24A, B.

Photograph not
available
at press time

Composition: Copper
Weight: 3.6 to 3.9 g
Diameter: N/A
Die Axis: ↑↓
Edge: Plain
Ref.Nos.: Co 9BT; W 652; Wo 9

Cat.No.	Description	AG	G-4	VG-8	F-12	VF-20
BL-25	Copper, ↑↓		Fewer than five known. Extremely Rare.			

BL-26 *SHIPS COLONIES & COMMERCE — (SHIP DESIGN)*

OBVERSE: A frigate sailing to the right flying a straight, rectangular pennant from the mainmast, with no square hollow next to the mast. There are no balls where the guys join the mainmast and the balls of the other masts are small. A short spike projects from the stern and the afterbrace of the mizzenmast joins the flagstaff. The ensign droops slightly. As BL-25.

REVERSE: SHIPS COLONIES & COMMERCE in four lines. The first "S" in SHIPS a little to the right of the first "O" in COLONIES.

Composition: Copper
Weight: 3.6 to 3.9 g
Diameter: N/A
Die Axis: ↑↓
Edge: Plain
Ref.Nos.: Br 999 (R-4); Lees 5; Lr 793 (R-2); W 653; Wo 9a

Cat.No.	Description	AG	G-4	VG-8	F-12	VF-20
BL-26	Copper, ↑↓	1,250.	1,750.	2,500.	3,500.	4,500.

BL-27   *NO LISTING*

BL-28   *SHIPS COLONIES & COMMERCE — (HARP DESIGN)*

OBVERSE: Similar to the reverse of BL-4, a harp facing left. From a badly cracked die.
REVERSE: Similar BL-24B. Struck on thick or thin flans.

Composition: Copper
Weight: 3.3 to 6.5 g
Diameter: 26.4 mm
Die Axis: ↑↑
Edge: Plain
Ref.Nos.: Br 998 (R-3); Co 12BT;
               W 656; Wo 10

Varieties: Flans
        A1 Thick flan, Weight 6.5 g
        A2 Thin flan, Weight 3.3 to 3.7 g

Cat.No.	Description	AG	G-4	VG-8	F-12	VF-20
BL-28A1	Copper, Thick flan	—	250.	500.	750.	—
BL-28A2	Copper, Thin flan	—	250.	500.	750.	—

BLACKSMITH IMITATIONS OF NOVA SCOTIA TOKENS

Towards the end of the period of private tokens in Nova Scotia, John Brown, and possibly others, had recourse to an anonymous manufacturer and issued halfpenny tokens of crude fabric on thin flans.

BL-29   *(HARP DESIGN)* —
HALF PENNY TOKEN (BUST OF GEORGE III)

OBVERSE: Laureate bust of George III facing right. Crudely fashioned.
REVERSE: Crowned harp, facing left, within a wreath.

Composition: Copper
Weight: 3.7 g
Diameter: 24.5 mm
Die Axis: ↑↓
Edge: Plain
Ref.Nos.: Co 361aNS; W 347

Cat.No.	Description	AG	G-4	VG-8	F-12	VF-20
BL-29	Copper, ↑↓		Only four known. Extremely Rare.			

BL-30   *(HARP DESIGN)* — *HALFPENNY (WAREHOUSE DESIGN)*

OBVERSE: Warehouse building.
REVERSE: Crowned harp facing left, within a wreath, as BL-29.

Photograph not
available
at press time

Composition: Copper
Weight: 5.2 g
Diameter: N/A
Die Axis: N/A
Edge: Plain
Ref.Nos.: Co 361NS; W 346

Cat.No.	Description	AG	G-4	VG-8	F-12	VF-20
BL-30	Copper			Extremely Rare.		

BL-31   *JB (SCRIPT INITIALS)—*
                  HALFPENNY (WAREHOUSE DESIGN)

OBVERSE: Warehouse building, as BL-30.
REVERSE: Script letters "JB."

Composition: Copper
Weight: 4.1 to 4.2 g
Diameter: 28.5 mm
Die Axis: ↑→
Edge: Plain
Ref.Nos.: Co 360NS; W 345

Cat.No.	Description	VG-8	F-12	VF-20	EF-40	AU-50	AU-55	MS-60
BL-31	Copper, ↑→	750.	1,250.	1,750.	2,500.	4,000.	—	—

BLACKSMITH IMITATIONS OF "TIFFIN" TOKENS

BL-32   *(COMMERCE SEATED) 1820 — (BUST DESIGN)*

OBVERSE: Laureate bust facing right, with an aquiline nose, a long, pointed chin and
a broad truncation. Three tufts of hair stand on the head. Ribbon ends
curve outward.
REVERSE: Commerce, with cornucopia and scales, seated left on a bale. Dated
1820.

Composition: Brass, copper
Weight: 4.3 to 5.5 g
Diameter: 26.7 to 27.6 mm
Die Axis: ↑↑, ↑↓
Edge: Plain
Ref.Nos.: Br 1008 (R-4); W 649;
                  See below

Varieties: Composition, Die axis
A1 Copper, Medal, Coinage; Co 1BT; Wo 19
A2 Brass, Coinage; Co 1aBT; Wo 20

Cat.No.	Date	Description	AG	G-4	VG-8	EF-40	F-12	VF-20
BL-32A1	1820	Copper, ↑↑, ↑↓	—	—	500.	1,000	1,500.	2,500.
BL-32A2	1820	Brass, ↑↓	—	—	750.	1,500.	2,000.	3,000.

BL-33

OBVERSE: Bust facing right, small nose and weak chin. Ribbon ends point inward.
REVERSE: As BL-32.

Composition: Copper
Weight: 4.2 g
Diameter: 26.0 mm
Die Axis: ↑→
Edge: Plain
Ref.Nos.: Co 2BT; W 650; Wo 21

Cat.No.	Date	Description	AG	G-4	VG-8	F-12	VF-20
BL-33	1820	Copper, ↑→		Unique. Baker Sale 1987, $6,850.			

BLACKSMITH IMITATIONS OF "BUST AND HARP" TOKENS

BL-34

OBVERSE: As BL-33.
REVERSE: A harp facing left.

Composition: Copper
Weight: 3.8 to 4.4 g
Diameter: 25.8 to 26.2 mm
Die Axis: ↑→
Edge: Plain
Ref.Nos.: Co 3BT; W 651; Wo 22

Cat.No.	Description	AG	G-4	VG-8	F-12	VF-20
BL-34	Copper, ↑→	—	1,000.	1,500.	2,000.	3,000.

BL-35

OBVERSE: Bust facing left. Very crude with poorly cut side curls, the cuirass has six flaps and the shirt frill has four ruffles.

REVERSE: Harp facing left. The harp has eight strings with the first attached to the wing. The foot of the harp points between "I" and "8" of the date, if the date is present. A large, centrally positioned dot appears among the strings.

Composition: Brass, copper
Weight: 4.9 to 5.5 g
Diameter: 27.4 to 27.5 mm
Die Axis: ↑↑, ↑→
Edge: Plain
Ref.Nos.: Br 1012 (R-0);
Co 25, 26;
Lr 786 (R-3);
McL 1-24; W 603;
See below

Varieties: Composition
A1 Copper; Co 25
A2 Brass; Co 26

Cat.No.	Date	Description	VG-8	F-12	VF-20	EF-40	AU-50	AU-55	MS-60
BL-35A1	1820	Copper	375.	525.	900.	2,250.	—	—	—
BL-35A2	1820	Brass	150.	225.	450.	—	—	—	—

BL-36

OBVERSE: Laureate bust facing right with nine leaves in the chaplet. A meaningless legend sometimes appears as CHCOBRDGES III RUBUS.

REVERSE: Harp facing right with nine strings and an ornamental top. The foot of the harp points to the "2" in the date. The legend may read RUMG EBUCAO BOUGO SO.

Composition: Copper
Weight: 7.1 to 7.8 g
Diameter: 25.9 to 27.5 mm
Die Axis: ↑→
Edge: Plain
Ref.Nos.: Co 20; W 604

Cat.No.	Date	Description	AG	G-4	VG-8	F-12	VF-20
BL-36	1820	Copper, ↑→	400.	600.	750.	1,000.	1,500.

THE BITIT TOKENS

This series of tokens, of which the most common has legends, has been considered by some as an English Bungtown token or coinage for the state of Vermont.

BL-37

OBVERSE: Large laureate head facing right with a pug nose. Legend reads: GLORIOVS III. VIS.

REVERSE: Crude seated figure of Hibernia seated left, holding a shamrock. Legend: BITIT; blank exergue.

Composition: Copper
Weight: 5.6 to 6.1 g
Diameter: 26.5 to 26.8 mm
Die Axis: ↑↓
Edge: Plain
Ref.Nos.: W 658; Wo 33

Cat.No.	Description	AG	G-4	VG-8	F-12	VF-20
BL-37	Copper, ↑↓	—	—	10.	30.	50.

BL-38

OBVERSE: Crude laureate bust facing left with a long nose. The legend is illegible.

REVERSE: Crude Britannia seated left holding a shamrock. An oval shield rests at her side. Legend: IIII; this is an imitation of BL-37.

Composition: Copper
Weight: 4.9 to 5.2 g
Diameter: 25.7 mm
Die Axis: ↑↑, ↑↓
Edge: Plain
Ref.Nos.: W 659; Wo 34

Varieties: Die Axis
A1 Medal
A2 Coinage

Cat.No.	Description	AG	G-4	VG-8	F-12	VF-20
BL-38A1	Copper, ↑↑	—	500.	1,000.	1,500.	—
BL-38A2	Copper, ↑↓	—	500.	1,000.	1,500.	—

BL-39

OBVERSE: Similar to BL-38 but cruder with a turned-up nose.
REVERSE: A crude harp facing left.

Composition: Copper
Weight: 3.3
Diameter: 26.5
Die Axis: ↑→
Edge: Plain
Ref.Nos.: BH-32; W 660; Wo 35

Cat.No.	Description	AG	G-4	VG-8	F-12	VF-20
BL-39	Copper, ↑→			Fewer than five known, Extremely Rare		

DANIEL AND BENJAMIN TRUE TOKENS

A number of American Hard Times tokens were struck by Daniel and Benjamin True of Troy, New York, after 1830. About 1835 they began to produce lightweight tokens for export to Canada, including one of the more common "Blacksmith" pieces. The dies of this piece were later muled with badly dilapidated dies of American store cards to produce some extremely rare pieces.

BL-40

The heaviest specimens are the earliest and the best while the lightest are struck from the worst of the dies. It is possible to arrange specimens to show the progressive deterioration of the dies. The reverse die was often touched up, producing many variations.

OBVERSE: Laureate bust facing right with a double chin and a prominent lower jaw. The ribbons are tied with a single bow. A large die crack runs through the shoulder to the border behind the head.
REVERSE: Seated Britannia facing right, as on the English regal copper of the period. Coarsely toothed borders.

Composition: Copper
Weight: 3.6 to 5.8 g
Diameter: 26.5 to 28.1 mm
Die Axis: ↑↓, ↑↑
Edge: Plain
Ref.Nos.: Co 20BT; W 661; Wo 23

Cat.No.	Description	AG	G-4	VG-8	F-12	VF-20
BL-40	Copper, ↑↓	—	—	30.	75.	100.
BL-40A	Copper, ↑↓	—	—	30.	75.	100.
BL-40B	Copper, ↑↑	—	—	30.	75.	100.

BL-41

The reverse of this token is so poor that only the examination of more than one specimen simultaneously could result in its proper identification. There were in this period many "Riseing Sun" taverns in Upper and Lower Canada. Ferguson considered it to have been issued by James Watson, the owner of a tavern of this name in Toronto between 1833 and 1837. Troy had almost no business dealings with Upper Canada, but had plenty with Lower Canada through Montreal. For this reason it is generally believed that the token is for a Lower Canadian tavern of this name.

OBVERSE: As BL-40. The die is badly cracked.
REVERSE: RISEING SUN TAVERN in large letters is close to and parallel to a coarsely toothed border.

Composition: Copper
Weight: 3.8 to 4.8 g
Diameter: 26.6 to 27.0 mm
Die Axis: ↑→
Edge: Plain
Ref.Nos.: Co 21BT; W 662; Wo 24

Cat.No.	Description	AG	G-4	VG-8	F-12	VF-20
BL-41	Copper, ↑→	—	200.	400.	600.	—

BL-42

OBVERSE: As BL-40.
REVERSE: A screw. Legend: MACHINE SHOP, SCREEN FOR PAPER, OIL AND CIDER MILLS, TURNING AND BORING.

Compositon: Copper
Weight: 3.2 to 3.4 g
Diameter: 25.8 mm
Die Axis: ↑↓
Edge: Plain
Ref.Nos.: Co 22BT; W 665; Wo 25

Cat.No.	Description	AG	G-4	VG-8	F-12	VF-20
BL-42	Copper, ↑↓	—	500.	750.	1,000.	1,750.

BL-43

OBVERSE: As BL-40, from a very badly worn and cracked die.
REVERSE: An eagle with a thin neck and clear wing feathers. Toothed borders.

Composition: Copper
Weight: 3.2 to 3.4 g
Diameter: 25.9 mm
Die Axis: ↑→
Edge: Plain
Ref.Nos.: Co 23BT; W 663; Wo 26

Cat.No.	Description	AG	G-4	VG-8	F-12	VF-20
BL-43	Copper, ↑→	—	400.	800.	1,200.	1,750.

BL-44

OBVERSE: As the reverse of BL-43.
REVERSE: As the reverse of BL-42.

Photograph not
available
at press time

Composition: Copper
Weight: 3.2 g
Diameter: 25.7 mm
Die Axis: N/A
Edge: Plain
Ref.Nos.: Co 24BT; W 666; Wo 27

Cat.No.	Description	AG	G-4	VG-8	F-12	VF-20
BL-44	Copper	Four known, two of which are in public collections. J. Hoare Auction, Fall 1989, Lot 2467, F-VF - $3,300.				

BL-45

OBVERSE: As the reverse of BL-43.

REVERSE: Legend: PECK'S PATENT TIN MACHINES enclosing the words INCOMPLETE SETS MADE AT TROY N.Y., with a spindle or windlass.

Composition: Copper
Weight: 5.0 to 5.2 g
Diameter: 26.7 mm
Die Axis: ↑→
Edge: Plain
Ref.Nos.: Co 25BT; W 667; Wo 28

Cat.No.	Description	AG	G-4	VG-8	F-12	VF-20
BL-45	Copper, ↑→	—	500.	1,000.	1,500.	—

BL-46

OBVERSE: LEGEND: PECK'S PATENT TIN MACHINES, INCOMPLETE SETS MADE AT TROY, N.Y., with a spindle or windlass. As BL-45.

REVERSE: Seated Britannia facing right as on the reverse of BL-40.

Composition: Copper
Weight: 3.3 to 3.4 g
Diameter: 25.9 mm
Die Axis: ↑↑
Edge: Plain
Ref.Nos.: Co 26BT; W 669

Cat.No.	Description	AG	G-4	VG-8	F-12	VF-20
BL-46	Copper, ↑↑	Four known. J. Hoare Auction, Fall 1989, Lot 2469, VF - $1,900.				

BL-47

OBVERSE: LEGEND: PECK'S PATENT TIN MACHINES, INCOMPLETE SETS MADE AT TROY, N.Y., with a spindle or windlass. As BL-45.

REVERSE: As BL-42.

Composition: Copper
Weight: See below
Diameter: 25.6 to 27.1 mm
Die Axis: ↑↓, ↑←
Edge: Plain
Ref.Nos.: Co 27BT; W 668; Wo 29

Varieties: Flan
A1 Thick flan, Weight. 6.7 to 6.8 g
A2 Thin flan, Weight. 3.4 g

Cat.No.	Description	AG	G-4	VG-8	F-12	VF-20
BL-47A1	Copper, Thick flan	—	75.	150.	300.	600.
BL-47A2	Copper, Thin flan	—	75.	150.	300.	600.

BL-48

OBVERSE: An eagle with a thick neck.
REVERSE: Same as obverse.

Composition: Copper
Weight: 5.2 g
Diameter: N/A
Die Axis: ↑↓
Edge: Plain
Ref.Nos.: Co 28BT; W 664; Wo 30

Cat.No.	Description	AG	G-4	VG-8	F-12	VF-20
BL-48	Copper, ↑↓	Fewer than five known. Baker Sale 1987, $300.				

BLACKSMITH IMITATIONS OF UPPER CANADA TOKENS

BL-49

OBVERSE: Sloop.
REVERSE: Crossed shovels.

Photograph not
available
at press time

Composition: N/A
Weight: N/A
Diameter: N/A
Die Axis: N/A
Edge: N/A
Ref.Nos.: Wo 31

Cat.No.	Description	AG	G-4	VG-8	F-12	VF-20
BL-49				Unique		

BL-50

OBVERSE: Bust facing right.
REVERSE: Legend: TO FACILITATE TRADE

Composition: Brass
Weight: 6.1 g
Diameter: 28.2 mm
Die Axis: ↑↓
Edge: Plain
Ref.Nos.: Wo 45

Cat.No.	Description	AG	G-4	VG-8	F-12	VF-20
BL-50	Brass, ↑↑			Extremely Rare		

BLACKSMITH IMITATION OF LOWER CANADA TOKENS

BL-51

OBVERSE: Mexican-Bouquet.
REVERSE: Standing Indian (Copy of 1850, Copper Mexican coin, State of Chihuahua).

Composition: Copper
Weight: 7.1 g
Diameter: 28.0 mm
Die Axis: ↑↑
Edge: Plain
Ref.Nos.: Not previously listed

Cat.No.	Description	AG	G-4	VG-8	F-12	VF-20
BL-51	Copper, ↑↑	J. Hoare Auction, October 1999, Lot 595, AVF - $3,520.				

BL-52

OBVERSE: Bust similar to LC-51.
REVERSE: U.S. Hard Times token, similar to Wood 25, 27, 28 and 29 which are the Starbuck and U & C Peck reverse.

Photograph not
available
at press time

Composition: N/A
Weight: N/A
Diameter: N/A
Die Axis: N/A
Edge: N/A
Ref.Nos Not previously listed

Cat.No.	Description	AG	G-4	VG-8	F-12	VF-20
BL-52				Extremely Rare		

MISCELLANEOUS BLACKSMITH TOKENS

BL-53

OBVERSE: A Union Jack in an oval shield and a partial wreath. The border is large dots.

REVERSE: A fouled anchor between two branches in a border of large dots.

Composition: Brass, copper
Weight: 3.1 to 5.8 g
Diameter: 26.0 to 28.0 mm
Die Axis: ↑→, ↑←
Edge: Plain
Ref.Nos.: W 670; Wo 32

Varieties: Composition; Flan
A1 Copper, Thick flan, Weight. 5.7 g
A2 Copper, Thin flan, Weight. 3.2 g
A3 Brass

Cat.No.	Description	AG	G-4	VG-8	F-12	VF-20
BL-53A1	Copper, Thick flan	J. Hoare Auction, October 1997, Lot 1142, EF - $1,265.				
BL-53A2	Copper, Thin flan	Extremely Rare				
BL-53A3	Brass	J. Hoare Auction, Fall 1989, Lot 2475, $1,500.				

BL-54

OBVERSE: A crude, dog-like head.
REVERSE: Same as above.

Photograph not
available
at press time

Composition: Copper
Weight: 4.7 g
Diameter: 27. 3 mm
Die Axis: N/A
Edge: Plain
Ref.Nos.: W 671; Wo 44

Cat.No.	Description	AG	G-4	VG-8	F-12	VF-20
BL-54	Copper	Four known of which three are in Public Institutions. J. Hoare Auction, Fall 1989, Lot 2479, F - $2,000.				

BL-55

OBVERSE: Part of a head facing right.
REVERSE: A safe on the back of a tortoise with a partial legend.

Photograph not
available
at press time

Composition: N/A
Weight: N/A
Diameter: N/A
Die Axis: N/A
Edge: N/A
Ref.Nos.: W 672; Wo 46

Cat.No.	Description	AG	G-4	VG-8	F-12	VF-20
BL-55			Fewer than five known. Extremely Rare.			

BL-56

OBVERSE: A very large laureate bust facing left. Crudely rendered numerals 1417 below.
REVERSE: Uniface.

Photograph not
available
at press time

Composition: N/A
Weight: N/A
Diameter: N/A
Die Axis: N/A
Edge: N/A
Ref.Nos.: W 673; Wo 36

Cat.No.	Date	Description	AG	G-4	VG-8	F-12	VF-20
BL-56	1417			Fewer than five known. Extremely Rare.			

BL-57

OBVERSE: A windmill between two vines.
REVERSE: A horse tied in front of a tavern. Legend: NO CREDIT.

Composition: Copper
Weight: 9.1 g
Diameter: 28.0 mm
Die Axis: ↑←
Edge: Plain
Ref.Nos.: W 674

Cat.No.	Date	Description	AG	G-4	VG-8	F-12	VF-20
BL-57	1810	Copper, ↑←	—	500.	1,000.	1,500.	2,000.

BRIDGE TOKENS
(BOUT DE L'ISLE TOKENS)

The earliest bridge tokens are the famous Bout de l'Isle tokens, struck in 1808 and used to pay tolls across a series of bridges connecting the east end of Montreal Island (the Bout de l'Isle) with the mainland via Isle Bourdon. Three sets of four tokens were issued to pay the four kinds of tolls across the bridges. Anyone on foot paid sixpence. The charge for a horse or beast of burden was tenpence. For a cart, sleigh or wagon drawn by two beasts the toll was two shillings and threepence, or two shillings if drawn by one beast. For a calèche or buggy drawn by two horses the toll was two shillings and ninepence, two shillings and sixpence if drawn by one horse. The tokens were in use for a very short time, for the bridges were all carried away by ice in the spring of 1808. Most of the Lachesnaye tokens are clipped. This was done because the toll collector at this bridge was illiterate and could not identify his own tokens any other way.

The word Repentigny was misspelled in the inscription on these tokens. The letter N was mistaken for U in the carelessly written manuscript order, resulting in Repentiguy rather than Repentigny.

COUNTERFEIT BRIDGE TOKENS

Fakes of Breton 536 (Cheval) and 545 (Personne) were first seen soon after 1890. They were traced to the Ottawa area. Their early exposure prevented their being produced in quantity, and they are as rare as the originals. The fakes are in bronze on thicker flans. The reverse inscriptions are in taller, thinner, and bolder lettering, and there is a small five-pointed star under the word MONTREAL instead of the small radiate symbol of the original issues.

Please note: Since this section has yet to be finalized catalogue numbers have not been assigned.

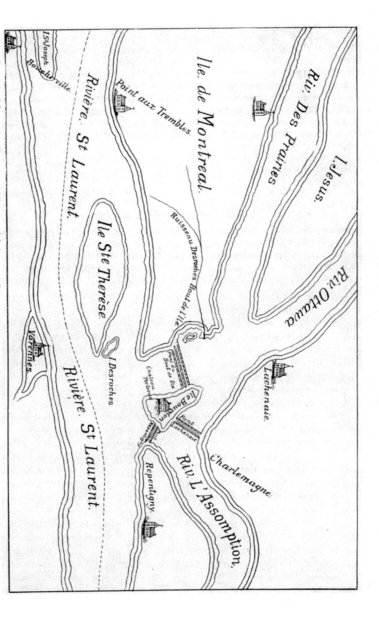

Riv. Des Prairies

I. Jesus.

Ile. de Montreal.

Point aux Trembles

Rivière. St Laurent.

Riv. Ottawa

Ile Ste Thérèse

Ruisseau Desroches Bout de l'Ile

Lachenaie.

I. Desroches

Varennes.

I. St Joseph
Boucherville

Bout de l'Ile
Ile Bourdon
Coulerie Perlare

Pont
Lachenaie

Charlemagne

Rivière. St Laurent.

Riv. L'Assomption.

Repentigny.

FROM LACHESNAYE TO L'ISLE DE MONTREAL OR REPENTIGNY

Obv.: Original Issue

Rev.: CALÈCHE

Rev.: CHARRETTE

Rev.: PERSONNE

Obv.: "Clipped" Issue

Rev.: CHEVAL (clipped)

Obv.: Clipped
Counterfeit

Rev.: Clipped
Counterfeit

Six Pointed Star
(Original)

Five Pointed
Star
(Counterfeit)

Composition: Copper
Weight: 6.6 to 7.0 g
Diameter: 28.0 to 28.1 mm
Thickness: 1.6 to 1.7 mm
Die Axis: ↑↓
Edge: Plain

Ref. Nos.:
Calèche: Br 534 (R-4½); Lr 585 (R-6); McL 45
Charrette: Br 535 (R-4½); Lr 586 (R-4); Mcl 42
Cheval: Br 536 (R-4½); Lr 587 (R-7); McL 37
Personne: Br 537 (R-4½); Lr 588 (R-7); McL 36

Cat.No.	Date	Description	G-4	VG-8	F-12	VF-20	EF-40
—	(1808)	Calèche (Carriage)		Extremely Rare			
—	(1808)	Calèche (Carriage) Clipped	400.	450.	500.	650.	950.
—	(1808)	Charrette (Wagon)		Extremely Rare			
—	(1808)	Charrette (Wagon) Clipped	400.	450.	500.	650.	950.
—	(1808)	Cheval (Horse)		Extremely Rare			
—	(1808)	Cheval (Horse) Clipped	400.	450.	500.	650.	950.
—	(1890)	Cheval (Horse) Counterfeit	200.	250.	300.	450.	—
—	(1808)	Personne (Person)		Extremely Rare			
—	(1808)	Personne (Person)	400.	450.	500.	650.	950.

FROM L'ISLE DE MONTRÉAL TO REPENTIGNY OR LACHESNAYE

Obv.: Original Issue   Rev.: CALÈCHE   Rev.: CHARRETTE

Rev.: CHEVAL   Rev.: PERSONNE

Composition: Copper
Weight: 7.1 to 7.4 g
Diameter: 28.0 to 28.3 mm
Thickness: 1.7 to 1.9 mm
Die Axis: ↑↓
Edge: Plain

Ref. Nos.:
Calèche: Br 538 (R-4); Lr 589 (R-6); McL 43
Charrette: Br 539 (R-4); Lr 590 (R-6); McL 40
Cheval: Br 540 (R-4); Lr 591 (R-7); McL 39
Personne: Br 541 (R-4); Lr 592 (R-7); McL 34

Cat.No.	Date	Description	G-4	VG-8	F-12	VF-20	EF-40
—	(1808)	Calèche (Carriage)	400.	450.	500.	650.	950.
—	(1808)	Charrette (Wagon)	400.	450.	500.	650.	950.
—	(1808)	Cheval (Horse)	400.	450.	500.	650.	950.
—	(1808)	Personne (Person)	400.	450.	500.	650.	950.

FROM REPENTIGNY TO L'ISLE DE MONTRÉAL OR LACHESNAYE

Obv.: Original Issue   Rev.: CALÈCHE   Rev.: CHARRETTE

Rev.: CHEVAL   Rev.: PERSONNE

Six-pointed Star   Five-pointed Star
(Original)   (Counterfeit)

Composition: Copper
Weight: 6.9 to 9.0 g
Diameter: 27.9 to 28.0 mm
Thickness: 1.5 to 1.9 mm
Die Axis: ↑↓
Edge: Plain

Ref. Nos.:
Calèche: Br 542 (R-4); Lr 593 (R-6); McL 44
Charrette: Br 543 (R-4); Lr 594 (R-6); McL 41
Cheval: Br 544 (R-4); Lr 595 (R-7); McL 38
Personne: Br 545 (R-4); Lr 596 (R-7); McL 35

Cat.No.	Date	Description	G-4	VG-8	F-12	VF-20	EF-40
—	(1808)	Calèche (Carriage)	400.	450.	500.	650.	950.
—	(1808)	Charrette (Wagon)	400.	450.	500.	650.	950.
—	(1808)	Cheval (Horse)	400.	450.	500.	650.	950.
—	(1808)	Personne (Person)	400.	450.	500.	650.	950.
—	(1808)	Personne (Person) Counterfeit	350.	400.	450.	550.	850.

REPENTIGNY TOKENS

The so-called Repentigny tokens appeared in 1890 and purported to be patterns for the Bout de l'Isle tokens. Many authorities, including Breton, accepted them as genuine, Breton publishing a detailed account of the circumstances surrounding their discovery. McLachlan denounced the pieces as fraudulent on the grounds that their fabric was too modern for the pieces to have been struck in 1808. He was proved to be right when the source was traced in England by W. J. Davis, who forced the maker to give up the dies in 1904. According to McLachlan six full sets were made. Sets exist in bronze and silver. They are very rare in bronze and extremely so in silver. The sets were struck in proof.

OBVERSES

 ON (OR) REPENTIGNY

 A (TO) REPENTIGNY

 **DE (FROM) REPENTIGNY**

REVERSES

CALÈCHE   CHARRETTE   CHEVAL   PERSONNE

VARIETIES

Varieties: Three sets containing four tokens
- **A** Obv.: On Repentiguy; Reverses: Caleche; Charette; Cheval; Personne
- **B** Obv.: A Repentiguy; Reverses: Caleche; Charette; Cheval; Personne
- **C** Obv.: De Repentiguy; Reverses: Caleche; Charette; Cheval; Personne

Composition: Bronze, silver
Weight: N/A
Diameter: N/A

Thickness: N/A
Die Axis: N/A
Edge: Plain

ON (OR) REPENTIGUY

Ref. Nos.:
Calèche: Br 546 (R-3); Lr 596f (R-7)
Charrette: Br 547 (R-3); Lr 596g (R-7)
Cheval: Br 548 (R-3); Lr 596h (R-7)
Personne: Br 549 (R-3); Lr 596i (R-7)

A (TO) REPENTIGUY

Ref. Nos.:
Calèche: Br 554 (R-3); Lr 596a (R-7)
Charrette: Br 555 (R-3); Lr 596b (R-7)
Cheval: Br 556 (R-3); Lr 596c (R-7)
Personne: Br 557 (R-3); Lr 596d (R-7)

DE (FROM) REPENTIGUY

Ref. Nos.:
Calèche: Br 550 (R-3); Lr 596j (R-7)
Charrette: Br 551 (R-3); Lr 596k (R-7)
Cheval: Br 552 (R-3); Lr 596l (R-7)
Personne: Br 553 (R-3); Lr 596m (R-7)

Cat.No.	Date	Description	Proof-63	Proof-65
—	(1890)	Bronze, Singles	300.	500.
—	(1890)	Bronze, Set of 12 tokens	4,000.	8,000.
—	(1890)	Silver, Singles	500.	1,000.
—	(1890)	Silver, Set of 12 tokens	6,000.	12,000.

FUR TRADE TOKENS

HUDSON'S BAY COMPANY

The issue of fur trade tokens was begun by the Hudson's Bay Company in the middle of the nineteenth century. The land north and west of the Province of Canada was the domain of the Hudson's Bay Company. The fur trade was the only industry, and it relied on barter. Barter gradually gave way to the use of tally sticks and ivory counters to make it easier for the Indians and Inuit to understand how business was transacted. Reckoning in those times was in terms of an adult beaver skin. The skin was stretched and tanned and was called a made beaver.

EAST MAIN DISTRICT

These brass pieces were used in the East Main District, south and east of Hudson Bay. It is not yet possible to establish the exact date of their issue, some authorities giving the date 1854 and others 1857. They are said to have been issued at the instigation of George Simpson McTavish, the factor at Fort Albany. It is said that they were designed by McTavish, and the dies were cut by Henry Smith of Birmingham. The tokens are denominated in N.B., the letters standing for new beaver. This was an engraver's error, the trade unit being the made beaver. Eventually the tokens were recalled, those presented for redemption being punched between the letters N . B on the reverse. The two smaller pieces are much scarcer punched than the larger pieces.

The tokens were soon afterwards withdrawn from circulation as the Indians preferred to trust their balances to the Company's books rather than to these checks, which were liable to be lost. The inscription when extended means: **HB** for Hudson's Bay, **EM** for East Main, and **1 NB** or **MB** for 1 Made Beaver or good for one made beaver skin. The made beaver was the unit of currency among the Company's forts, and was usually written **MB** for Made Beaver, thus **MF** for Moose Factory and **MR** for Moose River, hence the reason for the mistake **N** for **M**. A made beaver might be worth more or less than the beaver skin according to rise or fall in prices. It was a value fixed by usage long ago. The East Main district, which is really north east instead of north west, is situated east and south of Hudson's-Bay, and was for a long time the most productive of the districts occupied by the Company.

There is a current hypothesis that the tokens were not cancelled but punched for purposes of identification to be used in another district. One of the arguments put forth is that the punches are too uniform to be random cancellations.

GOOD FOR ONE MADE BEAVER
(HB E M 1 N B)

Composition: Brass
Weight: 5.9 to 8.2 g
Diameter: 29.4 to 29.8 mm
Thickness: 1.3 mm

Die Axis: ↑↑
Edge: Reeded
Ref. Nos.: Br 926 (R-3); G220c;
Lr 486 (R-8)

Varieties: Reverse
A Not punched
B Punched

Not Punched   Punched

GOOD FOR ONE HALF MADE BEAVER

Composition: Brass
Weight: 6.7 to 6.9 g
Diameter: 27.1 to 27.3 mm
Thickness: 1.8 mm
Die Axis: ↑↑
Edge: Reeded
Ref. Nos.: Br 927 (R-3); G220b;
Lr 487 (R-7)

Cat.No.	Date	Description	VF-20	EF-40	AU-50	AU-55	MS-60
—	(1857)	1/2 Made Beaver, Not punched	450.	550.	600.	650.	750.
—	(1857)	1/2 Made Beaver, Punched	450.	550.	600.	650.	750.
—	(1857)	1 Made Beaver, Not punched	400.	500.	550.	600.	700.
—	(1857)	1 Made Beaver, Punched	400.	500.	550.	600.	700.

Note: Sets exist of the "without punch" variety in presentation cases.

GOOD FOR ONE QUARTER MADE BEAVER

Composition: Brass
Weight: 3.9 to 4.5 g
Diameter: 24.6 to 24.7 mm
Thickness: 1.2 mm
Die Axis: ↑↑
Edge: Reeded
Ref. Nos.: Br 928 (R-3); G220a;
　　　　　　 Lr 488 (R-8)

GOOD FOR ONE EIGHTH MADE BEAVER

Composition: Brass
Weight: 2.6 to 3.0 g
Diameter: 19.2 to 19.6 mm
Thickness: 1.5 mm
Die Axis: ↑↑
Edge: Reeded
Ref. Nos.: Br 929 (R-3); G 220;
　　　　　　 Lr 489 (R-8)

Cat.No.	Date	Description	VF-20	EF-40	AU-50	AU-55	MS-60
—	(1857)	1/8 Made Beaver, Not punched	400.	500.	550.	600.	650.
—	(1857)	1/8 Made Beaver, Punched	400.	500.	550.	600.	650.
—	(1857)	1/4 Made Beaver, Not punched	350.	450.	500.	550.	600.
—	(1857)	1/4 Made Beaver, Punched	350.	450.	500.	550.	600.

NORTH WEST COMPANY

The North West Company was organized in Montreal about the year 1784. It carried on operations until about 1821 in the district south and west of Hudson Bay. This token was good for a beaver skin. Most tokens have been holed for stringing.

Composition: Brass, copper
Weight: 10.0 g
Diameter: 28.8 mm
Thickness: 1.9 mm

Die Axis: ↑↑
Edge: Plain
Ref. Nos.: Br 925 (R-5); Lr 485 (R-8)

Cat.No.	Sate	Description	AG	G-4	VG-8	F-12	VF-20
—	1820	Brass		Extremely Rare			
—	1820	Brass, holed	1,300.	2,000.	2,750.	4,000.	6,500.
—	1820	Copper		Extremely Rare			
—	1820	Copper, holed	2,000.	3,000.	4,000.	6,000.	10,000.

Note: Struck copies of the North West token exist.

MERCHANT TOKENS

M. BACQUET
HOTELKEEPER
QUEBEC, QUEBEC

Bacquet was a hotelier in Quebec City's Lower Town in 1852.

Composition: Lead
Weight: 13.3 to 14.2 g
Diameter: 31.2 to 31.5 mm
Thickness: 2.0 mm

Die Axis: Uniface
Edge: Plain
Ref. Nos.: Br 663 (R-2½); Lr 1067f

Cat.No.	Description	G-4	VG-8	F-12	VF20	EF-40
—	Lead, Uniface	50	100.	250.	—	—

DEVINS & BOLTON
DRUGGISTS
MONTREAL, QUEBEC

On arrival from England these tokens were held by Canadian customs and eventually destroyed. These tokens did not circulate; however, a few did escape the melting pot and those that did are found in high grade condition.

Composition: Copper
Weight: 4.6 to 5.0 g
Diameter: 25.5 mm
Thickness: 1.1 mm
Die Axis: ↑↑
Edge: Plain
Ref. Nos.: Br 569 (R-2½);
Lr 970 (R-5)

Cat.No.	Description	VF-20	EF-40	AU-50	AU-55	MS-60
—	Copper	—	—	125.	175.	250.

COUNTERSTAMPED TOKENS

Starting in the early 1860s the druggist Devins & Bolton devised a clever advertising plan, that of counterstamping their message on pennies and halfpennies that passed through their till. Over four hundred different varieties of counterstamped tokens exist.

Composition: Bronze
Weight: Various
Diameter: Various
Thickness: Various
Die Axis: Various
Edge: Various

Counterstamped "Habitant" Half Penny Token

Counterstamped Wellington Halfpenny Token

Cat.No.	Description	G-4	VG-8	F-12	VF-20	EF-40
—	Common types	30.	40.	50.	60.	75.

HUNTERSTOWN LUMBERING COMPANY
HUNTERSTOWN, QUEBEC

Located some thirty-five miles from Louiseville, Quebec, on the Rivière du Loup, this firm ran a lumbering operation. To support the operation a supply store was opened for the employees who were paid in scrip and halfpenny tokens.

Composition: Lead
Weight: N/A
Diameter: N/A
Thickness: N/A
Die Axis: N/A
Edge: N/A
Ref. Nos.: Br 567 (R-4);
Lr 597 (R-7)

Cat.No.	Description	G-4	VG-8	F-12	VF-20	EF-40
—	Lead			Extremely Rare		

Note: Cast copies exist.

I. S. KOLLMYER
MONTREAL, QUEBEC

Breton recorded that Kollmyer carried on business as a merchant tailor in Montreal during the 1850s.

Composition: Copper gilt
Weight: N/A
Diameter: N/A
Thickness: N/A
Die Axis: N/A
Edge: N/A
Ref. Nos.: Br 654 (R-4)

Cat.No.	Date	Description	G-4	VG-8	F-12	VF-20	EF-40
—	(1859)	Copper Gilt			Extremely Rare		

ROBERT PURVES, MERCHANT
WALLACE, NOVA SCOTIA

Composition: Copper
Weight: 4.8 to 5.4 g
Diameter: 26.0 mm
Thickness: 1.4 mm
Die Axis: ↑↑
Edge: Plain
Ref. Nos.: Br 897 (R-1);
Lr 451 (R-3); McL 315

Cat.No.	Description	VF-20	EF-40	AU-50	AU-55	MS-60
—	Copper	35.	50.	65.	75.	100.

R. SHARPLEY, WATCHMAKER
MONTREAL, QUEBEC

Rice Sharpley's cards were struck in Birmingham, England, to advertise his business located on Notre Dame Street in Montreal.

Composition: Copper, Gilt brass
Weight: 4.3 to 4.5 g
Diameter: 22.5 mm
Thickness:
Die Axis: ↑↑
Edge: Reeded
Ref. Nos.: Br 570 (R-2);
Lr 982 (R-5)

Cat.No.	Description	VG-8	F-12	VF-20	EF-40	AU-50
—	Gilt brass	50.	75.	100.	125.	175.
—	Copper	100.	125.	150.	175.	250.

WEIR & LARMINIE, BANKERS AND SPECIE BROKERS
MONTREAL, QUEBEC

The process for encasing postage stamps for use as currency was developed and patented by John Gault, of Boston.

Weir and Larminie were exchange brokers in Montreal during the early 1860s. Along with thirty American merchants, they issued a series of encased stamps for circulation during the Civil War in the United States. The various denominations of U.S. stamps were protected with a layer of mica, all enclosed in a brass metallic case.

Composition: Brass / mica
Weight: N/A
Diameter: N/A
Thickness: N/A
Die Axis: N/A
Edge: N/A
Ref. Nos.: Br 568 (R-4);
              Lr 598 (R-6)

Cat.No.	Date	Description	G-4	VG-8	F-12	VF-20	EF-40
—	(1862)	10 cents, Washington, Green.	—	—	900.	1,000.	2,000.
—	(1862)	5 cents, Jefferson, Red brown	—	—	900.	1,000.	2,000.
—	(1862)	3 cents, Washington, Pink	Extremely Rare				
—	(1862)	1 cent, Franklin, Blue	Extremely Rare				

TRANSPORTATION TOKENS

HALIFAX STEAMBOAT COMPANY

The Halifax Steamboat Company was founded in 1817 to take over the operation of a ferry service between Halifax and Dartmouth. A ferry service had existed since 1753. The company was acquired by the Dartmouth Ferry Commission in 1890. The tokens were very rare until the discovery of a very large hoard of uncirculated specimens during the demolition of the old company offices. It has not been possible to date them accurately because there are no records to show that the company ever used tokens. A hoard, wrapped in paper bearing the date 1846, was discovered some years ago.

Composition: Copper
Weight: 3.0 g
Diameter: 19.4 to 19.5 mm
Thickness: 1.5 mm
Die Axis: ↑↑
Edge: Plain
Ref. Nos.: Br 900 (R-2);
Lr 455 (R-4); McL 327

Cat.No.	Description	VF-20	EF-40	AU-50	AU-55	MS-60
—	Halifax Steamboat Company	20.	40.	50.	65.	75.

LAUZON FERRY

The Lauzon tokens were issued in 1821 to pay the fourpenny fare from Quebec to Point Levis aboard the ferry "Lauzon". The ship was owned by John Goudie, who later sold it to J. McKenzie. Some of the tokens were countermarked J McK to signify the change of ownership. When the ship was sold to J. Thompson, other specimens were countermarked JT to mark this second change of ownership. The tokens were struck in lead and wore easily. Fakes were made in an alloy containing bismuth.

Composition: Lead
Weight: 8.9 g
Diameter: 26.3 mm
Thickness: 1.7 mm
Die Axis: ↑↑
Edge: Plain
Ref. Nos.: Br 560 (R-4½);
Lr 599 (R-8); McL 33

Varieties:
- **2A** Plain, not counterstamped
- **2B** Counterstamped J McK (James MaKenzie)
- **2C** Counterstamped J T (J. Thompson)

Cat.No.	Date	Description	AG	G-4	VG-8	F-12	VF-20	EF-40
—	1821	Plain	500.	650.	750.	1,000.	1,500.	—
—	1821	Counterstamp J McK	400.	550.	650.	900.	1,250.	—
—	1821	Counterstamp J T	1,000.	1,250.	1,500.	2,000.	2,500.	—

Note: Counterfeit copies exist.

MONTREAL & LACHINE RAILROAD

Railway tokens were seldom used in Canada. The earliest is the third class token of the Montreal & Lachine Railroad, issued in 1847. It was inconvenient to use cardboard tickets for third class passengers, who were mostly Indians and labourers working on the Lachine Canal, so the company imported perforated tokens from Birmingham. These were strung on a wire as they were collected by the conductor. They were used until 1862, when the remaining stocks were melted down. In 1947 there was a souvenir issue of copies bearing the dates 1847 and 1947 flanking the locomotive on the obverse to mark the centenary of the opening of the line.

Original Issue

100th Anniversary Issue

Composition: See below **Thickness:** See below
Weight: See below **Die Axis:** ↑↓
Diameter: See below **Edge:** Plain
Ref. Nos.: Br 530 (R-2½); Lr 600 (R-5); McL 46

Varieties: Obverse
A Original Issue; Copper; 15.6 to 16.1 g; 34.5 mm; 2.1 mm
B Issue dated 1847 1947; Gold, N/A
C Issue dated 1847 1947; Silver; 17,3 g; 35.0 mm; 2.4 mm
D Issue dated 1847 1947; Bronze, N/A

Cat.No.	Date	Description	VG-8	F-12	VF-20	EF-40	AU-50	AU-55	MS-60
—	(1847)	Original, Copper	300.	400.	500.	750.	—	—	—
—	1947	Gold				Extremely Rare			
—	1947	Silver	—	—	—	—	600.	650.	700.
—	1947	Bronze	—	—	—	—	400.	450.	500.

NON-CANADIAN TOKENS

ANCHOR MONEY, 1822

These coins were designed by William Wyon, and struck at the Royal Mint, London, England. While listed by Breton and LeRoux, this coinage was never intended for Canada – it was struck for Mauritius and the British West Indies. The total issue of 1820 was shipped to Mauritius, with the 1822 issue divided between Mauritius and the West Indies. When Mauritius abandoned the sterling monetary system in 1826, the coins were withdrawn from circulation and shipped to the West Indies.

Trade between Canada and the British West Indies brought some of these coins to Canada.

HALF DOLLAR

Composition: Silver
Weight: 13.0 g
Diameter: 1.8 mm
Thickness: 1.5 mm
Die Axis: ↑↓
Edge: Reeded
Ref. Nos.: Br 857 (R-3½);
Lr 760 (R-5);
McL 369

1822 Plain   1822 2 over 1

Varieties: Obverse
   A Plain date
   B 2 over 1

Cat. No.	Date	Description	VG-8	F-12	VF-20	EF-40	AU-50	AU-55	MS-60
—	1822	Plain date	225.	300.	425.	600.	800.	900.	1,000.
—	1822	2 over 1	325.	400.	575.	800.	1,000.	1,150.	1,300.

QUARTER DOLLAR

Composition: Silver
Weight: 6.3 to 6.6 g
Diameter: 25.6 mm
Thickness: 1.5 mm
Die Axis: ↑↓
Edge: Reeded
Ref. Nos.: Br 858 (R-1½);
Lr 761 (R-4); McL 370

Photograph not
available
at press time

1822 Plain

Last 2 over 1

First 2 over 2

Photograph not
available
at press time

Open 8

Open 8, First 2 over 2

Varieties: Obverse
  A Plain date
  B Last 2 over 1
  C First 2 over 2
  D Open 8
  E Open 8, First 2 over 2

Cat. No.	Date	Description	VG-8	F-12	VF-20	EF-40	AU-50	AU-55	MS-60
—	1822	Normal date	15.	25.	50.	100.	300.	400.	500.
—	1822	Last 2 over 1	20.	30.	55.	150.	375.	450.	525.
—	1822	First 2 over 2	20.	30.	55.	150.	375.	450.	525.
—	1822	Open 8	30.	40.	65.	175.	425.	525.	600.
—	1822	Open 8, First 2 over 2	40.	50.	70.	200.	450.	575.	700.

ONE EIGHTH DOLLAR

Composition: Silver
Weight: 3.3 g
Diameter: 20.5 mm
Thickness: 1.2 mm
Die Axis: ↑↓
Edge: Reeded
Ref. Nos.: Br 859 (R-1½);
Lr 762 (R-4); McL 371

1822 Plain

Last 2 over 1

First 2 over 2

Varieties: Obverse
   A Plain date
   B Last 2 over 1
   C First 2 over 2

Cat. No.	Date	Description	VG-8	F-12	VF-20	EF-40	AU-50	AU-55	MS-60
—	1822	Normal date	15.	25.	50.	100.	200.	250.	300.
—	1822	Last 2 over 1	20.	30.	55.	150.	250.	300.	350.
—	1822	First 2 over 2	20.	30.	55.	150.	250.	300.	350.

ONE SIXTEENTH DOLLAR

Composition: Silver
Weight: 1.6 g
Diameter: 15.9 to 16.1 mm
Thickness: 0.8 to 1.0 mm
Die Axis: ↑↓
Edge: Reeded
Ref.Nos.: Br 860 (R-1½);
          Lr 763 (R-4); McL 126

1822 Wide 8

Narrow 8 over wide 8

Photograph not
available
at press time

First 2 over 2

Varieties: Obverse
   A Plain date, Wide 8
   B Narrow 8 over wide 8
   C First 2 over 2

Cat. No.	Date	Description	VG-8	F-12	VF-20	EF-40	AU-50	AU-55	MS-60
—	1822	Wide 8	15.	25.	50.	100.	175.	225.	275.
—	1822	Narrow 8 over wide 8	20.	30.	55.	150.	225.	275.	325.
—	1822	First 2 over 2	30.	40.	65.	175.	250.	300.	350.

COLONIAL PATTERN COINAGE

The coins were designed and engraved by William Wyon and struck by the Royal Mint, London, England. They were struck to accompany a proposal to establish a decimal system in British West Africa. They were not put into circulation; however, they are listed in Breton and LeRoux.

COLONIAL 1/50 DOLLAR 1823

Composition: Copper
Weight: N/A
Diameter: N/A
Thickness: N/A

Die Axis: N/A
Edge: N/A
Ref. Nos.: Br 861 (R-5); Lr 764 (R-8)

Cat. No.	Date	Description	PROOF
—	1823	Copper	Extremely Rare

COLONIAL 1/100 DOLLAR 1823

Composition: Silver
Weight: N/A
Diameter: N/A
Thickness: N/A
Die Axis: N/A
Edge: N/A
Ref. Nos.: Br 862 (R-5);
　　　　　　Lr 765 (R-8)

Cat. No.	Date	Description	PROOF
—	1823	Copper	Extremely Rare

**CANADIAN COLONIAL TOKENS CROSS REFERENCED BY BRETON,
COURTEAU AND WILLEY NUMBERS TO
CHARLTON CATALOGUE NUMBERS**

Breton Number	Courteau Number	LeRoux Number	Willey Number	Charlton Number
520	—	495	500	LC-1
521	8-11H	528,528a	745-748	LC-9A
521	12-14bH	530,530a	757-759	LC-9B
521	16-17dH	505	764-765	LC-9C
521	24-29BM	510,511	772-775	LC-9D
522	1-2IH	529	736-744	LC-8A
522	3-4iH	531	749-756	LC-8B
522	6-7bH	506	760-763	LC-8C
522	14-22BM	512	766-771	LC-8D
523	36-37BM	513	779-780	LC-11A
523	38BM	513	784	LC-11B
524	30-32BM	514	776-778	LC-10A
524	33-35BM	514	781-783	LC-10B
525	39BM	507	785	LC-11C
526	71-87BM	515	861-872	PC-2B
527	41-45, 47-63 66-70BM	—	852-853, 855-856 858-859,	PC-1B
527	40, 46, 64-65BM	516	851, 854, 857	PC-1A
527	—	516	860	PC-1C
528	15fH	532	877-878	PC-4
529	5-5hH	533	873-876	PC-3
531	47W	502	541	LC-12
532	—	503	575	LC-13A, B
533	—	504	574	LC-14
558	—	500	675-676	VC-1-2
559	—	501	677	VC-3
561	—	573	576-577	LC-15
562	—	576	579	LC-16
563	—	577	573	LC-17
564	—	578	572	LC-18
565	—	580	578	LC-19
670	71B	574	C28	LC-45
671	72B	579	580	LC-20
672	1B	534	692	LC-6
673	2B	535	693	LC-7
674	63-70B	547	734	LC-40
675	61B	548	694	LC-23A
676	57B	559	695	LC-22A
677	58B	555	696	LC-23B
678	56B	554	697	LC-23C
679	54-55B	557	699	LC-24
680	53B	539	700	LC-21
681	60B	565	701	LC-22C
682	59B	558	702	LC-22B
683	51-52B	536	703	LC-25
684	49-50B	545	732	LC-41
685	47	566	705	LC30C
686	48B	567	706	LC-30D

Breton Number	Courteau Number	LeRoux Number	Willey Number	Charlton Number
687	42B	552	707	LC-32A
688	41B	542	709	LC-31A
689	24B	549	733	LC-43
690	40B	553	G2	LC-44
691	43-44B	563	710	LC-27
692	39B	556	711	LC-32B
693	37B	541	712	LC-31B
694	38B	540	713	LC-31C
695	46B	538	714	LC-29A
696	45B	537	715	LC-29B
697	33-34B	564	716	LC-29E
698	36B	551	717	LC-30A
699	35B	550	718	LC-30B
700	32B	543	719	LC-29C
701	31B	544	720	LC-29D
702	29B	561	721	LC-28
703	30B	562	722	LC-30F
704	27-28B	560	723	LC-33A
705	25-26B	546	725	LC-33C
706	23B	572	726	LC-34
707	22B	571	727	LC-35
708	20B	570	728	LC-36
709	21B	525	729	LC-37
710	19B	569	730	LC-38A
711	18B	568	731	LC-39
712	—	548a	G3	LC-38B
713	8-13B	—	678-683	LC-2
714	3B-7B	—	684-688	LC-3
715	15-17B	508, 508a	690-691	LC-5
716	14B	509	689	LC-4
717	—	698	823	UC-3
718	—	699	824-828	UC-2
719	208-319UC	693, 694	880	PC-6A-D
720	1-207UC	695	879	PC-5A-D
721	—	696	A2	UC-1
723	—	680	801	UC-5
724	—	682	802-808	UC-6
725	—	681	809	UC-7
726	—	683, 688	819, 820	UC-8
727	—	684, 689	810-814	UC-9
728	—	685	815	UC-10
729	—	686	816	UC-11
730	—	687, 690	817-818	UC-12A
730	—	687, 690	821	UC-12B
731	—	691	—	UC-13
732	—	692	831	UC-14
867	251-257NS	410-412	351-358	NS-1A-B
868	260-264NS	413-414	361-365	NS-2A
869	258-259NS	416, 417	359-360	NS-1C
870	284-285aNS	418-421	381-383	NS-2B
870	286-289aNS	418-421	391-393	NS-4

Breton Number	Courteau Number	LeRoux Number	Willey Number	Charlton Number
871	265-276NS	422-424	366-380	NS-1D
871	277-279NS	—	384, 386	NS-3A
871	281NS	—	388	NS-3C
871	282-283NS	—	389-390	NS-3D
872	280NS	426	385	NS-3B
873	309-314NS	427	415-420	NS-2C-D
874	290-308NS	428	394-413	NS-1E-F
875	318-319NS	429	423	NS-6
876	315-316NS	430	421	NS-5
879	325-329NS	435	313-317	NS-7A-B
880	333-334NS	436	318	NS-8
881	331NS	447	319	NS-9
882	335NS	449	321	NS-10A
883	336-337NS	450	322-323	NS-10B
884	338-339NS	452	340	NS-11
885	340NS	437	341	NS-12
886	347-350NS	438	333-336	NS-25
887	346NS	784	337	NS-26
888	353-356NS	439	329-332	NS-23
889	351-352NS	440	324-325	NS-27
890	341NS	453	342	NS-13
891	342-345NS	444	326-328	NS-14
892	358NS	441	343	NS-15A
893	357NS	445	344	NS-15B
894	3NL	442	348	NS-24
895	330NS	443	339	NS-28
896	359NS	446	338	NS-16
899	362-363NS	454	349-350	NS-17
909	21-29NB	373	465-468	NB-2A
910	3-20NB	374	453-464	NB-1A
911	42-52NB	375	474-475	NB-2B
912	30-41NB	376	469-473	NB-1B
913	1NB	379	451	NB-4
914	2NB	380	—	NB-3
916	3PEI	352	238	PE-4
917	4-12PEI	357	239-246	PE-5A-B
918	13-15PEI	353	251-253	PE-7A
919	16-23, 25-28 33-40PEI	354	254-269	PE-7B-C
920	41-44PEI	355	247-250	PE-6
921	45PEI	356	272	PE-8
952	1-2NF	319-320	180, 182	NF-1A-B
953	3-8NF	321-322	183-186	NF-1C
954	9NF	316	187-188	NF-3
955	10NF	317	189	NF-4
956	11NF	318	—	NF-2
957	39-40T	767	C26-27	LC-47A
958	34-35,37-38T	768	C22-25	LC-47B-C
959	28-33T	769	C17-21	LC-47D
960	9-24T	770-772	606-620	LC-48A-B
960	25-27T	770-772	C14-16	LC-46
961	1-8T	773	621-628	LC-48C

Breton Number	Courteau Number	LeRoux Number	Willey Number	Charlton Number
962	8-13NL	777	304-309	NS-20A-B
963	6-7NL	775	302	NS-19A-B
964	5NL	—	301	NS-18
965	15-17NL	776	310-312	NS-21
966	18NL	791	152	AM-1
967	14NL	789	B8	NS-22
969	26W	799	522	WE-1
970	31W	807b	527	WE-4A
971	30W	807	526	WE-2A
972	27-28W	806	523-524	WE-2B
973	—	807a	528	WE-2C
974	29W	807c	521	WE-3
975	—	—	C1	AM-2
976	1-2W	794	C7-8	WE-5
977	43W	795	C9	WE-6
978	44W	797	C10	WE-7
979	33-38W	800	529-534	WE-8
980	39W	801	535	WE-9
981	40-42W	804	538-540	WE-10
982	40NL	809	542	LC-49
983	36NL	—	C5	AM-3
984	23W	798	520	WE-12
985	24W	805	C11	WE-13
986	12-21W	810	509-518	WE-11B-C
987	4-11W	811	502-508	WE-11A
988	22W	812	519	WE-11D
989	34NL	780	C4	LC-52
990	33NL	779	C3, 571	LC-51
991	32NL	778	C2	LC-50
992	47-48NL	787	561-562	LC-53A
994	25-31NL	781, 782	543-548	LC-54A-D
995	1PEI	783	206	PE-9A
996	2PEI	783a	207	PE-9B
997	—	793	208-234, 555-557, 559-560, 654-655	PE-10-1-44 BL-24A-B
998	12BT	—	656	BL-28
999	—	—	653, 657	PE-10-5, BL-24C
1000	—	793	558	PE-10-5B
1001	—	—	567	LC-55
1002	41-43NL	813	549-551	LC-58A
1002	44NL	813	552	LC-58B
1003	46W	802	537	WE-14
1004	20-24NL	774	569-570	LC-56A-B
1005	19NL	774a	568	LC-56C
1006	45W	803	536	WE-15
1007	45-46NL	808	553-554	LC-59A-B
1008	1-1aBT	—	649	BL-32
1009	4NL	792	153	AM-4
1010	—	790	829-830	UC-4
1011	37-39NL	785	564-565	LC-57
1012	1-26BH	786	581-604	LC-60A-F,BL-35-36
1013	1-2NL	766	151	AM-5

CANADIAN COLONIAL TOKENS CROSS REFERENCED BY CHARLTON CATALOGUE NUMBERS TO BRETON, COURTEAU AND WILLEY

Charlton Number	Breton Number	Courteau Number	LeRoux Number	Willey Number
NF-1A	952	1NF	320	180
NF-1B	952	2NF	319	182
NF-1C	953	3, 5, 7, 8NF	321-322	183-186
NF-2	956	11NF	318	—
NF-3	954	9NF	316	187-188
NF-4	955	10NF	317	189
PE-1	—	—	—	201-202
PE-2	—	—	—	236
PE-3	—	—	—	237-237a
PE-4	916	3PEI	352	238
PE-5A	917	4-8PEI	357	239-243
PE-5B	917	9-12PEI	357	244-246
PE-6	920	41-44PEI	355	247-250
PE-7A	918	13-15PEI	353	251-253
PE-7B	919	16-18PEI	354	254-256
PE-7C	919	19-23, 25-28, 33-40PEI	354	257-269
PE-8	921	45PEI	356	272
PE-9A	995	1PEI	783	206
PE-9B	996	2PEI	783a	207
PE-10-1, 2	997	—	—	556-557
PE-10-3 to 5A	997, 999	—	793	653-655
PE-10-5B	1000	—	793	558
PE-10-6 to 9	997	—	793	208, 555, 559-560
PE-10-10A to 13	997	—	793	209-211
PE-10-14 to 17	997	—	793	212
PE-10-18 to 22	997	—	793	213
PE-23, 24, 26	997	—	793	214, 216, 218
PE-10-25	997	—	793	215
PE-10-27, 33	997	—	793	217, 222
PE-10-28 to 32	997	—	793	218-221
PE-35, 40	997	—	793	223-224, 229
PE-36-37, 42, 45-46	997	—	793	225-226, 231, 234
PE-38, 39	997	—	793	227-228
PE-10-41, 43, 44	997	—	793	—
NS-1A	867	251-253NS 256-257NS	410	351-354 357-358
NS-1B	867	254-255NS	411-412	355-356
NS-1C	869	258-259NS	416-417	359-360
NS-1D	871	265-276NS	422-424	366-380
NS-1E	874	290-298NS	428	394-402
NS-1F	874	299-308NS	428	403-413
NS-2A	868	260-264NS	413-414	361-365
NS-2B	870	284-285aNS	418-421	NS381-383
NS-2C	873	309-311NS	427	415-417
NS-2D	873	312-314NS	427	418-420
NS-3A	871	277-279NS	—	384, 386
NS-3B	872	280NS	426	385
NS-3C	871	281NS	—	388

Charlton Number	Breton Number	Courteau Number	LeRoux Number	Willey Number
NS-3D	871	282-283NS	—	389-390
NS-4	870	286-289aNS	418-421	391-393
NS-5	876	315-316NS	430	421
NS-6	875	318-319NS	429	423
NS-7A	879	325NS	435	313
NS-7B	879	326-329NS	435	314-317
NS-8	880	333-334NS	436	318
NS-9	881	331NS	447	319
NS-10A	882	335NS	449	321
NS-10B	883	336-337NS	450	322-323
NS-11	884	338-339NS	452	340
NS-12	885	340NS	437	341
NS-13	890	341NS	453	342
NS-14	891	342-345NS	444	326-328
NS-15A	892	358NS	441	343
NS-15B	893	357NS	445	344
NS-16	896	359NS	446	338
NS-17	899	362-363NS	454	349-350
NS-18	964	5NL	—	301
NS-19A	963	6NL	775	302
NS-19B	963	7NL	—	302
NS-20A	962	8-11NL	777	304-307
NS-20B	962	12-13NL	777	308-309
NS-21	965	15-17NL	776	310-312
NS-22	967	14NL	789	B8
NS-23	888	353-356NS	439	329-332
NS-24	894	3NL	442	348
NS-25	886	347-350NS	438	333-336
NS-26	887	346NS	784	337
NS-27	889	351-352NS	440	324-325
NS-28	895	330NS	443	339
NS-30	—	35NL	—	154
NB-1A	910	3-20NB	374	453-464
NB-1B	912	30-41NB	376	469-473
NB-2A	909	21-29NB	373	465-468
NB-2B	911	42-52NB	375	474-475
NB-3	914	2NB	380	—
NB-4	913	1NB	379	451
NB-5	—	—	—	452
LC-1	520	—	495	500
LC-2	713	8-13B	—	678-683
LC-3	714	3-7B	—	684-688
LC-4	716	14B	509	689
LC-5	715	15-17B	508, 508a	690-691
LC-6	672	1B	534	692
LC-7	673	2B	535	693
LC-8A	522	1-2lH	529	736-744
LC-8B	522	3-4iH	531	749-756
LC-8C	522	6-7bH	506	760-763
LC-8D	522	14-22BM	512	766-771
LC-9A	521	8-11H	528, 528a	745-748

Charlton Number	Breton Number	Courteau Number	LeRoux Number	Willey Number
LC-9B	521	12-14bH	530, 530a	757-759
LC-9C	521	16-17dH	505	764-765
LC-9D	521	24-29BM	510, 511	772-775
LC-10A	524	30-32BM	514	776-778
LC-10B	524	33-35BM	514	781-783
LC-11A	523	36-37BM	513	779-780
LC-11B	523	38BM	513	784
LC-11C	525	39BM	507	785
LC-12	531	47W	502	541
LC-13	532	—	503	575
LC-14	533	—	504	574
LC-15	561	—	573	576-577
LC-16	562	—	576	579
LC-17	563	—	577	573
LC-18	564	—	578	572
LC-19	565	—	580	578
LC-20	671	72B	579	580
LC-21	680	53B	539	700
LC-22A	676	57B	559	695
LC-22B	682	59B	558	702
LC-22C	681	60B	565	701
LC-23A	675	61B	548	694
LC-23B	677	58B	555	696
LC-23C	678	56B	554	697
LC-23D	—	62B	—	698
LC-24	679	54-55B	557	699
LC-25	683	51-52B	536	703
LC-26	—	—	—	704
LC-27	691	43-44B	563	710
LC-28	702	29B	561	721
LC-29A	695	46B	538	714
LC-29B	696	45B	537	715
LC-29C	700	32B	543	719
LC-29D	701	31B	544	720
LC-29E	697	33-34B	564	716
LC-30A	698	36B	551	717
LC-30B	699	35B	550	718
LC-30C	685	47B	566	705
LC-30D	686	48B	567	706
LC-30E	—	—	—	708
LC-30F	703	30B	562	722
LC-31A	688	41B	542	709
LC-31B	693	37B	541	712
LC-31C	694	38B	540	713
LC-32A	687	42B	552	707
LC-32B	692	39B	556	711
LC-33A	704	27-28B	560	723
LC-33B	—	—	—	724
LC-33C	705	25-26B	546	725
LC-34	706	23B	572	726
LC-35	707	22B	571	727

Charlton Number	Breton Number	Courteau Number	LeRoux Number	Willey Number
LC-36	708	20B	570	728
LC-37	709	21B	525	729
LC-38A	710	19B	569	730
LC-38B	712	—	548a	G3
LC-39	711	18B	568	731
LC-40	674	63-70B	547	734
LC-41	684	49-50B	545	732
LC-42	—	—	—	735
LC-43	689	24B	549	733
LC-44	690	40B	553	G2
LC-45	670	71B	574	C28
LC-46	960	25-27T	770-772	C14-16
LC-47A	957	39-40T	767	C26-27
LC-47B	958	34-35T	768	C22-23
LC-47C	958	37-38T	—	C24-25
LC-47D	959	28-29, 31-33T	769	C17-21
LC-47E	—	36T	—	A1
LC-47F	—	30T	—	C12
LC-47G	—	41T	—	C13
LC-48A	960	21-24T	770-771	606-608
LC-48B	960	9-20T	772	609-620
LC-48C	961	1-8T	773	621-628
LC-49	982	40NL	809	542
LC-50	991	32NL	778	C2
LC-51	990	33NL	779	C3, 571
LC-52	989	34NL	780	C4
LC-53A	992	47-48NL	787	561-562
LC-53B	—	49NL	—	563
LC-54A	994	25NL	781	543
LC-54B	994	26-27NL	781	544
LC-54C	994	28-29NL	781	545-546
LC-54D	994	30-31NL	782	547-548
LC-55	1001	—	—	567
LC-56A	1004	20-22NL	774	569-570
LC-56B	1004	23-24NL	774	570
LC-56C	1005	19NL	774a	568
LC-57	1011	37-39NL	785	564-565
LC-58A	1002	41-43NL	813	549-551
LC-58B	1002	44NL	813	552
LC-59A	1007	45NL	808	554
LC-59B	1007	46NL	808	553
LC-60A	1012	21-22BH	786	581-582
LC-60B	1012	23BH	786	583
LC-60C	1012	9-13, 24-26BH	786	584-589
LC-60D	1012	4-8, 18BH	786	590-594
LC-60E	1012	1, 3, 14-17,19BH	786	595-601
LC-60F	1012	2BH	786	602
LC-61	—	—	—	605
WE-1	969	26W	799	522
WE-2A	971	30W	807	526
WE-2B	972	27-28W	806	523-524

Charlton Number	Breton Number	Courteau Number	LeRoux Number	Willey Number
WE-2C	973	—	807a	528
WE-3	974	29W	807c	521
WE-4A	970	31W	807b	527
WE-4B	—	32W	—	525
WE-5	976	1-2W	794	C7-8
WE-6	977	43W	795	C9
WE-7	978	44W	797	C10
WE-8	979	33-38W	800	529-534
WE-9	980	39W	801	535
WE-10	981	40-42W	804	538-540
WE-11A	987	4-11W	811	502-508
WE-11B	986	12-19W	810	509-516
WE-11C	986	20-21W	—	517-518
WE-11D	988	22W	812	519
WE-12	984	23W	798	520
WE-13	985	24W	805	C11
WE-14	1003	46W	802	537
WE-15	1006	45W	803	536
UC-1	721	—	696	A2
UC-2	718	—	699	824-828
UC-3	717	—	698	823
UC-4	1010	—	790	829-830
UC-5	723	—	680	801
UC-6	724	—	682	802-808
UC-7	725	—	681	809
UC-8	726	—	683, 688	819, 822
UC-9	727	—	684, 689	810-814
UC-10	728	—	685	815
UC-11	729	—	686	816
UC-12A	730	—	687, 690	817-818
UC-12B	730	—	687, 690	821
UC-13	731	—	691	—
UC-14	732	—	692	831
PC-1A	527	40, 46,64-65BM	516	851, 854, 857
PC-1B	527	41-45, 47-63, 66-70BM	516	852-853, 855-856, 858-859
PC-1C	527	—	516	860
PC-2A	—	88BM	514a	G13
PC-2B	526	71-87BM	515	861-872
PC-3	529	5-5hH	533	873-876
PC-4	528	15fH	532	877-878
PC-5A	720	1-75UC	695	879
PC-5B	720	76-110UC	695	879
PC-5C	720	111-158UC	695	879
PC-5D	720	159-207UC	695	879
PC-6A	719	208-233UC	693	880
PC-6B	719	234-257UC	693	880
PC-6C	719	258-274UC	693, 694	880
PC-6D	719	275-319UC	693	880
AM-1	966	18NL	791	152
AM-2	975	—	—	C1

Charlton Number	Breton Number	Courteau Number	LeRoux Number	Willey Number
BL-5	—	11BT	—	633
BL-6	—	8BT	—	634
BL-7	—	13BT	—	635
BL-8	—	14BT	—	636
BL-9	—	15BT	—	638
BL-10	—	16BT	—	637
BL-11	—	17BT	—	639
BL-12	—	18BT	—	640
BL-13	—	19BT	—	641
BL-14	—	—	—	642
BL-16	—	—	—	643
BL-17	—	—	—	644
BL-18	—	—	—	645
BL-19	—	—	—	646
BL-20	—	—	—	647
BL-21	—	—	—	648
BL-24A	997	—	793	655
BL-24B	997	—	793	654
BL-24C	999	—	793	657
BL-25	—	9BT	—	652
BL-26	997	—	793	653
BL-28	998	12BT	—	656
BL-29	—	361aNS	—	347
BL-30	—	361NS	—	346
BL-31	—	360NS	—	345
BL-32	1008	Co 1, 1ABT	—	649
BL-33	—	2BT	—	650
BL-34	—	3BT	—	651
BL-35	1012	25-26	786	603
BL-36	—	20	—	604
BL-37	—	—	—	658
BL-38	—	—	—	659
BL-39	—	—	—	660
BL-40	—	20BT	—	661
BL-41	—	21BT	—	662
BL-42	—	22BT	—	665
BL-43	—	23BT	—	663
BL-44	—	24BT	—	666
BL-45	—	25BT	—	667
BL-46	—	26BT	—	669
BL-47	—	27BT	—	668
BL-48	—	28BT	—	664
BL-53	—	—	—	670
BL-54	—	—	—	671
BL-55	—	—	—	672
BL-56	—	—	—	673
BL-57	—	—	—	674

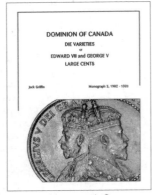
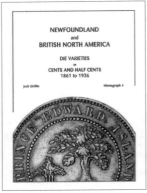